SYMPTOMS OF
VISCERAL DISEASE

SYMPTOMS OF
VISCERAL DISEASE

A Study of the Vegetative Nervous System in Its Relationship to Clinical Medicine

By

FRANCIS MARION POTTENGER
A.M., M.D., LL.D., F.A.C.P.

Medical Director, Pottenger Sanatorium and Clinic for Diseases of the Chest, Monrovia, California; Professor Emeritus of Clinical Medicine, University of Southern California; Author of "Clinical Tuberculosis," "Tuberculin in Diagnosis and Treatment," "Muscle Spasm and Degeneration," Etc.

SIXTH EDITION

WITH EIGHTY-SEVEN TEXT ILLUSTRATIONS AND TEN COLOR PLATES

ST. LOUIS
THE C. V. MOSBY COMPANY
1944

Printed in the
United States of America

Press of
The C. V. Mosby Company
St. Louis

PREFACE TO SIXTH EDITION

The fact that a sixth edition of *Symptoms of Visceral Disease* should be called for is an indication of an ever-growing interest in visceral neurology.

Clinicians are always dealing with symptoms. Some, they can readily interpret; others, they are forced to admit are beyond their understanding. Many of the most difficult symptoms to explain are of a reflex nature. The clinician's failure to understand is often not because the cause is not known to physiology but because physiology and the clinic are too widely separated.

The practice of medicine is a continuous attempt on the part of physicians to understand the manner in which the patient expresses disease through his physiologic systems.

This book attempts to bring an important phase of physiology to the physician. It is preeminently a discussion of man as a segmented organism. On the one hand, it describes visceral and somatic relationships to neurons which take origin in the various segments of the cord; and, on the other hand, it describes the reflexes which result from this association.

Reflex spasms, pains (referred pain), and degenerations are described and assigned to the various neurons which mediate impulses from inflamed or irritated viscera. Physiologic reflexes do not shift, so if the clinician knows his segmental relationships, he can reason from organ to the zone of the reflex or from the zone of the reflex back to the organ.

While the importance of reflexes is emphasized throughout the book, an attempt has been made to show that man is a unit, acted upon by many forces—some physical, some psychical, some physiologic, some pathologic—which determine and alter nerve reaction, thus making for variability of symptoms.

FRANCIS MARION POTTENGER.

Monrovia, Calif.

PREFACE TO FIFTH EDITION

When the first edition of *Symptoms of Visceral Disease* appeared in 1919, the subject of visceral neurology was little discussed in clinical medicine, but year by year interest has increased. The interest in recent years has been especially keen in the surgical aspects of the visceral nerves as related to angina and peripheral vascular diseases. However, the subject of visceral pain, the functional changes in blood pressure, the clinical syndromes which are expressed through the nerves supplying the heart, gastrointestinal tract, and lungs, have all been given considerable attention; but many medical men still fail to appreciate the myriads of visceral reflexes which are produced by the organism in adjusting its body functions to its external and internal environment.

The vegetative nervous system is the correlating system upon which the body relies for quick action whenever the organism is threatened, and upon which it depends for the proper distribution of those stimuli which are necessary for its normal physiologic function. Therefore, it should be earnestly studied by medical men that they may understand the everyday reactions of their patients. The importance of this system depends upon the fact that it controls the action of all smooth muscle, the striated heart muscle, and all secreting glands of the body.

In the present edition I have dealt with visceral pain in a separate chapter. I have also added a chapter describing the vegetative centers in the brain and cord which will help to clarify some of the more complicated effects which result from a specific stimulation or a stimulation applied to some definite site in the brain or cord. I have given more emphasis to the endocrines in their relationship to bodily function than in previous editions. Nearly every chapter has been partially or wholly rewritten.

As physiologic medicine becomes better understood, the vegetative nervous system will occupy an ever more important position in its relationship to body function. I hope that this new edition may be of further aid in solving the problems of physiologic medicine.

FRANCIS MARION POTTENGER.

Monrovia, Calif.

PREFACE TO SECOND EDITION

The fact that the first edition of this book was exhausted so soon after its publication came as a welcome surprise. It indicates an awakened interest in that phase of medicine which makes the patient himself the chief object of study. In the present edition I have followed the same arrangement as in the preceding one. No new chapters but much new material has been added. The text has been amplified and clarified throughout. Factors which offer a basis for the classification of symptoms; the segmental relationships of tissues and organs with reference to the mediation of reflexes; principles and laws governing reflexes; particular factors which operate to cause variability of symptoms; and effects of certain internal secretions upon the vegetative nerves and their power to modify nerve response both in health and disease, have all been discussed more fully than in the previous edition. The effect of psychical states in the initiation of symptoms or in modifying them when due to disease processes has been given considerable attention. Some new material will also be found in Part II, in those chapters which deal with the innervation and common symptoms of the important viscera. The changes in Part III are of minor importance and mainly for the purpose of clarifying the text.

Some criticism has been made to the effect that the names of the reflexes are cumbersome, but this same criticism is made of the terms used in other new fields of knowledge and is largely due to unfamiliarity with the subject. They are not as cumbersome as they seem and they have the advantage that the name suggests a description of the reflex.

In describing and classifying reflexes I followed a plan, in which the name indicates both the organ and the nerve path through which the reflex is produced. Sympathetic reflexes had previously been designated by the prefix "viscero." This I have continued. Among sympathetic reflexes we have (1), *muscle tension* which is described as a pulmonary, cardiac, gastric or other, "visceromotor reflex"; (2) *pain*, which, while not a true reflex, is, for clinical convenience, described as a "viscerosensory reflex," with the name of the organ involved accompanying it; (3) *degenerations* such as we find when

7

the lung and kidney are involved are described as, ·'viscerotrophic reflexes,'' with the name of the organ attached, and (4) the various reflex *"functional symptoms"* which are for the most part of parasympathetic origin are designated as "parasympathetic secretory,'' "parasympathetic motor,'' "parasympathetic sensory,'' and "parasympathetic trophic'' reflexes with the name of the organ attached.

The conception which has dominated recent advances in medicine has been an anatomic one; but that which must dominate in the future or, at least, that which must be considered as of equal importance, is the physiologic one. This study not only shows the physiologic basis for many of the symptoms commonly met in disease, but offers a means for understanding their vagaries as met in practice. I hope that this work may continue to stimulate interest in the patient's reactions, and at the same time afford a basis for their better understanding.

FRANCIS MARION POTTENGER.

Monrovia, Calif.

PREFACE TO FIRST EDITION

Though I have devoted myself to the study of diseases of the chest—a so-called "specialty''—for more than twenty years, experience has led me to see that such a thing as a medical specialty in the accepted sense of the term, cannot exist. Diseases cannot be divided into those of this and that organ; for the human body is a unit. One part cannot be diseased without affecting other parts. No organ can be understood except in its relationship to other organs and to the body as a whole.

In this monograph an attempt is made to interpret so far as may be possible in terms of visceral neurology, symptoms which are found in the everyday clinical observation of visceral disease. It is a study of visceral disease not from the standpoint of the *disease process,* important as that is, but from the no less important standpoint of the *patient* who has the disease. It is an attempt to show how pathologic changes in one organ affect other organs and the organism as a whole, through the medium of the visceral nerves. In contradistinction to the usual treatment of disease processes in their pathologic anatomic relationships this is a study in pathologic physiology. It is largely a discussion of "viscerogenic'' reflexes; and, as

such, causes us to examine somewhat carefully into the problems connected with the vegetative nervous system. It aims to show the importance of careful clinical observation and analysis.

The idea of the viscerogenic reflex is developed more fully than is
usual in medical discussions; and the parasympathetic reflexes have
been given as much attention as those of sympathetic origin. In this
respect my discussion will differ from that of Mackenzie in his
book on "Symptoms and Their Interpretation," to which I have referred so often in these pages. I have also emphasized the importance
of the "viscerotrophic" reflex, a subject which has been almost
wholly omitted from other works.

While the importance of the vegetative nervous system has long
been known to physiologists, clinicians generally have ignored it and
failed to see its intimate relationship to clinical medicine; yet it is
the key which unlocks the door to many of the secrets of visceral activity. An understanding of the vegetative nervous system and the
activities of the endocrine glands will explain to the clinician most of
the physical acts connected with visceral function and furnish the
bridge between the pathologic changes in tissues and the expression
of the disease in altered organic function. In other words, the vegetative nerves and the products of the endocrine glands are the me-
diums through which visceral symptoms are expressed.

The study of the vegetative nervous system here presented is brief;
at the same time it is sufficiently complete to furnish the essential
facts which one should have in order to understand the manner
in which body activities, both physiologic and pathologic, express
themselves through it. It is hoped that a brief presentation of this
kind will be appreciated and that it may help popularize the subject
among medical men.

The monograph is arranged in three parts: Part I. The Relationship Between the Vegetative Nervous System and the Symptoms
of Visceral Disease; Part II. Innervation of Important Viscera,
with a Clinical Study of the More Common Viscerogenic Reflexes;
Part III. The Vegetative Nervous System. A natural order would
be to consider the vegetative nervous system first, since it is the
basis of the study. Owing to the fact, however, that its consideration must necessarily be somewhat technical, it seemed best to
place the more practical subjects first. Parts I and II, therefore,
which contain the practical application of the principles of visceral

neurology to clinical medicine, including many of my original discussions, are placed first; while a brief review of the vegetative
nervous system will be found in Part III.

The discussion of the reflexes arising in or expressed in each
organ as described in Part II is preceded by a statement of the
innervation of the organ in question. The difficulty which the
writer experienced in gathering this data from books on anatomy
and physiology is sufficient assurance of the importance of making
this data easily accessible to the clinician.

This book is an attempt to show the relationship between physiologic facts and clinical observation and is given forth with the
hope that it may stimulate greater interest in clinical observation
and interpretation.

My thanks are due to Messrs. Marion, Alcorn and Shumway for
assistance in preparing the illustrations and to my secretary, Miss
Donahue, for aid in preparing the manuscript.

I shall be gratified if this monograph helps in any degree to emphasize the importance of more accurate clinical observation and interpretation of symptoms, thus aiding in the better understanding
and enjoyment of that phase of clinical medicine upon which we
are just entering, in which the patient who has the disease is to receive a consideration equal to the disease which has the patient. I
realize that the suggestions contained herein are not all final; but
I trust that they may stimulate observation and call out discussion
which will lead to a better understanding and interpretation of
clinical phenomena. This work, however, must be looked upon as
being only a brief excursion in a large field.

Francis Marion Pottenger.

Monrovia, Calif.

CONTENTS

CHAPTER I

PART I

THE VEGETATIVE NERVOUS SYSTEM

CHAPTER II

CHAPTER III

CHAPTER IV

CHAPTER V

CHAPTER VI

CHAPTER VII

PART II

THE RELATIONSHIP BETWEEN THE VEGETATIVE NERVOUS SYSTEM AND THE
SYMPTOMS OF VISCERAL DISEASE

CHAPTER XV

PART III

INNERVATION OF IMPORTANT VISCERA WITH A CLINICAL STUDY OF THE MORE IMPORTANT VISCEROGENIC REFLEXES

CHAPTER XVI

CHAPTER XVII

CHAPTER XVIII

CHAPTER XIX

COLOR PLATES

"THERE IS A PATIENT
WHO HAS THE DISEASE,
AS WELL AS
THE DISEASE WHICH HAS
THE PATIENT."

SYMPTOMS OF VISCERAL DISEASE

CHAPTER I

INTRODUCTORY

THE EVOLUTION OF MODERN MEDICINE

As our studies in medicine penetrate deeper into the problems of each individual branch or specialty one fact stands out with ever increasing emphasis; namely, that medicine is a unit and not divisible into specialties. The superior man in the medicine of the future will not be the great laboratory worker, or the man who is known for his studies in metabolism or the expert gastroenterologist, or neurologist, or surgeon or he who stands preeminently above his confreres in his knowledge of diseases of the heart and arterial system or of the lungs, but the man who recognizes the fact that the truths derived from all of these sources of study and investigation must be interpreted as belonging to the human patient as a whole—in other words, the internist who recognizes both the psychical and the physical man and appreciates the unity of medicine. The distinguished specialist will be one who regards his field of study in its intimate relationships to the body as a whole.

Modern medicine is a wonderful illustration of the triumphant force of truth and knowledge. It is not necessary to go back more than a few decades to find that the greatest clinical teachers were almost wholly ignorant of the scientific basis of disease. Many of them were good clinical observers, but they were armed with few of the scientific facts which form the basis of modern medicine. Their knowledge was almost wholly gained from observing the sick patient, and this without anything more than the most rudimentary ideas of physiologic function. It was a medicine founded upon clinical observation based upon a smattering of anatomic and pathologic knowledge.

The state of mind which ruled medicine at that time is well illustrated by Pasteur's biographer, Vallery-Radot, who cites as an

21

example of the lack of appreciation of scientific effort the manner in which Claude Bernard's lectures on experimental physiology applied to medicine were received by the Académie de médicine in 1870. His hearers affirmed that "Physiology can be of no practical use in medicine; it is but a *science de luxe* which could well be dispensed with." The wonderful epoch-making contributions of Pasteur which laid the foundation of modern scientific medicine were received with no greater enthusiasm; but, on the other hand, met with the same opposition born of ignorance and conservatism. Nor is this to be wondered at, for his new idea, of diseases being due to microbes, was opposed to the theory of spontaneous generation which up to this time had held absolute sway in the minds of scientists. It is difficult for most men to change their opinions, even though they have never examined the reasonableness of those to which they subscribe; for "If it is painful to tenants to leave a home in which they have spent their youth, what must it be to break with one's whole education."

The status of every branch of science, every profession, every business rests upon a mass of supposedly established and accepted facts. Whether these are true or not does not matter, as far as their influence upon the branch of science, the profession or the business is concerned. They dominate it; and progress can be made only as increased knowledge displaces error or as these "facts" are changed to meet new conditions. This "consensus of opinion" makes for and establishes a "conservatism," which forces the discoverer of new truths not only to promulgate them but to fight for their acceptance. Such conservatism prevents many unproved and false theories from being accepted, and in this manner renders valuable aid to science. At times, it prevents; at other times, it postpones the acceptance of truths and hinders progress. This delay in recognizing truths caused Claude Bernard to say: "Those who sow on the field of science are not destined to reap the fruit of their labors," meaning that recognition is so slow that it comes after the scientist is dead. New discoveries depend upon increased knowledge or new application of known facts; but alas, those who sit in judgment upon them too often render their opinion without familiarizing themselves with the facts upon which they are based.

The conservatism of the medical profession in the last quarter of the nineteenth century opposed the findings of the laboratory and made the proponents of many fundamental discoveries fight for recognition; but when they had been understood and accepted, they seemed so plain that the ignorance and conservatism which had opposed them was in turn opposed, and clinical observation, which had previously been the cornerstone of medicine, was now discredited. One by one, the basic truths underlying modern scientific medicine have been established, each emphasizing the particular branch of medicine in which it originated; now bacteriology, now pathology, now biochemistry and biophysics and again one or the other of the clinical specialties; and all further emphasizing the lack of scientific foundation upon which medicine had previously rested. The result of this movement was that the physician of the old school was discredited. He either accepted the new advances that were being made or dropped by the wayside. The laboratory and the clinical specialist and those who could think in terms of the laboratory and of the specialties came into the ascendancy. This is where medicine stands today, but it is an illogical position in which the parts are emphasized at the expense of the whole. The mass of established facts in each of these branches, however, is now sufficient to call for a constructive unification. Fundamentally there is no antagonism between laboratory and clinical observation, none between the specialties and general clinical medicine. They must be brought together in the construction of the future unified medicine. Any study or analysis, therefore, which will show the interdependence of the various tissues and organs of the body and any study or analysis which will show the interdependence of the various branches and specialties of medicine will further this end and should be welcomed.

NECESSITY OF A NEW VIEWPOINT IN CLINICAL MEDICINE

The one outstanding need of modern medicine is accurate clinical observation and interpretation. This statement is not made to underrate or belittle the truly great observations that hereofore have been made, nor in a spirit of ingratitude toward those who have blazed the way. It is rather an admission that clinical observation has lagged behind when compared with the various phases of laboratory investigation. In fact, clinical medicine has been in danger of becoming not the master but the willing servant of the laboratory. Medical laboratories are operated for two purposes, to aid in the prevention of disease and to aid in the study and cure of those afflicted with disease.

The transposition by which the laboratory has been placed above clinical observation, has been due to many influences. Medicine has developed unevenly. Laboratory medicine has been an inviting field and has succeeded in interesting many of the brightest minds among the best trained of the younger men, who by dint of hard work have observed and correlated many important facts. The laboratory era, too, opened at a time when clinical medicine was losing some of its former prestige. The former reverence for the physician and the blind faith in his remedies were waning. Instead of seizing upon the new laboratory discoveries as being an aid to clinical observations, the clinician almost ceased to observe and made his opinions secondary to the laboratory findings; "laboratory diagnosis" became an accepted fact in medicine, and was over and above the observations of those who saw and studied the patients.

Laboratory workers deserve the greatest credit for the untiring energy which they have exerted and the invaluable contributions which they have made to medicine, through which it has been placed upon a scientific basis, but we are now able to look further ahead; and as we do, we recognize the clinician, the one who sees and studies the patient, as the one who must evaluate diagnostic data from all sources and give the final opinion. In order to be able to do this, he must not only be familiar with laboratory methods and be able to interpret properly such findings, but he must also cultivate the same accuracy of observation for the study of the patient as the laboratory worker has developed in the study of his subject. The clinician's subject, however, is the patient, with all his departures from normal function and all the abnormal tissues, secretions, and excretions found by whatever method of examination.

PATHOLOGY AND MODERN MEDICINE

Modern medicine has been dominated by a one-sided pathology which has devoted itself to the earnest study of *disease* and to the changes which this disease produces in the various tissues, secretions, and excretions of the body. Pathologic anatomy, bacteriology, serology, and biochemistry under conditions of disease, have thus received most of the thought of our rapidly developing science.

It readily can be seen that, no matter how interesting and how valuable studies of tissues, secretions, and excretions are, they leave much to be desired from the standpoint of the everyday practice of our profession. As long as clinical medicine exists, the *patient* must be the subject of our earnest study and solicitation.

The one who is suffering from annoying or serious symptoms does not care nearly so much for the pathologic changes as he does for the annoyance which the symptoms give him or the harm that may accrue from them. While it is necessary for scientific physicians to have all the aid that pathologic anatomy, bacteriology, serology, biochemistry, and biophysics are able to give them, yet this is all on one side of the question. In this the patient does not see the intimate relationship which is borne to his sufferings. Is there nothing on the side of the patient that we may also study? By studying the patient can we not learn how and through what agencies disease processes effect changes? These questions must be answered in the affirmative. *There is no study today that offers us greater hope for the future practice of medicine than the study of the individual who has the disease and the means by which the disease expresses itself in his tissues, secretions, and excretions—the study of pathologic physiology or "functional pathology" as it is often called.* Increased knowledge in this line of research is absolutely indispensable if we are to make the greatest use and application of the principles and facts revealed by the modern laboratory.

INACCURACY OF CLINICAL OBSERVATIONS

No one who has experienced the difficulties which beset the physician in his examination of the patient, can doubt that great inaccuracies are bound to creep into the data obtained through studying the patient. Much of this inaccuracy arises because of our own lack of knowledge; part of it to inaccurate and insufficient observation. It is not all due to the wrong application of knowledge, nor is it all due to misinformation furnished by the patient.

If one compares clinical observations and interpretations with laboratory data and their interpretations, there is not so much difference in the degree of accuracy of the two as is generally believed. Too much dependence is put in laboratory findings, while clinical observation is underrated and often belittled. Nothing at our command will detect clinical tuberculosis as early as careful study and examination of the patient and the evident departures from normal physiologic function which he manifests; while dependence on the laboratory will often postpone diagnosis until the chances of cure are greatly reduced. In the examination of sputum for rare tubercle bacilli, J. E. Pottenger[1] has shown that the percentage of diagnoses increases with any given method up to a certain point, according to the amount of time spent in the search. In examining sputums containing few bacilli, the most accurate method of examination reveals on a two-minute search of the specimens, only 10 per cent of the positive diagnoses that are shown in a fifteen-minute search. Nearly all diagnoses made in clinical laboratories depend upon a method much inferior to this. As a rule, the search is carried on for only a few minutes, there being no definite time of search, yet the findings are often taken as final. Syphilis, as a clinical entity, is often determined by the clinical observer when the laboratory shows doubt. The real estimate of the heart when this organ is diseased can only be derived, as is so well emphasized by Mackenzie, by studying the patient.

Both laboratory and clinical observations should go hand in hand; but that method of examination which comes in intimate relationship with the patient—clinical observation—must assume more and more responsibility in diagnosis and prognosis as observers familiarize themselves more with the normal physiologic processes in the body. Let us recognize the fact that good clinical observation can be made as valuable and probably about as accurate as good laboratory observation. Neither method is free from error, nor is one so vastly superior that the other should be deprecated. Without an accurate knowledge of the physiologic processes going on within the body, and the pathologic changes wrought in them by disease, proper interpretation cannot be placed on laboratory data.

MODERN CLINICAL TEACHING AT FAULT

While students are taught to reason for themselves more than they were in former times, yet the study of medicine is made too much a matter of memory. Principles should be taught and then the pupil should be guided in the careful study of their application. If students were to become familiar with the basic studies, anatomy, physiology, chemistry, physics, psychology, bacteriology, pathologic anatomy, pathologic physiology, pathologic chemistry and physics, and pathologic psychology, it would make little difference in what branch of medicine they were taught the application of the principles. The application of principles, however, involves higher mental processes than their memorizing; every student should be given a thorough drill in clinical analysis in which he should be made to see the relationship which exists between the fundamental facts and their clinical application.

There has been too much of a tendency in modern medicine to underrate the value of theorizing. Science cannot unfold alone as a succession of facts. The active inventive mind looks at things not only as entities, but also in their broad relationships. From facts, theories spring up which must be followed out and proved or disproved. Theorizing is a legitimate instrument for the advancement of science. It was ably championed by Pasteur, who said: "Without theory, practice is but routine born of habit. Theory alone can bring forth and develop the spirit of invention."

One must not, however, be a slave to any theory no matter by whom propounded. One should be ready to change when knowledge of fundamental facts warrants change. This has been well stated by Claude Bernard as follows: "When you meet with a fact opposed to a prevailing theory, you should adhere to the fact and abandon the theory, even when the latter is supported by great authorities and generally adopted."

Imagination should be cultivated in medicine. How dull our practice of medicine when we see no relationship between our primary facts and our end-results. How interesting and how wonderful the unfolding when one can see relationships in all the branches of this wonderful science. A fact is worth little unless it can be applied, and it cannot be applied unless the one who knows the fact has vision enough to see where it fits in.

Many relationships which should be obvious to the clinician are facing him each day, but are unrecognized because of his lack of imagination. He fails to connect the cause and the effect because he fails to recognize the instrument through which the cause operates.

In this monograph I shall attempt to gather together from the labors of physiologists, data with which we may construct a bridge between cause and effect in certain disease processes.

NORMAL CONTROL OF BODY ACTIVITIES

The cells of the body consist of colloidal substances which unite with crystalloids according to physical and chemical laws. The ionic content of the cell is unstable and changes during activity. So does the permeability of the cell membrane change, being permeable to many substances during activity and impermeable to most substances during rest (Bayliss[2] and Burns[3]). Each cell has within itself the power of action which is accompanied by changes in its colloidal make-up or its ionic content. Thus action on the part of cells may take place without the intervention of nerve impulse; but this does not mean that cells are independent of nerves, for they are stimulated to activity or inhibited in their action, and their activity is brought into harmony with action in other structures by stimuli which course through the nerves.

While it has been suggested, from a failure to find nerve connection to a few minor structures, that they may be free from direct nerve influence, yet this has not been proved; and, in our discussion of practical clinical relationships, we are safe in assuming that action presumes nerve connection. There is a chemical control which depends upon the colloidal state and ionic content of the cell, and others consisting of various metabolic substances and the products of the glands of internal secretion, which act centrally through, or with, the nerves as they influence tissues. Correlation of body activities cannot occur except through nerves and chemical substances, such as the products of the glands of internal secretion.

Nöel Paton[4] in the introduction to his monograph, *Regulators of Metabolism,* says: "It is now universally recognized that the chemical changes in protoplasm which constitute its metabolism, are the basis of all the phenomena of life, alike of the manifest activities of movement and of the less visible but no less real activities of development, growth and repair. In fact, we no longer look upon protoplasm as a substance; we now recognize that it is protoplasm only in virtue of its constant cycle of chemical changes." These chemical changes result from activity in the cell itself or in its nerve control.

1. **Chemical Control.**—The lowest forms of life have no nervous system, yet they live and change, which means chemical action. They adapt themselves to their surroundings, that is, they react to physi-

cal stimulation. The human embryo, in its earliest development, likewise, has no nervous system, yet growth and change take place, which is evidence of chemical activity. Paton attributes the first impulse to development to hereditary inertia, but considers that it is superseded by chemical control and later by nervous control.

All cells, whether muscular or secretory, possess rhythm. They show periods of activity followed by periods of rest. This rhythm is influenced by, but is partly independent of, nerves and internal secretions. It is dependent upon a continuous chemical change which takes place in the ions which are found in the cells. The stimulus which produces the chemical exchange is either of nervous origin or due to the presence of free ions in the fluids surrounding the cells which are able to displace those which are already combined within it.

After development proceeds and the viscera are formed, there are certain ones which produce secretions which are discharged into the blood stream and have as their function the influencing of growth and body activities. These are called "internal secretions." They have the power of influencing distant tissues and, to a limited degree, have the property possessed so highly by the nervous system, of correlating activities. The glands which produce the principal substances having such control, are the thyroid, parathyroid, thymus, hypophysis, pituitary, adrenals, pancreas, mucosa of small intestines, and gonads.

These glands are under nerve control, but may be influenced by electrolytes and other internal secretions. These internal secretions also influence the nervous system. They control, and in turn are controlled by, the calcium, sodium, and potassium, and the water and sugar balances of the body.

The internal secretions, the vegetative nervous system, the ionic content, and physical state of the cell must all be considered together in order to understand normal physiologic control and pathologic disturbance in function of smooth musculature and secretory structures of the body; in other words, in order to understand normal and pathologic physiologic activity.

2. **Nerve Control.**—As the human embryo develops, it becomes necessary that there be a quicker response and a greater correlation of activity; so, before the viscera are formed, the neural canal comes into existence and the motor cells which are to give origin to the

fibers of the vegetative nervous system, escape and start their migration peripheralwards. They send out their fibers which enter the various organs even before the tissues of the organs are fully differentiated.

Nerves, however, are dependent upon the ionic content of the cells for their activity. When a stimulus passes to cells over nerves, it causes them either to discharge ions or to combine with certain ions as is discussed more fully in Chapter VII.

With the development of the central nervous system, the reflex comes into its greatest perfection. Some lower forms of life seem to be physically influenced by their surroundings. Reflex control is not perfected until the central nervous system is formed, and does not come into its highest perfection without the fullest development of the brain and spinal cord. This latest development makes possible the greatest degree of integrative action and makes the physical man superior to all other forms of animal life.

The vegetative nervous system, being that system which influences those functions without which the animal cannot exist, is given an intimate and direct control over metabolic activity.

It is especially necessary to emphasize this because it is so often inferred that metabolism is controlled only by the endocrines. There is an intimate relationship between these two vegetative systems, and physiologic activity may be expressed both in terms of the vegetative nerves and in syndromes of endocrine activity. The study of the physiologic activity of the vegetative nervous system becomes a duty of clinicians. Its pathologic activity expresses itself in disturbed function and it is a most important bridge between pathologic stimuli and the pathologic changes in tissues, secretions, and excretions. *The vegetative nervous system then, when its normal action is disturbed, furnishes one of the chief paths through which symptoms of visceral disease are expressed.* It affords the common bridge between activator and end-result. See Part I for discussion of the Vegetative Nervous System.

PHYSICAL CONDITION CHANGES BODY CONTROL

The chief factor in adjustment to man's environment is the afferent or ingoing impulse of the reflex. In this the nervous system is like a telephone exchange; the call is put in through a wire, the connection is made, and the action is then carried out over the out-going wire—afferent neuron, synapse, and efferent neuron.

The first part of every reflex is a sensory stimulus; every portion of the body is provided with sensory nerves, which, when acted upon, carry the impulse to the central nervous system. If the sensory stimulus is slight, it may not be enough to overcome the resistance in the synapse. In such case, no effect would be transmitted beyond the sensory system. If the stimulus is greater, however, then it is transmitted to other neurons, either motor or sensory, or both, and some near-by or distant structure is influenced: it may be a pain is felt, a muscular contraction occurs, or secretory activity is influenced. These sensory nerves may be the nerves of sight, smell, hearing, taste, or touch, or nerves excited by chemical and mechanical stimuli. The immediate result is motor or sensory action; if normal physiologic activity is sufficiently disturbed, symptoms of disease will appear.

Man is a receptor mechanism, influenced by every force in his environment. He receives all impulses which come through sensory nerves whether they are those of meteorologic and cosmic origin, such as changes in atmospheric temperature, changes in humidity, barometric pressure, light, and variation in wind movement; or those more generally recognized, such as those due to physical or chemical contact. All such forces are carried centralward over sensory nerves and transferred to the visceral system; acting through visceral nerves, they produce changes throughout the organism and affect man both physically and psychically.

PSYCHIC ACTIVITY CHANGES BODY CONTROL

Man is further endowed with a psychic system which is capable of influencing nerve and chemical control. As the *reflex* is the basis of physical action, the *idea* is the basis of psychic action; *and as normal function on the part of the nervous system is essential to physical equilibrium, so are normal trends of thought necessary to a mental or psychical equilibrium.*

While we do not understand fully the relationship which exists between the physical and the psychic, we do know that they bear a close relationship to each other. The psychic condition is influenced greatly by man's physical condition and the manner in which he reacts or has reacted to his environment; his physical condition, on the other hand, depends much upon the equilibrium or loss of equilibrium in his psychic being. Of the two it would seem that the psychic influence over physiologic body function is greater than the physical over the psychic. We occasionally see those physically weak with apparently perfect trends of thought, but it is rare to see one with a disturbed psychic equilibrium who does not have some disturbed physiologic function. Wrong trends of thought, if persisted in, are usually followed by pathologic change in physiologic action. This result is brought about through nerve stimulation and changes in internal secretions.

Modern thought requires that we get away from the idea that the psyche resides in a certain portion of the brain. It is a *force*, an *energy* which we must conceive of as being present in all body structures (Mathews[5]). Its normal activity results in normal conduct, its pathologic activity in abnormal conduct. As the action of the body depends on the manner in which the physical man reacts to outward and inward stimuli, so man's conduct results largely from his psychologic reaction towards his environment.

DISEASE EXPRESSES ITSELF BOTH PHYSICALLY AND PSYCHICALLY

Diseases affect both the physical and psychic equilibrium. The nature and extent of the harm done depends upon the previous condition of the patient as well as upon the nature and duration of the disease.

Disease affects the physical being by influencing the physics of the cell directly, or indirectly through changes in its own and in its environmental electrolytes which may be brought about by the vegetative nervous system and the glands of internal secretion.

The influence of disease upon psychic reaction manifests itself in both acute and chronic maladies. Sometimes acute, serious, psychic reactions follow acute diseases, which run their course in a few days. Chronic pathologic conditions, however, result in prolonged harmful stimulation of nerve cells which produce in them a condition of fatigue and irritability which leads to a more or less general disturbance in body function. This often results in a change in the individual's reaction toward his social as well as his physical surroundings. The former results in wrong trends of thought and shows in instability of conduct. Nearly all patients who suffer from chronic disease, and this is especially true of chronic infections, show some degree of neurasthenia and psychasthenia. No patient with well-marked neurasthenia or psychasthenia can escape disturbance in physiologic equilibrium. Irritability on the part of nerve cells means unstable action, which has as its necessary concomitant, disturbed function; and this when long continued is prone to disturb the individual's method of thought and influence his conduct.

There can be no doubt that psychic unbalance affords a basis for disease. By altering nerve and chemical control, it produces pathologic metabolic states; it is but natural that these should lower resistance and predispose to infection.

A RATIONAL BASIS FOR STUDY OF DISEASE

The study of medicine in the future should give more attention to the individual who has the disease, a phase of the subject which has been sadly neglected in the past. The fact should be emphasized that *there is not only a disease which has the patient but a patient who has the disease.* It is necessary to continue study along the lines of pathologic anatomy, bacteriology, serology, and laboratory chemistry; but it is equally important to seek out the means through which bacteria and other harmful agencies produce the pathologic changes in tissues, secretions, and excretions. This we find by studying the normal nerve and chemical body controls and the disturbances in function which result from their pathologic stimulation.

In previous papers,[6,7] I suggested that, *since much of the normal physiologic equilibrium of the body is maintained through nerves and internal secretions, and inasmuch as most symptoms of disease are expressions of disturbances in this normal physiologic control, therefore most symptoms are due to altered nerve and endocrine activity. I further suggested that the stimuli which disturb this physiologic control may be either physical or psychic in origin and that the resulting action depends upon the cell and its electrolytic balance.* Mackenzie[8] suggested that the causes of most symptoms are *disturbances in normal reflexes.* In this he recognizes the endocrine system as a modifier of nerve action.

The rational study of disease, whether it be for the purpose of diagnosis, prognosis, or therapy, demands an understanding above all else of the physics of the cell and the influence exerted upon the cell through the nervous and endocrine systems. In the discussion which follows, the internal secretions will be connected up with the vegetative nerves where the action is evident, but it would make the task too great to undertake a complete discussion; it would lead me too far from my purpose, which is particularly to show the relationship of the visceral nerves to the symptoms of disease, and to show how symptoms are produced and what symptoms may be expected with a given disease.

ORGANIC VERSUS FUNCTIONAL DISEASE

The inevitable result of the rapid strides in the study of bacteriology, and pathologic change in tissues and secretions, and the comparatively slow progress which has been made in studying the patient, has been an undue emphasis of the importance of the disease and a minimizing of the importance of the patient who has it. This, in the recent past, had gone to such an extent that no matter how annoying or distressing the symptoms on the part of any organ, if no anatomic changes could be found in the organ, the symptoms were disregarded and turned aside as being "functional." The only kind of disease that was worthy of accurate study seemed to be one attended by a definite injury to or destruction of tissue. The dawning of a better day in medicine, however, is now evident; a day in which the patient and the disturbances in function of his various organs will receive due study and investigation. This requires a study of the electrolytes without which there could be no cellular activity, and the nervous and hormonal correlation and integration which cause the body to function as a whole.

It matters nothing to the comfort of the patient who is suffering from a distressing symptom, whether or not it has an underlying pathology in the particular organ in which the symptom manifests itself. It is of great importance, however, for the physician to know that symptoms on the part of one organ or system may be caused either by disturbed physiologic equilibrium in the organ or system in question, or reflexly by pathologic changes in some other organ or system.

This is well illustrated in pulmonary tuberculosis, in which reflex symptoms for the most part group themselves in organs and tissues outside of the respiratory system, thus: hoarseness, tickling in the larynx, and cough, refer to the larynx; the digestive disturbances, whether motor or secretory, refer to the gastrointestinal canal; the rapid or slow heart to the cardiovascular system; while the reflex motor and trophic changes in the superficial soft structures may wrongly be interpreted as being due to local nerve lesions. It is necessary to understand reflex relationships in order to interpret these symptoms correctly. Because of the reflex nature of these symptoms, patients suffering from pulmonary tuberculosis are continually consulting specialists in other lines, particularly laryngologists and gastroenterologists, who, also, too frequently treat the functional derangement as an entity. The chest specialist, on the other hand, often approaches a case of asthma as though it were a disease of the lungs, when in reality it is a fundamental condition of the tissues acted upon by substances which stimulate the vagal neurocellular mechanism, the cause of which may be as varied as the causes which stimulate the pulmonary branches of the vagus.

It shall be the purpose of this study to show the interrelationship of organs and systems of the body; to point out the manner in which they are bound together by the nervous system and how the action of different parts is correlated and integrated; and, further, how a disturbance in one organ influences others through this nervous system. It is a study of symptoms, the interpretation of which is the basis of clinical medicine. In this, I hope that the true worth of functional disturbances on the part of organs will appear.

References

1. Pottenger, F. M.: Clinical Tuberculosis, St. Louis, 1917, The C. V. Mosby Co., Vol. 1, p. 542 (Chapter on Laboratory Methods).
2. Bayliss, William M.: Interfacial Forces and Phenomena in Physiology (Herter Lectures, 1922), London, Methuen and Co., Ltd., p. 133.
3. Burns, David: An Introduction to Biophysics, New York, 1921, The Macmillan Co., pp. 111 and 133.
4. Paton, Nöel: Regulators of Metabolism, London, 1913, The Macmillan Co.
5. Mathews, Albert P.: Some General Aspects of the Chemistry of the Cells. General Cytology, Edited by E. V. Cowdry, Chicago, 1924, Univ. Chicago Press.
6. Pottenger, F. M.: The Patient's Reaction: A Neglected But Important Phase in the Study of Medicine, Ann. Med. 1: No. I, April, 1920.
7. Pottenger, F. M.: The Importance of the Study of Symptoms With a Discussion of MacKenzie's Law Governing Their Production, Tr. Sect. Practice Med., A. M. A., 1921, p. 230.
8. Mackenzie, Sir James: The Theory of Disturbed Reflexes in the Production of Symptoms of Disease, Brit. M. J. 1: 147, 1921.

PART I

THE VEGETATIVE NERVOUS SYSTEM

CHAPTER II

THE VEGETATIVE NERVOUS SYSTEM: GENERAL CONSIDERATIONS

For the anatomy and physiology of the vegetative nervous system, I am compelled to rely on the works of others. Frequent reference will be made to these various authors, but exact citations will be given only where they are quoted literally. My material has been drawn from such works as those of Gaskell,[1] Langley,[2] Sherrington,[3] Lucas,[4] Bechterew,[5] Lewandowsky,[6] Higier,[7] Müller,[8] Jelliffe and White,[9] Starling,[10] Bayliss,[11] Luciani,[12] Tigerstedt,[13] Eppinger and Hess,[14] Guillaume,[15] Cannon,[16] Keith,[17] Bailey and Miller,[18] Biedl,[19] Falta,[20] Paton,[21] Lereboullet, Harvier, Carrion and Guillaume,[22] Gley,[23] and Kuntz.[24]

My hope is that I may be able to present to the clinician the important facts of vegetative neurology in such a manner that they may be understood and applied in the everyday practice of medicine.

Control of Protoplasmic Activities.—A study of body activity must be directed to chemical, physical, and nerve control.

The nervous system is divided into voluntary and involuntary, or somatic and visceral. It is further made up of efferent and afferent neurons. The efferent neurons which supply somatic structures have their cell bodies within the central nervous system. Those which supply visceral structures have their cell bodies either in ganglia outside of the central nervous system or in the walls of the structures which they supply. The visceral nervous system is a system of efferent neurons only. It borrows its sensory or afferent neurons from the somatic system. These afferent neurons, since they supply tissues and organs which are shielded from outside injury, have not developed that property of keenly expressing pain which belongs

36

to the somatic sensory neurons; in fact, their most important function seems to be that of carrying impulses centralward from the viscera and mediating reflexes with efferent neurons in other organs and tissues of both the somatic and visceral systems.

Stimulation of an efferent nerve either directly or reflexly brings about action. This action may result in the contraction of muscles, in increased secretory activity, or in inhibition of these. Stimulation of an afferent nerve may result in some form of sensation or an impulse which starts reflex action. Whenever a muscle comes intimately in contact with the outside world, it is innervated by voluntary nerves. Such control seems necessary for the protection of the organism.

The voluntary system consists of some of the cranial nerves and the spinal nerves. These nerves supply muscles which are under the direct control of the will; because of this they are spoken of as voluntary muscles. The voluntary muscles consist of those belonging to the skeletal or somatic system. Their fibers differ from those belonging to the involuntary or vegetative system in being striated.

While the power to act in skeletal muscles is derived from nerves which belong to the voluntary system, the metabolism of these muscles depends upon the vegetative system, the same as that of all other structures of the body.

The phenomena of life are manifestations of activity in colloidal systems controlled by chemical laws and subject to nerve stimulation. Child[25] states that: "Protoplasm, instead of being a peculiar living substance with a peculiar complex morphological structure necessary for life, is on the one hand a colloid product of the chemical reactions, and on the other a substance in which the reactions occur and which influences their course and character both physically and chemically."

The colloids of the body cells combine according to physical and chemical laws with crystalloids and form true chemical compounds. Activity in the cells consists of physical and chemical reactions which depend upon the surface charge and the particular ions in the cell and in the medium which surrounds it as well as upon their relative proportion. Nerve stimulation produces its effect by causing the colloids to give up certain ions, to bind them more closely or to take up others, as discussed in Chapter VII.

Protoplasmic activity under physiologic and pathologic conditions is the subject under investigation in scientific medicine. Not only the activity in cells but the correlation of activity of the cells throughout the body must be considered, if we would understand body activities. This leads to the study of that particular part of the nervous system—the vegetative—through which processes necessary to life and tissue change, or metabolism, are influenced.

Nöel Paton[21] calls the forces which act in embryonic life "hereditary inertia" or "inherited developmental tendencies." He assumes that these unknown and uncomprehended tendencies are working to shape a definite form and determined action prior to the appearance of the regulating forces which later control the organism. Later in the period of growth they become less important in their control and are replaced by definite nerve and chemical forces which act partly with and partly without the action of the will.

While body activities are greatly influenced through the nervous system there are chemical substances in the form of internal secretion which also exert control. The action of hormones is sometimes exerted through nerves and sometimes without nerve innervation.

Stimuli may be either physical or psychic in origin. Psychic conditions affect body activities through both the nervous system and the products of internal secretion in much the same manner as afferent stimuli which arise in physical structures. The importance of this fact has not yet been sufficiently appreciated by practitioners of medicine, yet every practitioner has seen the equilibrium of the nervous system as thoroughly disturbed from psychic as from physical causes. I have referred to this subject briefly in Chapter XVIII, but since it is so intimately connected with activities of the vegetative nerves and their influence on protoplasmic activity, I deem it best to discuss the subject more fully at this time.

Chemical Control of Body Activities.—With our newer study of physiology, we are learning that there are many substances circulating in the body fluids which have to do with metabolic activity. Some of these are the products of physiologic action, others are the products of pathologic action. Some, when provided in normal quantities, keep up normal physiologic activity, but when present in abnormal amounts produce harmful effects. Others produce functional disturbances even if present only in small amounts.

Aside from the so-called "ductless glands" many other glands, such as those of the gastrointestinal mucosa, the liver, and the pancreas, produce internal secretions which exert an influence upon physiologic activity. In fact, we may not be far from the truth if we state that probably every tissue of the body produces an internal secretion or chemical substance which has some physiologic action. Pathologic action which results from substances entering the circulation when tissues are injured is also extremely common in disease.

The higher organisms are complex structures made up of many independent cells. In order to bring the whole to any degree of efficiency, it is necessary that the action of these cells be correlated. This is brought about through chemical substances and the nervous system. The chemical control is a much slower, and a much less efficient control than that produced by the nervous system, yet its action is extremely definite. This may be illustrated by *secretin* (Bayliss and Starling), a substance which is produced by the duodenal glands when stimulated by the acid contents of the stomach. Secretin passes into the circulation, and circulating through the body, comes in contact with cells of the pancreas and increases the flow of pancreatic juice. It also has a lesser effect upon the cells of the liver, producing a flow of bile. The marvelous part of this action is its selectivity, as emphasized by the fact that *secretin* must pass through the liver, right heart, lungs, left heart, and then the systemic structures; it must pass through practically all structures of the body but, as far as we know, stimulates only the pancreatic and liver cells. Thus the production of bile and pancreatic juice, two substances which are necessary to further digestion, is stimulated by a secretion which is brought about by the acid when poured into the duodenum. *Secretin* will produce the flow of pancreatic juice when all the connector neurons going to the pancreas are severed. This does not necessarily mean that the action of secretin is independent of nerves, for it may act upon the parasympathetic cells in the organ.

The glands of internal secretion have been known to medicine for many decades, but their intensive study has taken place only within the last quarter of a century. The effects of the internal secretions are now known to be vital to the growth, development, and proper functioning of the organism. They are a vital part of the physiologic mechanism. They affect cellular activity in various organs and circulating in the fluid systems of the body correlate and integrate visceral function, supplementing the action of the visceral nerves. They exert an influence on fecundation, the maturation of the embryo, and sexual development. They are determining factors in both somatic and psychic spheres. They influence metabolic activity, exert a control over the electrolytes and pH of the blood, and so assume an important place in preserving physiologic equilibrium.[26]

One of our best known internal secretions is adrenalin. This is a chemical substance which is produced by the chromaffin tissue found in the medulla of the adrenals. It passes into the blood stream, circulates, and stimulates structures which react to central stimulation of the sympathetic nerves. Adrenalin acts peripherally at the junction of the sympathetic filament and the muscle cell or in the lateral or collateral ganglia as shown by Hartman, page 364. When adrenalin is thrown into the blood stream, it produces an effect on the structures on which it acts like that produced when the sympathetic nerves are centrally stimulated. According to Swale Vincent, Hoskins and Stewart,[27] adrenalin is not found in the circulating blood in normal states of activity. Others believe differently.

An illustration of a chemical substance which results from general body activity is that of CO_2, which is a product of all tissue activity. It acts on the respiratory center in the medulla, and automatically governs the frequency and depth of respiratory effort. In this connection, insulin,[28] the active substance of the pancreas, must also be mentioned. See Chapter XXXV for further discussion.

Nerve Control of Body Activities.—While a slow coordination of body activity such as that maintained by the "internal secretions," may be carried on by chemical substances circulating in the blood, yet, if a quick response and a rapid correlation are required, they must be brought about through the nervous system.

In nerve action there is a difference between the voluntary system and the vegetative system. In the voluntary system the response is almost immediate. In the vegetative system it is somewhat delayed. In all cases in which a quick response is necessary, nerve conduction must be provided. Acts of defense, such as closing the eyelids at the approach of dust, drawing the hand away from the fire, the contraction of muscles for escape from danger, all depend upon rapid and correlated action. The rapidity with which such action is called forth may be illustrated by the muscle response which is necessary in order to remove the foot from a harmful stimulation. Within a very small fraction of a second, a stimulus arising from an injury applied to the toe may be carried through the sensory nerves to the cells in the ganglion on the posterior root of the lower spinal nerves, thence be conducted through other fibers to the thalamus, and then by another neuron to the sensory cortical area. By a complicated route it is transferred from the cortical sensory area to the cortical motor area. An act of will results. The impulse is sent out over fibers to the motor cells in the spinal nerves, which send fibers to the muscles of the leg, and the leg is withdrawn. The control of the internal viscera is through reflexes brought about by sensory stimuli which are not necessarily transferred to the sensory areas in the cortex. While the path of the reflex is often shorter, the response is not as rapid.

In the voluntary system, action and inhibition of action are under the influence of the will. Nerves supplying different sets of muscles come into play. In reciprocal sets of muscles, if one is contracted, the other, as a part of the same act, is relaxed; as for example, contraction of the biceps and inhibition of the triceps. In the vegetative (involuntary) system, on the other hand, there are two methods by which action and inhibition of action are produced. One is through a single system of nerves but through different fibers in which the motor effect varies according to the strength of the stimulus; the other is through two opposing sets of neurons, the one belonging to the sympathetic, the other to the parasympathetic system. When the same tissues are supplied by both sets of nerves, usually one activates and the other inhibits action. The pilomotor muscles and the blood vessels for the most part are controlled by the sympathetic nerves only, relaxation and contraction depending on different fibers or different stimuli. All smooth muscle is maintained in a normal state of tonus. This tonus may be disturbed by nerve or chemical stimuli. In all structures belonging to the enteral system except the esophagus and the cardiac end of the stomach (lungs, pyloric end of stomach, small intestines, colon, liver, pancreas, and body of the bladder) a state of equilibrium is maintained as long as the action of the neurons of the sympathetics and parasympathetics equal each other; equilibrium is destroyed, however, and functional derangement is produced when one overbalances the other.

At the beginning and end of the intestinal tract there are some structures which have a combination of voluntary and involuntary nerve control.

Psychic Influence on Body Activities.—One of the features in which man differs from other animals is in the development of the faculty of reasoning. The psychic side, by which he is able to perceive, enjoy, hope and desire, or suppress these emotions, is able to affect greatly and modify both nerve impulses and chemical secretions; consequently, the psychic state of the individual assumes great importance in the human being. Its impress upon the physical body is made for the most part through the nervous system, and will be referred to from time to time in that connection. Its effect upon the physiologic activity of the organism through altered secretion of the endocrine glands is also well recognized.

Significance of the Nervous System.—Each body cell has its own action and each organ its own function. If each cell or organ should functionate without regard to other cells or organs, it would be equivalent to all citizens of a state living and acting without regard for others. A state of anarchy would result. Harmonious activity can come only through correlation of action. In the animal organism this correlation is brought about partly through chemical substances but mainly through the nervous system, as previously mentioned. Through it the action of every cell is subordinated to the good of the whole.

The central nervous system in its development is closely related to the surface of the body. This is exceptionally well shown in Figs. 1, 2, and 3. Fig. 1 represents a diagrammatic section across the back of an anencephalic child, in which the medullary plates were exposed on both head and spine. From this illustration the relationship of the medullary plates to the skin is evident and appears as modified parts of the ectoderm. The formation of the neural canal of the human embryo is well illustrated in Fig. 2, in which the infolding of the ectoderm is shown. Fig. 3 shows diagrammatically the differentiation of the ectodermal cells of the medullary

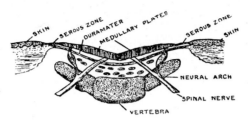

Fig. 1.—Diagrammatic section across the back of an anencephalic child in which the medullary plates were exposed on both head and spine. (Keith.)

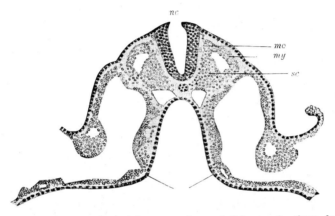

Fig. 2.—Transverse section of human embryo of 2.4 mm. to show developing neural canal. (T. H. Brice, from Starling.) *nc*, neural canal; *mc*, muscle plate; *my*, outer wall of somite; *sc*, sclerotome.

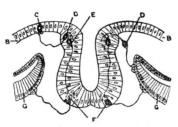

Fig. 3.—Diagram to show how the ectodermal cells of the medullary plates are differentiated into nerve cells or neuroblasts and supporting cells or spongioblasts. (After Prenant.)
The central canal is being enclosed by upgrowth of the medullary plates. *B*, *B*, ectoderm; *C*, sensory cell in ectoderm; *D*, *D*, cells which become enclosed in posterior root ganglion; *E*, *E*, nerve cells which connect the sensory and motor cells; *F*, *F*, motor cells in anterior horn; *G*, *G*, muscle plates. (Keith.)

plates into nerve cells or neuroblasts and supporting cells or spongio-blasts; and further gives a clear idea of the development of the various cell components of the cord.

In order that the organism may live and multiply, it must be endowed with means for preserving its life. Self-preservation becomes more important and more complex as evolution proceeds. It is in connection with this function of self-preservation that the central nervous system has developed.

If one would form an idea of what is going on within the body, he must know something of the nervous system. The normal body is continuously striving to adapt itself to its environment. The environment contains many hostile elements; but through various methods of defense which have been devised, deleterious influences are quickly perceived and a proper method of rendering them harmless is instituted.

The animal learns of harmful influences through its senses—sight, hearing, smell, taste, and touch. Aside from the organs of special sense, afferent nerves with receptors for detecting many types of sensory changes are distributed to every portion of the surface of the body and also to all internal tissues. Stimuli which are picked up by these receptors are carried centralward where they are translated into action; for this purpose a second group, the efferent nerves, becomes necessary. The impulse of the afferent nerve is not always transmitted directly to the efferent nerve, but passes through other connecting fibers before reaching it. In the voluntary nervous system these impulses may be carried up to the higher centers in order to call the will into judgment before action results.

The vegetative system comprises both efferent and afferent neurons. Unlike the voluntary system, the sensory or afferent neurons of the vegetative system possess the power of expressing pain only to a slight degree. (Mackenzie says, not at all.) They transmit sensory impulses, however, and join with sensory spinal nerves to cause referred pain on the surface of the body. This is discussed more fully in Chapter XII.

The individual is limited by the manner in which he responds to afferent stimuli; in other words, the manner in which he responds to his environment. Environment in this connection means both external and internal forces. The most constant forces to which man must react are those of meteorologic origin. He must hourly, daily, and seasonally adjust to differences in heat and cold, humidity, barometric pressure, and light intensity. These adjustments are made through both the somatic and the vegetative nervous systems. He must also adjust to changes within the body. The absorption of undigested food may start a train of symptoms. The toxins of disease may spread dysfunction throughout the entire body. Psychical upsets also disturb function generally throughout the tissues of the body. All such forces are mediated through the vegetative nervous system.

The actions of the body may be classified into those which are absolutely essential to life, and those which are not. Those essential to life must be carried on continuously without interruption, the others may be interrupted without harm.

The essential difference in these two classes of action calls for a difference in the type of nerve control, the one under the will, the other independent of it.

CHEMICAL TRANSMISSION OF NERVE IMPULSES

Since 1904 the time when Elliott,[29] noting the close resemblance between sympathetic stimulation and the action of adrenalin, first suggested that the nerve endings might liberate an adrenalin-like substance, Howell[30] and Howell and Duke[31] have shown that a relationship exists between vagus stimulation of the heart muscle and potassium, and Löwi[32] has shown that the perfusates from a heart in which the vagus is stimulated contain a different substance from the perfusate when the cardiac sympathetics are stimulated.

These observations have stimulated an earnest search to find out how nerve impulses are transmitted. In 1931 Cannon and Bacq[33] demonstrated that in normal animals, stimulation of the sympathetic nerves causes the passage of a sympathomimetic substance into the blood stream. This substance they called sympathin. It closely resembles adrenalin but has certain points of difference. It was later found that sympathin differs when stimulation of the sympathetic produces an excitatory and an inhibitory action. The important fact is that the nerve activity is transmitted by a release of sympathin which acts upon the cells.

Dale[34] had studied the pharmacologic effect of choline and found that it produced certain effects which were similar to muscarine and others similar to nicotine, thus producing both parasympathetic and sympathetic effects, and in 1933 he suggested a new classification of vegetative nerves into "cholinergic" and "adrenergic" according to which substance was used in transmitting the impulse.

Cholinergic fibers for the most part belong to the parasympathetics, while adrenergic fibers are of sympathetic origin.

Sweat, as is well known, is a sympathetically produced substance which does not respond to adrenalin. It responds to choline, so is cholinergic. Some of the sympathetic fibers supplying the stomach, uterus, nictitating membrane, and certain vasodilator fibers are also cholinergic.

Thus, some of the vagaries which were early noted in the action of the two components of the vegetative nervous system are being cleared up by a better understanding of how nerve impulses are transmitted.

Other important facts which have been established by these studies are that acetylcholine is the synaptic transmitter, and that the preganglionic fibers are the source of the substance. Acetylcholine is liberated when the nerve is stimulated and after transmitting the impulse is quickly hydrolyzed and gotten out of the way by esterase, which is found at the nerve terminals.

Significance of the Vegetative Nervous System.—As previously mentioned, the acts which are essential to life are carried out independently of the will. Cells possess the power of action independently of nerves; but efficiency of the working of the body as a machine could not be carried on without the regulatory and integrative action of the nervous system. Under all ordinary circumstances the human machine is so regulated by its neurons and its nerve centers which preside over essential functions that, whether awake or asleep, these functions are carried on in such a manner that life is maintained and the best interests of the individual are served. The scheme of the vegetative or involuntary nervous system is shown in Plates I and VII.

The vegetative system supplies the striated muscle of the heart, all smooth muscle of the body, and all secreting glands. The parts supplied by it are:

1. Certain subdermal structures; the pilomotor muscles and muscles of the sweat glands, possibly the glands themselves.

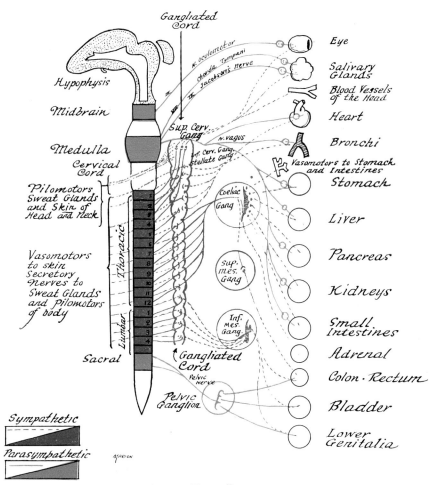

Ganglated Cord

Eye

Hypophysis

Salivary Glands

Midbrain

Blood Vessels of the Head

Heart

Medulla

Bronchi

Cervical Cord

Vasomotors to Stomach and Intestines

Pilomotors Sweat Glands and Skin of Head and Neck

Stomach

Liver

Vasomotors to skin Secretory Nerves to Sweat Glands and Pilomotors of body

Pancreas

Kidneys

Small Intestines

Sacral

Adrenal

Ganglated Cord

Colon · Rectum

Pelvic Nerve

Bladder

Pelvic Ganglion

Lower Genitalia

Sympathetic

Parasympathetic

PLATE I

SCHEMATIC ILLUSTRATION OF THE DISTRIBUTION OF THE TWO COMPONENTS OF THE VEGETATIVE NERVOUS SYSTEM, SHOWING ITS DIVISION INTO SYMPATHETIC AND PARASYMPATHETIC AND THEIR BRANCHES TO THE VARIOUS ORGANS.

The thoracicolumbar portion of the cord, which gives origin to the sympathetic nervous system, is represented in red. The portions of the midbrain and medulla, and sacral segments of the cord, which give origin to the parasympathetic system, are represented in blue. The peripheral nerves belonging to the parasympathetics are shown as solid blue lines, while those belonging to the sympathetic system are shown as red lines. This chart shows the double innervation of the structures of the head, heart, and the entire enteral system, and likewise indicates the single innervation for the blood vessels, pilomotor muscles and sweat glands of the body. (Modified from Meyer and Gottlieb.)

2. The heart and blood vessels.

3. The gastrointestinal tract, with the liver and pancreas.

4. The upper and lower respiratory tract.

5. The genitourinary tract.

6. Certain parts of the eye (pupil, ciliary body, Müllerian muscle, and lacrimal glands).*

7. All other smooth muscles and secretory glands of the body.

The vegetative nervous system consists of three distinct groups of neurons, one with its origin in the midbrain and bulb; one in the thoracic and upper lumbar segments of the cord; and a third in the sacral segments of the cord, as shown in Plates I and VII.

From these three groups of neurons, *all of the unstriped muscles, the heart, and all the secretory glands of the body, receive their motor power.* As will appear from our later discussion, the neurons which take their origin from the thoracic and upper lumbar portions of the cord (sympathetics) are quite generally opposed in their action in structures and organs supplied by both divisions of the vegetative system, by the neurons which take origin from either the midbrain, bulb, or sacral portion of the cord (parasympathetics) and vice versa. One group is the activator, the other the inhibitor, but this antagonism does not seem to be so absolute as was formerly taught. So often the action depends upon the state of activity of the organ or structure when stimulated. This is to be expected because action of cells depends on their electrolytic content and this varies with the rest and action periods of the cells and whether they are pathologically affected.

There are some structures, such as the pilomotor muscles, most of the blood vessels, and the structures derived wholly from the Müllerian and Wolffian ducts; viz., Fallopian tubes, uterus, vagina, vas deferens, seminal vesicles and ureter, which are supplied by filaments almost wholly from the sympathetics; likewise the cardiac end of the stomach, the esophagus and the ciliary muscle seem to be innervated wholly, or at least largely, by the parasympathetics.

As will be made plain as our discussion proceeds, there is a very close relationship between the sympathetic system and the chro-

---

*Hunter claims to have shown that striated muscle is composed of large and small fibers; the former, innervated by the voluntary nerves, contract muscles, the latter, innervated by the sympathetic nerves, produce a spastic state and hold the muscles in the position given them by the contracting fibers. Many have failed to confirm this.

maffin system of the lower vertebrates and invertebrates. Unstriated muscles which are brought into activity by stimulation of the sympathetic neurons, with a few exceptions, are also activated by adrenalin. This unstriated musculature includes that of the blood vessels and that lying immediately under the skin. Also related to the dermal musculature is that of the sphincter system and the musculature of the genitourinary tract. From this fact Gaskell suggests that the name ''vasodermal'' would be more appropriate than ''sympathetic'' for this system of nerves.

The dermal muscles supplied by the sympathetics are:

1. The pilomotor muscles and muscles of the sweat glands.

2. The urogenitodermal system, which includes all the involuntary muscles which originally surrounded the Wolffian and Müllerian ducts.

3. The alimentary canal system of involuntary muscles which consists of the sphincters of the gut, which according to Gaskell are probably of dermal origin.

There is another widespread group of involuntary muscles belonging to the alimentary canal and those organs derived from it. This may be called the ''endodermal'' (Gaskell) in contradistinction to the ''dermal'' musculature. This is found throughout the intestinal canal, the bronchial walls, the liver, gall bladder, pancreas, and urinary bladder, except the trigone. In order to understand these relationships, one must bear in mind that the lungs, gall bladder, liver, and pancreas are formed from diverticula from the esophagus and small intestine and that the body of the urinary bladder is formed from a diverticulum from the rectum. The innervation of these organs, therefore, is the same as that of the digestive tube from which they are derived.

This ''endodermal'' system of involuntary muscles is supplied with motor power by the cranial and sacral neurons of the vegetative system, and Gaskell has suggested that the entire system be called the ''enteral system'' to denote its embryologic relationship.

Aside from the endodermal structures just enumerated, there are certain structures in and about the eye and nasal chambers, and the salivary glands, which are innervated by vegetative fibers which course in the IIIrd, VIIth and IXth cranial nerves.

Confusion in Names.—There is so much confusion in the terms descriptive of that portion of the nervous system which is not under the control of the will, that it is necessary to make clear at the outset what is meant by the terms used.

The system as a whole is called by various writers: "Involuntary," "vegetative," "autonomic" and sometimes the "sympathetic."

The term "involuntary" is excellent except that all the acts performed by this system are not wholly independent of the will: for example, respiration may be either voluntary or involuntary; so may vomiting, defecation, urination, and many other acts. If this term is employed it is not fully descriptive of the system.

The term "autonomic" means self-governing and was suggested by Langley because those structures which are supplied by this system, although normally receiving impulses from the spinal cord through connector neurons, will continue for a time to functionate after they have been separated from the spinal cord; this term, however, has the same objection as "involuntary," in that it is not wholly adequate to describe the conditions. This system is not wholly independent. Another objection is that the term "autonomic" is applied to the system as a whole and is also used to designate one of the two divisions of the system, the bulbosacral outflow. Some physiologists speak of the entire system as the "sympathetic," but since there is almost general agreement in calling the division arising from the thoracic and upper lumbar segments of the cord, the "sympathetic," this term should be limited to that system, even though the term is without a rational meaning in a neurophysiologic sense.

"Vegetative," meaning pertaining to the functions which are necessary to life, is the term which characterizes this system best; and now that we are beginning to study this subject in clinical medicine it would be well to arrive at some definite use of terms so as to avoid confusion. I shall use the term *vegetative* throughout this monograph in speaking of the system as a whole.

DIVISIONS OF THE VEGETATIVE SYSTEM.—The vegetative system is made up of different parts taking their origin from widely separated portions of the central nervous system. Some of the fibers course in certain cranial nerves, the IIIrd, VIIth, IXth, and Xth. Others arise in the spinal cord. Those coming from the thoracic and upper lumbar segments of the cord are called the *sympathetic*, and those from the sacral portion constitute the *pelvic nerve*. The pelvic nerve is functionally related to the vegetative fibers in the IIIrd, VIIth, IXth, and Xth cranial nerves.

Functionally these various groups of nerves may be divided into two definite and distinct systems which produce more or less antagonistic effects in the structures in which they meet. Just as there are flexor and extensor actions in the superficial muscles supplied by the voluntary nervous system, so there are activating and inhibiting impulses carried to the structures supplied by the vegetative system. Sometimes these two types of impulses are carried by nerves of the same system, at other times by nerves of different systems (sympathetics and parasympathetics).

According to a similarity of function the vegetative system is divided into two component parts. In one of these groups are the fibers given off from the thoracic and upper lumbar segments of the cord, *the sympathetics;* in the other group those arising from the midbrain, bulb, and sacral portions of the cord, the *parasympathetics.*

The cell bodies which give origin to the neurons of the true sympathetic system lie in ganglia between the cord and the viscus innervated; those which give origin to the true parasympathetic system, on the other hand, are found in the walls of the organ supplied. It seems fitting then to group the vegetative fibers in the IIIrd, VIIth, IXth, and Xth cranial nerves and those in the sacral or pelvic nerve together. Various names have been applied to this group—"autonomic," "greater or extended vagus," and "parasympathetics." The use of the term "autonomic" will only confuse. "Greater or extended vagus," as used by Eppinger and Hess, classifies the neurons as being similar in action to the vagus, but also confuses and should be discarded. "Parasympathetic" has much in its favor, the prefix "para" meaning alongside of, or against. These fibers act against the sympathetics. In this monograph I shall use the term *parasympathetic* to designate the bulbosacral outflow of vegetative nerves.

Reflex.—One cannot proceed far in the study of visceral neurology without understanding the principles of reflex action. Luciani[35] defines a reflex thus: "The reflex act is the involuntary transformation of a centripetal into a centrifugal nerve impulse by means of a central organ represented by a group of nerve cells.'' A reflex arc is made up of at least two components, an afferent and an efferent neuron. The afferent neuron is always sensory because sensation is the only thing that may be perceived and carries the impulse to the cell bodies in the central nervous system. The cell bodies of the afferent neuron in the spinal cord are found in the ganglion of the posterior root. They are situated in this same ganglion, whether the afferent fibers supply the somatic or the visceral structures. The efferent component of a somatic motor neuron has its cell bodies in the anterior horn of the cord and in the motor nuclei of the cranial nerves, while the neurons which connect the central cells of the vegetative system with its motor cells which lie peripherally in ganglia and in the tissues of organs are situated in the lateral horn of the cord and in the motor nuclei of cranial vegetative nerves.

The connection of the two components of the reflex may be direct, but it is probable that such simple reflexes are comparatively rare. Other neurons are usually interposed between the two. The union which takes place between the axon of one neuron and the dendrites and cell bodies of another neuron in the reflex is called the *synapse*.

Some reflexes are extremely complex, others are very simple. This is illustrated in Figs. 4 and 5. In complex reflexes, several neurons may be interposed between the afferent and the efferent components of the reflex. Starling[36] in speaking of this complex nature of reflexes, says: ''When we study the structure of the central nervous system more fully, we find that although there are certain shortest possible paths, i.e., ones involving few neurons, for every impulse arriving at the central nervous system, yet so extensive is the branching of the entering nerve fibers and so complex are the neuron systems with which they come in connection, that an impulse entering along one given fiber could spread to practically every neuron in the spinal cord and brain.'' This does occur in strychnia poisoning, in which the resistance of the synapse is broken down so that an afferent impulse from any source may cause general contraction of muscles. Such impulse may be a sight, a sound, a smell, a touch, or any other sensory disturbance. While it is thus seen that a sensory stimulus conveyed to the cord might produce a very wide-

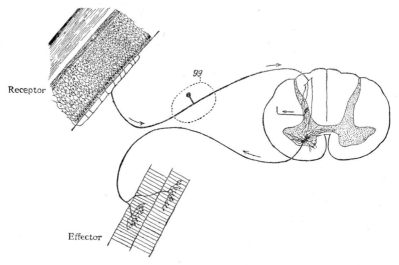

Fig. 4.—A two-neuron reflex arc in a vertebrate. *gg*, ganglion. (Van Gehuchten.)

The receptor or sensory neuron receives the impulse and carries it to or through the ganglion on the posterior root to the cells in the anterior horn of the cord and transmits them to a motor or effector nerve which produces action in another tissue. This is the simplest type of reflex, probably not commonly found in clinical medicine.

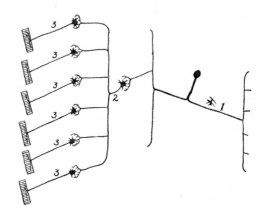

Fig. 5.—A three-neuron reflex arc. (Van Gehuchten.)

1, afferent peripheral neuron; *2*, intermediate or central neuron; *3*, efferent peripheral neurons.

The impulse is carried to the ganglion on the posterior route by sensory neuron *1*; and there or in the cord transmitted to the second neuron *2*; and then transmitted to the final effector neuron *3*. Several different types of complex neurons are shown in Fig. 24, page 161.

spread motor response, yet this is not the rule. There is for each afferent nerve root some efferent root which offers the least resistance to impulses which are conveyed centralward by it, and this is the one which usually completes the reflex act. This is often in the same segment of the cord, but as in case of the sympathetic afferent nerves from the lung, it may be found in segments somewhat removed, following out, however, the developmental relationships of the viscera. See Sherrington's Law, pages 168 and 169.

The laws governing reflexes will be discussed quite fully in Chapter XI, so they need not be repeated here. It is sufficient to state the following fact in this general discussion : *Reflexes are mediated by few or many neurons, hence affect few or many structures, according to the strength of the exciting stimulus. When a stimulus has once excited a neuron to activity, no amount of extra stimulus can cause further action in that neuron at that time. A stronger stimulus, on the other hand, excites action in more neurons, and causes the reflex action to be expressed more widely.* This fact is important in the clinical study of the reflex, for it shows why, at times, a large area of muscles is contracted; when again, with the same organ inflamed, a smaller muscle area is influenced, and probably the muscle tone is much less. An example, commonly found in clinical practice, illustrative of this fact is the boardiness of the lower intercostal muscles which is usually observed when acute pleurisy is present over the lower intercostal area. Under certain conditions of severe stimulation the reflex is not confined to the intercostal area but extends below the costal border to the muscles of the abdominal wall. We note the same spread of the reflex when the pain and muscle spasm of angina extend up into the neck.

Vegetative Nervous System Embryologically Considered.—One can best understand the vegetative system and its action in the tissues, if he is familiar with its embryologic development. The development of the vegetative nervous system can best be studied in the thoracicolumbar portion of the cord from which the sympathetic neurons originate. As previously mentioned, the neural tube is made from an infolding of the ectoderm. The tube is closed during the early days of the embryo by certain cells which form a band between the posterior borders of the neural plate as shown in Fig. 6. These cells are known as the neural crest.

The neural crest separates from the cord when the embryo is three weeks old, and forms two longitudinal bands running lengthwise of the cord. The ventral borders of these bands show segmentation, the cells arranging themselves into clumps, which later become completely separated, forming the spinal ganglia. These cells continue to proliferate, and then a differentiation takes place, from which the components of the spinal nerves as well as the white ramus communicans of the sympathetic system are formed. Many of the cells from the neural crest continue their migration as well as proliferation, and become deposited still further peripheralward, forming other sympathetic ganglia. Segmentation takes place

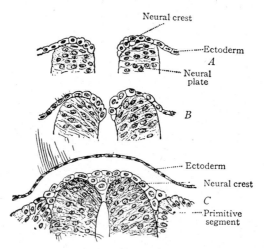

Fig. 6.—Three stages in the closure of the neural tube and formation of the neural crest (spinal ganglion rudiment). From transverse sections of a human embryo of 2.5 mm. (13 pairs of primitive segments, 14-16 days). Von Lenhossék. (Bailey and Miller.)

at the seventh week and the gangliated cord of the sympathetic system is then formed. Later cells of the gangliated cord proliferate and migrate still farther and are collected in ganglia near the organ or organs which they will later supply, such as the pulmonary, cardiac, celiac, renal, and pelvic. In the parasympathetic system the cells come to rest in contact with or into the tissues of the organs themselves, forming such plexuses as those of Auerbach's and Meissner's in the walls of the gastrointestinal canal.

The cell bodies of the *afferent neurons* of the sympathetic system are found in the ganglia of the posterior root, while the cell bodies of the *efferent* connector fibers are located in the anterior portion of the lateral walls of the neural tube. These efferent connector fibers connect the central nervous system with the true sympathetic motor cells which are found in the ganglia. It will then be seen that none of the true motor cells belonging to the vegetative system lie within the central nervous system, but that they are connected with it through the connector fibers which course in the IIIrd, VIIth, IXth, and Xth cranial nerves; in the white rami communicantes of the thoracicolumbar segments; and in the pelvic nerve.

During the stage of migration, when the motor cells of the vegetative system are separating from the central nervous system, it should be mentioned that some of the sympathetic cells differentiate into sympathoblasts which become cells in sympathetic ganglia and others phaeochromoblasts, from which arise the chromaffin cells of the adrenal bodies. This is the embryologic reason for the similar action of the sympathetic motor cells and adrenalin. Adrenalin is a secretion from cells belonging to the sympathetic system. The chromaffin cells are so named because of their property of being stained with chrom salts. We know them in physiology as belonging to the sympathetic nervous system and being the producers of adrenalin. They are found for the most part in the medulla of the suprarenal glands, although lesser deposits are found in some mammals at the branching of the aorta and carotids. In the lowest groups of vertebrates there are many scattered, segmentally arranged masses of chromaffin cells and few sympathetic cells; but in the higher vertebrates there are many sympathetic cells which form the sympathetic system.

Development of Afferent and Efferent Neurons.—Not only do the cells from the neural crest differentiate into ganglia and the chromaffin cells of the suprarenal glands, but also into the nerve fibers which complete the efferent neurons of the vegetative system.

The tissues supplied by both the voluntary and the involuntary systems possess neurons of an afferent and efferent character. The afferent or sensory neurons, whether of the voluntary or vegetative (involuntary) system, have their neuron bodies alike in the ganglia of the posterior root; in fact, all afferent fibers which arise in the cord, whether they supply somatic or vegetative structures, belong to the voluntary system. Schilf[37] states that afferent vegetative fibers have not yet been proved to exist. The efferent neuron bodies of the somatic system lie in the anterior horn of the neural tube, while the efferent neuron bodies of the vegetative system lie without the neural tube in ganglia, lateral, collateral, and terminal, which have wandered from the neural canal. These ganglia are brought into connection with the neural tube, however, by fibers which pass out from the central portions of the lateral walls in the white ramus communicans. Gaskell has given these fibers the name of "connector fibers." They connect the central receptor mechanism with the peripheral cells of effector neurons.

Relationship Between Cerebrospinal and Vegetative Nervous Systems.—The vegetative nervous system belongs to a lower stage of development of the animal than does the voluntary system. Its neurons, however, carry sensory, motor, and trophic impulses the same as the neurons of the cerebrospinal system, except the sensory neurons are endowed with only a modified power of expressing pain. To express pain they call into action the sensory spinal and Vth cranial nerves which are segmentally related to them. This is discussed more fully in Chapters XI and XII.

While the neurons of the vegetative system are capable of carrying on the activities of the tissues supplied by them for a time, in such a manner as to sustain life, independently of the cerebrospinal system; and the cerebrospinal system is able to carry on the functions presided over by its neurons in a certain sense independently of the vegetative system, yet these two systems are more or less intimately connected and action in one is correlated with action in the other.

We must conceive that there is a continuous flow of sensory impulses (afferent) passing to the central nervous system from the surface of the body. These may make their presence known not only to the brain, causing action in the skeletal tissues, but also through their intimate connection with the cell bodies of the visceral nerves, cause an outflow of impulses (efferent) through the vegetative nerves to the unstriped muscles and the secretory glands of the viscera.

We must also conceive that there is a continuous stream of impulses (afferent) traveling centralward from the viscera which are capable of expressing themselves involuntarily through efferent neurons and causing action in tissues supplied by both components of the vegetative system, some of which are described in Chapters XIII and XIV. Action is also brought about in skeletal tissues through mediation between vegetative and cerebrospinal neurons. Stimuli coming from the surface of the body may affect the function of internal viscera; and impulses coming from the viscera may influence skeletal structures.

Adequate Stimulus.—Afferent nerves are distributed to all structures of the body. A stimulus is any force, no matter what its character, that can transform nerve excitability into action. It is adequate if it is suited to the particular sensory receptor and motor effector cell, and if its strength is sufficient to discharge action.

Sensory nerves are normally excited to activity only by stimuli which are applied peripherally. Motor nerves are normally excited only by stimuli which are applied to the ganglion cells from which they originate.

To produce action it is not sufficient that a stimulus be brought in contact with a nerve at the proper place; the stimulus must be of the proper quality and of sufficient intensity to overcome the natural resistance to action. There is always a certain amount of inhibition exerted by higher centers over impulses arising in lower levels. For a stimulus to be perceived or for it to produce reflex action, it must break down whatever inhibition is placed in its way. It must overcome all resistance met at the synapses. In other words, it must be *adequate to express itself*.

When a stimulus is adequate, both as to quality and quantity, to overcome the resistance in the receptor neuron, it is carried centralward, and, if it is still able to overcome resistance met in central synapses, it may be transferred to the higher brain centers where its particular quality will be recognized and translated into its proper symbol, such as light, sound, heat, cold, or pain; or, it may be transferred in central ganglia to motor nerves and be expressed reflexly in muscular or secretory activity.

Adequate stimuli arising in sensory organs of the voluntary system are readily carried to the higher centers of consciousness; while those arising in vegetative structures for the most part stop short of consciousness, being transferred to motor nerves of the voluntary system to produce changes in the soft structures (skin, subcutaneous tissues, and muscles) or to other nerves belonging to the vegetative system to produce such changes in function as result from disturbances in action of both smooth muscle and glands.

Only when function is markedly disturbed in vegetative structures are we aware of it. All normal physiologic stimuli go by unheeded. Only those which are sufficient to overcome resistance, met in their path, call for action which may be recognized. This is discussed more fully in Chapter XIII, page 191, and in Chapter XIV, page 205.

Afferent Impulses over Sympathetics and Parasympathetics Cause Different Reflexes.—Reflex responses which are dependent upon impulses flowing over afferent neurons of the two divisions of the vegetative system, differ in a very important particular. Recognized responses which result from afferent impulses flowing centralward to the thoracicolumbar segments of the cord are expressed largely by reflex action in skeletal structures which receive their nerve supply from the same segments that the stimulus enters. The responses which result from afferent impulses flowing centralward over the parasympathetics express themselves reflexly in other neurons of the same system, or through either the cranial or the sacral spinal nerves. They usually produce reflex action in visceral structures, but sometimes in somatic structures.

Reflexes in which both afferent and efferent impulses are visceral and enter and leave the same segments of the cord, are probably much more common than we have been inclined to believe. It is probable that contraction of sphincters, dilatation of intestinal segments, and many vasomotor disturbances are of this nature.

From this the following two observations which are fundamental in the study of clinical aspects of visceral neurology and which are of great diagnostic import may be made:

1. *Reflexes resulting from afferent impulses from internal viscera express themselves through: first, the spinal nerves manifesting themselves in sensory, motor, and trophic changes in the skin, subcutaneous tissue, and muscles and, second, through vegetative nerves causing many visceral disturbances which we have as yet not fully learned to recognize.*

2. *Reflexes resulting from afferent impulses from internal viscera which flow centralward over the parasympathetic neurons, express themselves for the most part through other neurons of the parasym-*

pathetic system and to a lesser extent through cranial somatic and spinal nerves, and indirectly through the sympathetics, causing disturbance in function of other internal viscera.

References

1. Gaskell: The Involuntary Nervous System, New York, 1916, Longmans, Green & Co.
2. Langley: Autonomic Nervous System, Brain, 26: 1903; and The Autonomic Nervous System, Part I, Cambridge, 1921, W. Heffer and Sons, Ltd.
3. Sherrington: The Integrative Action of the Nervous System, New York, 1906, Charles Scribner & Sons.
4. Lucas: The Conduction of the Nervous Impulse, New York, 1917, Longmans, Green & Co.
5. Bechterew: Die Funktionen der Nervencentra, Jena, 1908, Gustav Fischer, Vol. I.
6. Lewandowsky: Die Funktionen des zentralen Nervensystems, Jena, 1907, Gustav Fischer.
7. Higier: Vegetative or Visceral Neurology, Ergebnisse der Neurologie und Psychiatrie 2: No. 1, 1912.
8. Müller, L. R.: Das vegetative Nervensystem, Berlin, 1920, Verlag von Julius Springer.
9. Jelliffe and White: Diseases of the Nervous System, Philadelphia, 1917, Lea & Febiger.
10. Starling: Principles of Human Physiology, Philadelphia, 1915, Lea & Febiger.
11. Bayliss: Principles of General Physiology, New York, 1915, Longmans, Green & Co.; also the Vaso-Motor System, London, 1923, Longmans, Green & Co.
12. Luciani: Human Physiology, London, 1911-1917, Macmillan Co., Vols. I-IV.
13. Tigerstedt: Textbook of Physiology (Translated by Murlin), New York, 1906, D. Appleton Co.
14. Eppinger and Hess: Die Vagotonie, Sammlung klinischer Abhandlungen, von Noorden, Nos. 9 and 10, 1910.
15. Guillaume, A. G.: Le Sympathique et les Systemes Associes, Paris, 1920, Masson et Cie Editeurs, Libraires de L'Académie de Médicine.
16. Cannon: Bodily Changes in Pain, Hunger, Fear, and Rage, New York, 1915, D. Appleton Co.
17. Keith: Human Embryology, London, Edward Arnold & Co.
18. Bailey and Miller: Text Book of Embryology, New York, 1916, Wm. Wood & Co.
19. Biedl: Innere Sekretion, ed. 4, Wien, 1922, Urban und Schwarzenberg.
20. Falta: The Ductless Glandular Diseases (Translated by Meyers), Philadelphia, 1916, P. Blakiston's Son & Co.
21. Paton, Nöel: The Nervous and Chemical Regulators of Metabolism, London, 1913, The Macmillan Co.
22. Lereboullet, P., Harvier, P., Carrion, H., and Guillaume, A. G.: Endocrine Glands and the Sympathetic System, Translated by E. Raoul Mason, Philadelphia, 1922, J. B. Lippincott Co.
23. Gley: Practitioner, London, January, 1915, xciv, Nos. 1 and 2.
24. Kuntz, Albert: The Autonomic Nervous System, Philadelphia, 1929, Lea & Febiger.
25. Child, Charles Manning: Senescence and Rejuvenescence, Chicago, 1915, Univ. Chicago Press, p. 19.
26. Pottenger, F. M.: Neural and Endocrine Factors in Bodily Defense, Endocrinology 21: 449-454, 1937.

27. Vincent, Hoskins, and Stewart: Recent Views as to the Function of the Adrenal Bodies, Endocrinology 1: 140-152, 1917.
28. Banting, F. G., and Best, C. H.: The Internal Secretion of the Pancreas, J. Lab. & Clin. Med. 7: 253-266, 1922.
29. Elliott, T. R.: J. Physiol. 31: 1904; ibid. 32: 1905.
30. Howell, W. H.: Vagus Inhibition of the Heart in Its Relation to the Inorganic Salts of the Blood, Am. J. Physiol. 15: 280, 1906.
31. Howell, W. H., and Duke, W. W.: The Effects of Vagus Inhibition on the Output of Potassium From the Heart, Am. J. Physiol. 21: 51-63, 1908.
32. Löwi, Otto: Humoral Transmissibility of Cardiac Nerve Activity, Arch. f. d. ges. Physiol. 193: 201, 1921.
33. Cannon, W. B., and Bacq, Z. M.: Am. J. Physiol. 96: 392, 1931.
34. Dale, H. H.: Jour. Physiol. 80: 10, 1933.
35. Luciani: Human Physiology, London, 1915, The Macmillan Co., Vol. 3, p. 310.
36. Starling: Human Physiology, Philadelphia, 1915, Lea & Febiger, p. 305.
37. Schilf, Erich: Das Autonome Nervensystem, Leipzig, 1926, Verlag von Georg Thieme, pp. 9 and 175.

CHAPTER III

THE VEGETATIVE NERVOUS SYSTEM ANATOMICALLY CONSIDERED

In order to understand the relationship between the activities of the body and the visceral nerves it is necessary for one to familiarize himself with the anatomy and physiology of the vegetative nervous system. In our discussion we shall be brief, yet we shall attempt to state a sufficient number of the more important facts to make the subject intelligible.

SYMPATHETIC NERVOUS SYSTEM

We shall first describe the sympathetic system. It takes its origin from that portion of the spinal cord which extends from the first thoracic to the third or fourth lumbar segments. By the term "origin" we are to understand that the motor neurons of the sympathetic system which have wandered out to supply the viscera as described on page 53 and whose motor cells lie in the sympathetic ganglia, originally came from this portion of the cord, and that they are still connected with these segments by connector fibers whose cell bodies lie in the lateral horn of this section of the cord, but which have followed them out, so to speak, in order to preserve their connection with the central system.

The sympathetic system consists of:

1. A chain of ganglia lying on each side of the vertebral column, there being as a rule one ganglion for each spinal nerve root. These ganglia are called *lateral ganglia* or *vertebral ganglia.*

2. Numerous ganglia situated farther away from the spinal canal which are termed *collateral ganglia* or *prevertebral ganglia,* and still others lying on or in the tissues of the viscera, as in the genital organs, which are termed *terminal ganglia.*

3. Numerous plexuses of fibers which supply the various tissues.

4. White rami communicantes.

5. Gray rami communicantes.

61

Gangliated Cord.—The *lateral* or *vertebral* ganglia are arranged in two rows along the ventral surface of the vertebral column, extending its full length. These ganglia are arranged for the most part segmentally, corresponding to the segmental spinal nerves. The connector fibers passing from the spinal segments to the sympathetic ganglia are known as the *white rami communicantes,* and the fibers passing from lateral sympathetic ganglia back to the spinal nerves to be distributed to the skeletal vessels, subdermal structures, and the blood vessels of the spinal cord, are known as the *gray rami communicantes.* The fibers passing from one of the lateral ganglia to another form a definite cord and taken in conjunction with the ganglia form the *gangliated cord,* which extends from the atlas to the coccyx. Fig. 7 shows the gangliated cord. It is also shown schematically in Fig. 23, page 158.

The sympathetic ganglia are masses of nerve cells. These cells with the nonmedullated fibers originating in them, form the motor neurons of the sympathetic nervous system.

The ganglia of the gangliated cord in certain areas fuse together. Thus the upper three or four thoracic ganglia fuse and form the stellate ganglion; the ganglia of the cervical portion are arranged sometimes in a superior and inferior, and sometimes a third, the medium ganglion, is interposed; the lumbar and sacral portions sometimes have three, sometimes four ganglia. The lower ends of the two gangliated cords either unite in a common ganglion behind the coccyx, called the ganglion of Walter, or unite by a simple loop.

The sympathetic ganglia are relay stations, so to speak, where impulses are transmitted from one neuron to another. Fibers will often pass through one or more ganglia without connecting with or forming relays with the neurons whose cells are found in those ganglia. Fibers which end in cells in a given ganglion enter it as *white medullated* fibers, while the fibers which carry the impulses onward emerge from the ganglion as *nonmedullated* fibers. *The only truly sympathetic motor fibers, then, are nonmedullated fibers;* while *all medullated motor fibers belonging to the sympathetic system are connector in function,* joining the ganglionic motor cells with the motor cells in the spinal cord.

The vertebral ganglia are the first relay stations. Many of the impulses transmitted from the cord are directed to the tissues which

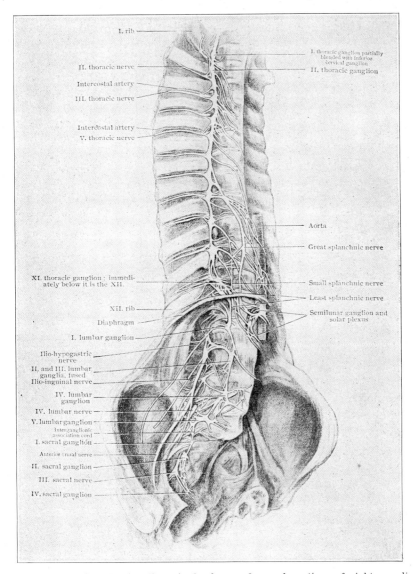

Fig. 7.—Dissection showing thoracic, lumbar, and sacral portions of right gangliated cord and their branches. (Piersol.)

they supply by the nerve cells in the vertebral ganglia. Here arise the sympathetic fibers which supply the skeletal blood vessels, the subdermal musculature and the blood vessels of the spinal cord. Many more pass through these ganglia and onward, to activate motor cells in some of the peripheral ganglia. This has a very important bearing upon the study of the paths of sympathetic reflexes and will be discussed more fully later.

Collateral and Terminal Ganglia.—The fibers of the sympathetics often form large plexuses before innervating the viscera. The fibers which make up these plexuses are nonmedullated, having originated from motor cells in the collateral ganglia. The more important collateral ganglia are: the ciliary, the celiac which is formed by the union of the semilunar and superior mesenteric, the inferior mesenteric, the renal and the ovarian or spermatic.

The sympathetic fibers pass to the viscera along with the blood vessels.

Some of the More Important Sympathetic Ganglia.—One should familiarize himself with a few of the more important ganglia of the sympathetic system.

THE SUPERIOR CERVICAL GANGLION.—The superior cervical ganglion receives its fibers from the Ist, IInd, IIIrd, and sometimes as low as the VIIth dorsal segments of the cord. It innervates the vessels of the head, the muscles of the hair bulbs and sweat glands of the head, the musculus dilatator pupillae, and the smooth orbital muscle of Müller.

It connects by means of gray rami communicantes with the Ist, IInd, IIIrd, and sometimes IVth cervical nerves. Aside from the fibers to the head, there are branches which go to the pharynx and larynx, and the superior cardiac nerve which must be considered.

In the superior cervical ganglion we find the following branches which are of interest in *exophthalmic goiter*.

1. The branches which go to the orbit supplying the muscle of Müller, the contraction of which produces exophthalmos.

2. The plexus thyreoideus and communicating branches to the plexus thyreoideus inferior, stimulation of which causes hypersecretion of the thyroid gland.

3. The superior cardiac nerve which carries accelerator fibers to the heart, and also sends fine fibers to the plexus thyreoideus inferior. Fig. 8 shows the structures supplied by the superior cervical ganglion.

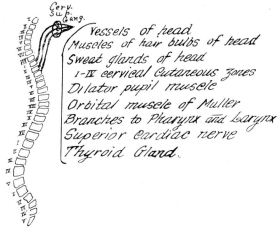

Fig. 8.—Superior cervical ganglion and tissues supplied by it, shown schematically. The connector fibers for the superior cervical ganglion arise from the upper three thoracic segments.

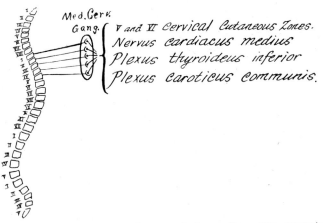

Fig. 9.—Structures supplied by medium cervical ganglion. The connector fibers arise from the Ist, IInd, IIIrd, IVth, and Vth thoracic segments.

The Medium Cervical Ganglion receives its fibers from the Ist, IInd, IIIrd, IVth, and Vth dorsal segments. It communicates by its gray rami communicantes with the Vth and VIth, sometimes also the IVth, cervical nerves. When the medium ganglion is absent, which it often is, the corresponding part of the cord takes its place. Fibers from the medium ganglion go through the nervus cardiacus medius to the heart, to the plexus thyreoideus inferior, and to the plexus caroticus communis as shown in Fig. 9.

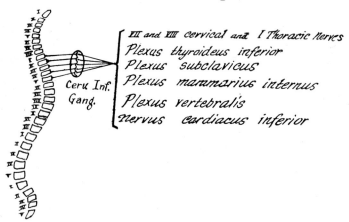

Fig. 10.—Structures supplied by the inferior cervical ganglion. Connector fibers to the inferior cervical ganglion arise from the Ist, IInd, IIIrd, IVth, and Vth thoracic segments.

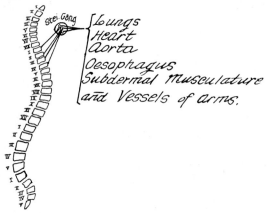

Fig. 11.—Structures supplied by the stellate ganglion. Connector fibers for the stellate ganglion arise from the Ist, IInd, IIIrd, and IVth thoracic segments.

THE INFERIOR CERVICAL GANGLION through gray rami sends communicating branches to the VIIth and VIIIth cervical and Ist dorsal nerves.

It sends vascular fibers to the plexus thyreoideus inferior, plexus subclavius, plexus mammarius internus, and plexus vertebralis. It also, in conjunction with the upper dorsal ganglia, gives origin to the nervus cardiacus inferior as shown in Fig. 10.

STELLATE GANGLION.—The upper three or four thoracic ganglia join together and form the stellate ganglion. The inferior cervical ganglion is also fused with this at times. This gives off visceral branches to the lungs, heart, aorta, and esophagus, and gray rami to the subdermal musculature and blood vessels of the arms as shown in Fig. 11.

THE CELIAC GANGLION is the most important of the abdominal sympathetic ganglia. It is formed by a union of the semilunar aorticorenal and superior mesenteric ganglia. It is connected with the cord by the greater and lesser splanchnic nerves; the former arising from the Vth, VIth, VIIth, VIIIth, and IXth thoracic segments, the latter from the IXth and Xth, or Xth and XIth.

Sympathetic, nonmedullated fibers from the celiac ganglion supply the stomach, liver, pancreas, spleen, kidney, suprarenal gland, ovary, testicle, and the intestines as far as the descending colon. This is shown in Fig. 12.

THE INFERIOR MESENTERIC GANGLION receives its connector fibers from the Ist, IInd, and IIIrd lumbar segments. It sends nonmedullated fibers to the descending colon and through the hypogastric nerves to the rectum, bladder, sphincter of the bladder, and genitals, as shown in Fig. 13.

DIFFERENCE IN NUMBER OF PREGANGLIONIC AND POSTGANGLIONIC FIBERS.—While the impulses which travel from the central nervous system to the sympathetic ganglia are all transmitted through fourteen white rami communicantes, eleven from the thoracic segments (II-XII) and three from the lumbar (I-III) as shown in Plate VII, before the tissues have been supplied the impulses have traveled over thousands of fibers which have originated from the motor cells in the various ganglia, lateral, collateral, and terminal. Before supplying the tissues, these fibers collect in networks of fibers which are known as plexuses and then follow the blood vessels to the structures to be supplied.

White Rami Communicantes.—It is impossible to understand the vegetative nervous system without understanding the *connector neuron*. The connector neurons of the sympathetic system course in the *white rami communicantes*. There is no other efferent connection between the cerebrospinal system and the sympathetic ganglia. They communicate to the motor cells of the ganglia impulses which have been brought to the cord but which are intended for the sympathetic

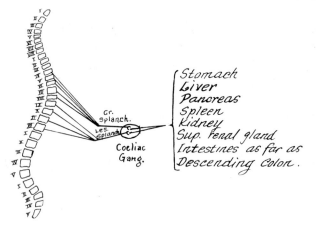

Fig. 12.—Structures supplied by the celiac ganglion. Connector fibers run through the greater splanchnic nerve, arising from the Vth, VIth, VIIth, VIIIth, and IXth thoracic segments, and from the lesser splanchnic arising from the IXth, and Xth or Xth and XIth thoracic segments.

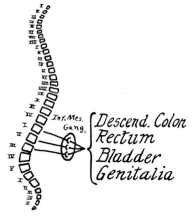

Fig. 13.—Structures supplied by the inferior mesenteric ganglion. Connector fibers arise from the Ist, IInd, and IIIrd lumbar segments.

system. Connector neurons terminate in ganglia around the cells from which originate neurons which supply motor power to the vascular and dermal structures; the sphincters of the gut and bladder, and parts of the eye muscles; and inhibitory power to structures such as the muscles of the vast enteral system and those structures which originated embryologically from it, such as the respiratory tract, liver, pancreas and urinary bladder except the trigone.

The connector neurons of the sympathetic system sometimes pass through several ganglia before they terminate. Thus fibers from the upper thoracic segments pass through the stellate and medium cervical ganglia and terminate around motor cells in the superior cervical ganglion. From there on they course as nonmedullated or true sympathetic fibers to certain tissues.

Aside from these efferent motor fibers, the white rami contain medullated fibers whose nutrient centers are in the posterior root ganglia. *These are the afferent fibers from the sympathetically innervated tissues.* They belong to the voluntary sensory system. They carry impulses from the tissues supplied by the sympathetics to the central nervous system, where they are transmitted to efferent neurons and manifest themselves as reflexes in many tissues. They are medullated throughout their entire course. The afferent fibers have no cell connection in sympathetic ganglia, but pass through them in their course from the cord and posterior root ganglia to the peripheral tissues.

Gray Rami Communicantes.—The lateral ganglia as previously stated are arranged segmentally. This arrangement corresponds to that of the spinal nerves. Each lateral ganglion sends sympathetic fibers to its corresponding visceral segment and also to its spinal nerve. These latter course with the spinal nerve for a time and then are distributed to the smooth muscle which is supplied by the given spinal segment. Langley has shown that fibers to the pilomotor muscles course in the sensory spinal nerves.

While the white rami are limited to that portion of the cord between the first thoracic and third or fourth lumbar segments, the gray rami pass from the vertebral sympathetic ganglia to all spinal nerve roots as shown in Plate II.

In the greater portion of the thoracic and upper lumbar segments of the cord, the relationship between the gray rami of the sympathetic ganglia and the corresponding spinal nerve is regular; but in the upper portion of the thoracic and cervical portions, where the ganglia have fused, there is a certain degree of irregularity. The superior cervical ganglion sends gray rami to the Ist, IInd, and IIIrd

THE ARRANGEMENT OF THE CONNECTOR FIBERS (BLACK) AND THE EXCITOR NEU-
RONS (RED) OF THE SYMPATHETIC SYSTEM IN THE SPINAL REGION.

All the spinal nerves are shown from the first cervical, *C1*, to the third coccygeal, *Co3*.

All the connector neurons leave the spinal cord in the thoracicolumbar outflow
which extends from the second dorsal, *D2*, to the third lumbar, *L3*. The lateral
chain of sympathetic ganglia is connected together by the further prolongation of
these processes which run from ganglion to ganglion, connecting in three or more
of them with the cells of excitor neurons. The lateral chain is therefore made
up of a series of groups of excitor neurons connected together by the processes
of connector neurons. Certain ganglia have become fused, those corresponding
to the first four cervical nerves being aggregated into superior cervical ganglion,
S.C.G., those of the last four cervical and the first four dorsal being aggregated
into the stellate ganglion, *St.G.*, which lies just caudal to the annulus of Vieussens,
A.V. For the sake of simplicity the ganglia on this annulus and the inferior
cervical ganglion have been omitted and considered part of the stellate ganglion.
The processes of the excitor neurons belonging to any ganglion run out in the
gray ramus communicans to join the spinal nerve and to be distributed with it.
The excitor fibers for the first four cervical nerves thus arise from the superior
cervical ganglion, *S.C.G.*; the excitor neurons for the last four cervical nerves
arise from the stellate ganglion, *St.G.*, and at first all run in the ramus vertebralis, *R. V.*, they finally branch from this and join their respective nerves. Similarly
the excitor fibers of the first four dorsal nerves all arise from the stellate ganglion,
St.G., to which the first three white rami communicantes run. The rest of the
spinal nerves are supplied with sympathetic excitor fibers from their corresponding sympathetic ganglia. (Gaskell.)

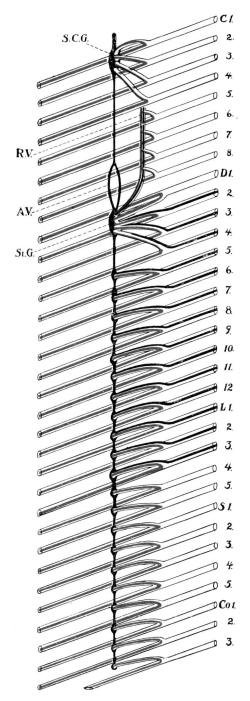

C1.
2.
3.
4.
5.
6.
7.
8.
D1.
2.
3.
4.
5.
6.
7.
8.
9.
10.
11.
12
L1.
2.
3.
4.
5.
S1.
2.
3.
4.
5.
Co1.
2.
3.

S.C.G.

R.V.

A.V.

St.G.

PLATE 11

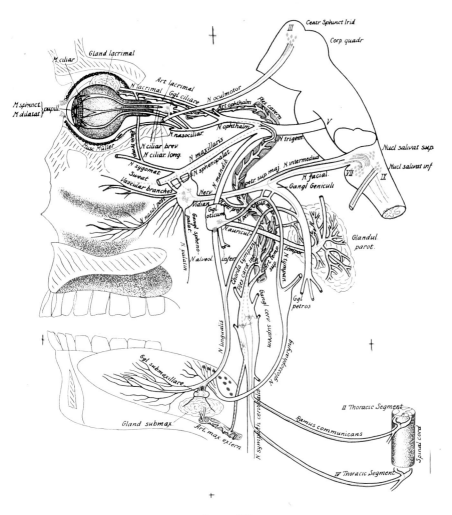

PLATE III

SCHEMATIC ILLUSTRATION OF THE DISTRIBUTION OF THE VEGETATIVE NERVOUS
SYSTEM IN INNERVATING THE TISSUES OF THE HEAD. (FROM HIGIER,
AFTER MUELLER AND DAHL.)

The parasympathetic fibers from the midbrain and medulla are in *green*.
Fibers of the sympathetic system are in *blue*. The visceral sympathetic ganglia
are in *blue*, the parasympathetic in *green*. The preganglionic fibers are shown by
continuous lines. The postganglionic by broken lines.

and sometimes the IVth cervical nerves, and the inferior cervical ganglion and the ramus vertebralis from the stellate ganglion when the medium ganglion is absent, send gray rami to the IVth, Vth, VIth, VIIth, and VIIIth cervical nerves. When the medium is present, it sends gray rami to the Vth and VIth.

Sacral Vegetative Nerves.—The sacral outflow is entirely different from the thoracicolumbar outflow. It belongs to the parasympathetic system. It passes out through the IInd and IIIrd sacral nerves. These fibers do not pass through lateral ganglia as do the sympathetics, but unite to form the pelvic nerve, also called *nervus erigens,* and then pass directly to ganglia lying on the surface of the bladder, rectum, and other structures supplied by them. In this, as well as physiologically, they resemble the craniobulbar outflow.

Cranial Vegetative Nerves.—It is characteristic of the craniobulbar outflow, the same as of the sacral, that the motor ganglia lie near or within the organs innervated, while the connector neurons run from the centers in the brain to the organ itself without passing through ganglia.

The IIIrd, VIIth, IXth, and Xth cranial nerves carry fibers which belong to the vegetative system. These are spoken of as belonging to the craniobulbar outflow.

The vegetative fibers of the IIIrd nerve pass to the ciliary ganglion and from there fibers go to innervate the sphincter pupillae.

The visceral fibers which course in the VIIth cranial nerve (facialis) are found in the chorda tympani, which carries vasodilator and secretory fibers to the sublingual and submaxillary glands, also to the mucous membranes of the nose and its accessory sinuses, soft palate and upper pharynx. The fibers in the IXth cranial nerve (glossopharyngeal) give vasodilator and secretory fibers to the parotid gland. The vegetative fibers in the IIIrd, VIIth, and IXth nerves are shown in Plate III from Higier.

Vagus.—The arrangement of the nuclei of the vagus in the medulla corresponds to the ventral, lateral, and posterior horns in the spinal cord.

The *nucleus ambiguus* corresponds to the ventral horn from which arise the motor nerves. It gives origin to those fibers of the vagus which supply the voluntary muscles of the larynx, pharynx, and esophagus.

The *nucleus solitarius* lies in a more dorsal position; all visceral afferent fibers (sensory) of the vagus terminate along with those of the seventh and ninth nerves in this nucleus.

The *nucleus dorsalis,* the largest nucleus of the vagus, gives origin to the visceral fibers and its ganglion cells correspond in form and size to the cells found in the lateral horn of the cord.

The fibers from these three nuclei pass through the foramen jugulare where they expand into the ganglion jugulare and a little below into the ganglion nodosum. These two ganglia correspond to the dorsal root ganglia of the spinal nerves and contain the cell bodies of the afferent neurons of the vagus. Many anastomoses are made with the glossopharyngeal and hypoglossal nerves, the superior cervical ganglion and the carotid sinus plexus. The vagus is illustrated in Plate IV.

The ganglion jugulare resembles spinal root ganglia. It supplies the ear, pharynx, and larynx with somatic fibers. The ganglion nodosum, on the other hand, contains cells from which neurons arise which provide afferent fibers for the structures which receive innervation from the visceral fibers of the vagus.

The sensory (afferent) fibers of the vagus supply:

1. The entire mucous membrane of the respiratory tract from the epiglottis downward.

2. The heart.

3. The following portions of the digestive tract: the base of the tongue, the palate, the pharynx and other portions of the mucous membrane of the throat, the esophagus, stomach, duodenum, jejunum, ileum, and ascending portion of the colon.

4. The mucous membranes of the biliary passages.

5. All musculature of viscera supplied by motor fibers of the vagus.

6. That portion of the dura mater around the foramen jugulare.

7. The concave surface of the auricula and the external auditory meatus.

The motor fibers of the vagus supply the following somatic structures:

1. Muscles of the soft palate (azygos uvulae).

2. Musculi constrictores pharynges.

3. The upper portion of the esophagus.

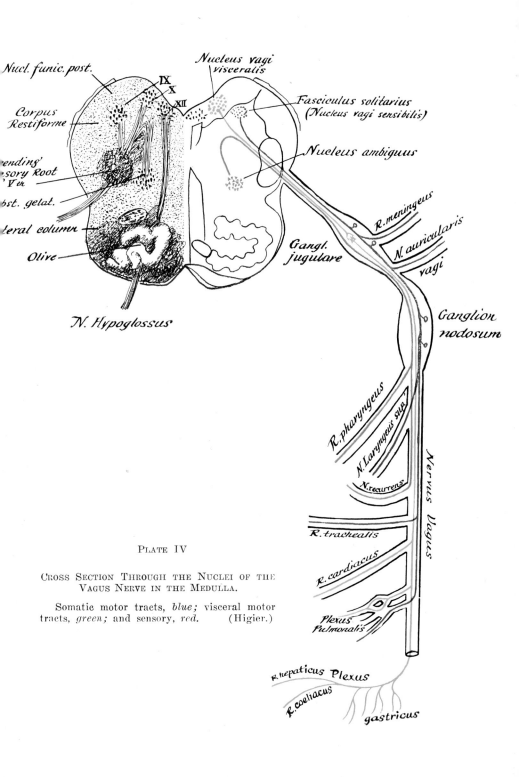

Nucl. funic. post.

Nucleus vagi
visceralis

IX
X
XII

Corpus
Restiforme

Fasciculus solitarius
(Nucleus vagi sensibilis)

Nucleus ambiguus

ending'
sory Root
V tr.

bst. gelat.

teral column

Olive

R. meningeus

N. auricularis
vagi

Gangl.
jugulare

N. Hypoglossus

Ganglion
nodosum

R. pharyngeus

N. Laryngeus sup.

N. recurrens

Nervus Vagus

R. trachealis

PLATE IV

CROSS SECTION THROUGH THE NUCLEI OF THE
VAGUS NERVE IN THE MEDULLA.

Somatic motor tracts, *blue;* visceral motor
tracts, *green;* and sensory, *red.* (Higier.)

R. cardiacus

Plexus
Pulmonalis

R. hepaticus Plexus

R. coeliacus

gastricus

4. The cricothyreoideus and, in conjunction with the accessorius, all other muscles of the larynx.

5. The stomach.

6. The small intestine.

7. The large intestine as far as the descending colon according to some observers.

8. The bronchi.

9. The liver and spleen.

10. The suprarenal bodies and kidneys.

One must realize that the sensory and motor nuclei of this nerve are closely bound by connecting fibers which cause reflex action to be readily transmitted from afferent fibers from one viscus to efferent fibers in another. A similar connecting relationship exists between all nerves of craniobulbar origin which carry vegetative fibers. There is also a close reflex relationship between the cranial parasympathetics and the sensory portion of the Vth cranial nerve. These furnish the basis for the parasympathetic motor, secretory, and trophic reflexes which I have described in Chapter XIV. In the thorax, the vagus forms connections with the sympathetics through the inferior cervical ganglion and with them forms the esophageal, cardiac, and pulmonary plexuses. In the abdomen they form the hepatic, celiac, hypogastric, enteric, and pelvic plexuses. Vagal connector fibers do not end in ganglia but find their cell bodies in terminal plexuses in the walls of the viscera.

The reflex relationship between the various cranial nerves is shown in Plate II, page 70, which should be carefully studied. As an illustration of this relationship we have the slowing of the pulse by pressure on the eyeball, the afferent impulse traveling through the sensory fibers of the Vth cranial nerve and being transferred through connecting neurons to the cardiac branches of the Xth nerve; or the provoking of bronchial spasm (asthma) by nasal irritation, the afferent impulse traveling through the sensory fibers of the Vth cranial nerve and being transferred to the pulmonary branches of the vagus.

CHAPTER IV

LOCATION AND FUNCTIONS OF VEGETATIVE CENTERS IN THE CENTRAL NERVOUS SYSTEM

Centers in Diencephalon.—While alteration in control of vegetative structures is often exerted segmentally through reflex activity, yet there are many general forces which produce visceral effects which are initiated in higher centers. Such are the various emotional stresses, and such conditions as pain, cold, heat, asphyxia, and toxemia.

Knowledge of these higher centers is still unsatisfactory, but the general, widespread visceral reactions that are brought about through the body's sympathetic system can only be accounted for by there being central areas from which the necessary stimuli may be released.

One cannot believe that the body in its wisdom would leave the adjustments which have to be made in case of such conditions as fright, anger, pain, asphyxia, and threatened disturbance in water, sugar, and acid-base balance to peripheral stimulation of the complex mechanisms which are necessary to combat the threats of these hostile forces. The organism would undoubtedly perish through inefficiency if it did.

Then, too, there is need for stations in the central nervous system in order that the cortical centers may exert through them a controlling influence on certain vegetative reactions and hold them within the realm of physiologic balance. Such centers are found in the diencephalon.

Clinical experience shows that these centers in the central nervous system are also subject to stimuli arising in the viscera, but, so far, no definite paths have been traced from the viscera through the cord and medulla to them. Nevertheless, Huber and Crosby[1] suggest: "It is possible that the general visceral afferent impulses are carried to the diencephalic centers by nonmedullated fibers, or even more probably by a chain of neurones similar to those associated with the lateral spinothalmic path."

Nearly all impulses which reach the cortex with the exception of those of olfactory origin, are relayed in the diencephalon.

The epithalamus and hypothalamus are the particular portions of the diencephalon which contain the centers for the reception of visceral or interoceptive impulses and for their correlation and discharge to the appropriate somatic and visceral mechanisms. The dorsal and ventral thalami receive chiefly exteroceptive and proprioceptive impulses and transfer them to the proper neurons for action. Thus the various portions of the thalamus seem to be related to special tracts in the cord which carry somatic and visceral stimuli.

As to the more definite localization of the brain centers Bard[2] discussed this matter and through his[3] studies on the decorticate cat was able "to state that the discharge of nerve impulses which evokes the extraordinary motor activity of the decorticate preparation is conditioned by central mechanisms which lie within an area comprising the caudal fractions of the hypothalamus and the most ventral and most caudal fractions of the corresponding segment of the thalamus."

The diencephalon is thus a very important substation in which mediation of impulses is carried on without cortical action, but, nevertheless, it is subject to cortical influence. It seems to be a receiving and distributing center for impulses which arise in any and all portions of the body.

Some of the functions over which special centers located here preside are carbohydrate metabolism; the rate and force of the heartbeat; regulation of temperature; water balance; dilatation of the pupil, bulging of the eyeball, and retraction of the nictitating membrane; the erection of hairs; the secretion of adrenalin; and regulation of the secretion of the lacrimal, salivary, and sweat glands.

Ranson[4] shows that the region just in front of the hypothalamus may perhaps represent a general parasympathetic center. Stimuli applied here "regularly cause contraction of the bladder, sometimes also a fall in blood pressure, rarely constriction of the pupil, and very rarely indeed slowing of the heart." Stimulation of this center also causes inhibition of respiration.

It can thus be seen how important the diencephalon becomes in aiding the body in maintaining a condition of homeostasis as described by Cannon[5, 6] in the presence of stimuli of both a physical and a psychic nature. It is evident that the centers in this portion of the brain receive stimuli from afferent neurons carrying all varieties of sensory phenomena, whether from the external or from the internal environment of the patient, and correlate and distribute them with that precision and nicety which is for the best interest of the individual. In case of disease they further attempt to inhibit or neutralize pathologic action and maintain the body functions in normal or as near normal conditions as possible.

Centers in Cord.—Aside from these centers in the diencephalon there are numerous centers in the spinal cord and medulla which control visceral function.

The thoracic and upper lumbar segments of the cord control vasomotor, pilomotor, and sweat secretion.

The second and third thoracic segments control the perspiration of the head, neck, and upper extremities. Perspiration of the upper portion of the trunk is regulated by the fourth to ninth thoracic segments and that below the umbilicus by those from the ninth thoracic to the third lumbar. Sweating in the lower extremities is controlled by centers in segments from the ninth thoracic to the third lumbar.

The second and third thoracic segments furnish sympathetic control of lacrimal secretion and, with the lower cervical segments, regulate the sympathetic activities of the eye.

Centers for the lung are found in the upper five or six thoracic segments.

The abdominal viscera have their sympathetic centers located in segments from the fourth thoracic to the second lumbar.

Genitourinary and anorectal structures are controlled by sympathetic centers in the segments of the lower thoracic and upper lumbar portions of the cord, and by parasympathetic centers in the sacral segments.

Aside from these spinal centers there lies in the floor of the fourth ventricle in close proximity to the sensory nucleus of the vagus the important center which presides over respiration.

Function of Vegetative Centers.—These spinal and medullary centers are largely free from control of the will. They regulate functions which are necessary to the existence of the individual. They distribute impulses which are brought to them and regulate activity of the organs to which the impulses are directed.

Many visceral impulses mediate reflexes in the same segment that receives the afferent stimulus. Stronger stimuli, however, may spread to other segments both upward and downward in the cord.

The importance of these centers may be best understood by considering some of the uses which they serve.

Man as a receptor organism must react to every stimulus which affects his body. Reaction means cellular activity which again means consumption of oxygen and formation of waste material. Increased oxygen consumption and elimination of waste means increased function on the part of certain vegetative mechanisms, one of which is the respiratory apparatus. The center in the floor of the fourth ventricle stimulated by acid waste products sends out impulses which cause the necessary augmentation of the rate. The greater the stimulus the greater the reaction.

Cold; heat; changes in barometric pressure; changes in air movement, the intensity of light, and humidity; the effects of storms as well as physical stimuli which act upon the surface of the body, all send stimuli centralward, which if strong are transferred upward in the cord to these centers in the brain which distribute them and provide for their proper correlation in the various visceral mechanisms that are required to come into play to aid the organism to maintain its state of normal physiologic activity. (Petersen,[7] Mills.[8, 9])

This is well illustrated when the individual is subjected to cold. The cold contacts the skin. Instantly general peripheral vasoconstriction takes place. While there are spinal vasomotor centers which control these mechanisms, the general vasoconstrictor reaction which takes place is most likely of cerebral origin; and the pilomotor muscles contract, producing goose flesh in man, but in animals and birds, erection of hairs and feathers, so as to surround the body with a covering which will further prevent the dissipation of heat.

The purpose to be served is to prevent the escape of heat and at the same time to produce more heat. If more heat is to be produced, oxidation must be increased. The tissues must burn more sugar, consequently the adrenals are called into action and sugar is forced from the liver. If this mechanism is not sufficient, then muscular activity is brought into play and the patient shivers and burns up the sugar in the muscles, liberating still more heat.

Thus we have the respiratory vasomotor, pilomotor, and sympathico-adrenal mechanisms all called into play. Central control alone could provide for the prompt, efficient response necessary to bring all of the mechanisms into action that are necessary to meet the emergency.

In fact the sympathetic system always shows a marked tendency to react vigorously and to react as a whole. Thus its response to all of these forces enumerated above and to the major emotions as well, is a reaction of the system in its entirety. No reaction on the part of the sympathetic system to a major force is limited in its response to a single viscus or mechanism.

The relation of the hypothalamus to the hypophysis has been studied by many observers. Formerly, adiposity, polyuria, subnormal temperature, somnolence and certain emotional disturbances were believed to be due to disease of the hypophysis.

Cushing[10] suggests that parasympathetic centers in the hypothalamus might be stimulated by hypophyseal hormones passing into the third ventricle and then through its walls.

Ranson[4] clears up the relationship between the hypothalamic centers and the hypophysis in polyuria by showing that the control of urine may be lost by properly placed lesions in both structures. He states that the posterior lobe of the hypophysis secretes an antidiuretic hormone, but that it is under nerve control from the hypothalamus, and that diabetes insipidus is due to a deficiency or absence of this antidiuretic hormone. It would seem, however, that most of the conditions which were originally thought to be due to the hypophysis have now been shown to be produced through the hypothalamic centers.

References

1. Huber, G. Carl, and Crosby, Elizabeth C.: Somatic and Visceral Connections of the Diencephalon, Research Publications of Association for Research in Nervous and Mental Diseases, Baltimore, 1930, Williams and Wilkins Co., Vol. IX, p. 244.
2. Bard, Philip: A Diencephalic Mechanism for the Expression of Rage, With Special Reference to the Sympathetic Nervous System, Am. J. Physiol. 84: 490-513, 1928.

3. —:   The Central Representation of the Sympathetic Nervous System as Indicated by Certain Physiological Findings, Research Publication of Association for Research in Nervous and Mental Diseases, Baltimore, 1930, Williams and Wilkins Co., Vol. IX, p. 67.
4. Ranson, S. W.:   Some Functions of the Hypothalamus, The Harvey Lectures, 1936-37, Baltimore, 1937, Williams and Wilkins Co., pp. 92-121.
5. Cannon, W. B.:   Physiologic Regulation of Normal States; Some Tentative Postulates Concerning Biological Homeostatics, Jubilee Volume for Charles Richet, Paris, 1926, pp. 91-93.
6. —:   The Sympathetic Division of the Autonomic System in Relation to Homeostasis, Research Publication of Association for Research in Nervous and Mental Diseases, Baltimore, 1930, Williams and Wilkins Co., Vol. IX, p. 181.
7. Petersen, W. F.:   The Patient and the Weather, Vol. I, Part I, Autonomic Integration, Ann Arbor, 1936, Edwards Brothers, Inc.
8. Mills, C. A.:   Climatic Stimulation in Relation to Resistance to Infection and General Metabolic Level, Tr. Am. Clin. and Clim. Assn., 1934, p. 27.
9. —:   Health and Disease as Influenced by Climatic Environment, Internat. Clin. 2: 143-167, 1936.
10. Cushing, Harvey: Papers Relating to the Pituitary Body, Hypothalamus and Parasympathetic Nervous System, Baltimore, 1932, Charles C. Thomas.

CHAPTER V

THE VEGETATIVE NERVOUS SYSTEM: GENERAL PHYSIOLOGIC CONSIDERATIONS

THE RÔLE OF THE VEGETATIVE NERVOUS SYSTEM IN ADJUSTING MAN'S PHYSIOLOGIC EQUILIBRIUM TO MEET VARYING EXTERNAL AND INTERNAL ENVIRONMENTAL FORCES

The study of visceral neurology has been delayed largely because students allow the lack of knowledge of its minute workings to obscure the important facts which are known.

There are sufficient facts known to show that the exploration of this field offers promise of great reward to medicine.

If only we consider the importance of the vegetative nervous system as a mechanism through which man adapts himself to his outward environment; to heat and cold, to humidity and dryness, to low and high barometric pressure, to light and darkness, to wind and calm, to the stresses of storms and to the changes of seasons, it at once assumes a position of highest importance to mankind.

The fact that metabolism may be carried on without the interposition of visceral nerves does not deny their importance. Cannon shows in denervated animals that while they are able to live in the sheltered conditions of the laboratory, they are not able to protect themselves against the forces of unfavorable environment. Studies made by Huntington, Petersen, Mills, and others show that one of man's greatest tasks is to adjust himself to meteorologic and cosmic factors. The slow and mild reaction of the residents of the tropics and the rapid and severe reaction of those who live in the colder climates are both conditioned by the environing atmospheric forces acting through the vegetative nerves.

The vegetative nervous system is essential to the efficient protection of the host. It receives the stimuli whether strong or weak and transmits them to the proper physiologic mechanisms through which the proper reaction is brought about to utilize the stimulus for the individual's benefit if favorable, and to nullify and protect against it if harmful. It is the function of these nerves to maintain normal physiologic balance in the face of varied types and degrees of stimulation.

In this connection it must not be forgotten that the endocrine glands and the electrolytes in the cells also have their important part. There could be no reaction of cells were it not for the electrolytes in the fluid matrix in which they bathe. On the other hand, it is possible for cells to act without the stimulus of nerves and without hormones. But we would expect that their action would be ineffective except for the bare carrying on of living processes. There could be no effectual work accomplished and the organism would perish because of its lack of adapting power.

The vegetative nervous system is the most effective correlating and integrating system of the body. Its action is general. A second system with correlating function is the endocrine system, but the action of the products of the glands of internal secretion is not general. Each gland has more or less specific effects which it produces; furthermore, it is not able to produce its effects with the dispatch that is necessary to protect or make the organism a rapidly adjusting individual.

Then too the correlation of internal forces, such as arise within the organism; the utilizing of the useful and protecting against the harmful could not be done quickly and efficiently except through a nervous network which is able to act promptly. The relief of such conditions as pain, fever, infection, asphyxia, hemorrhage, dehydration, hyper- and hypoglycemia, acidosis and alkalosis, and the effects which they produce upon the organism, are dependent not only partly but largely on visceral nerves. The action of all smooth muscle and all secreting glands including many of the endocrines is dependent upon the guiding stimulus of the vegetative nervous system.

The leading symptoms through which we recognize disease all have a nervous component; and reflex symptoms and visceral pain are wholly dependent upon nerves for their existence. When we realize how closely sympathetic stimulation is associated with calcium in the cell and how intimately parasympathetic stimulation is bound up with the potassium content, we can understand that even the pH of the tissues and the reactivity of the cell itself are influenced by stimuli which are carried over this efficient correlating mechanism.

RELATIONSHIP BETWEEN THE VEGETATIVE AND THE CENTRAL NERVOUS SYSTEM

As the animal ascends in the scale of development from the simple to the more complex forms, greater demands are made upon it in its relationship to its environment as well as in the various relationships which are concerned with its own body functions. This increased complexity is met by an expanded and more intricate nervous system and a greater degree of coordination of action.

Advancement is particularly associated with development of integration of action and of the higher centers. Quickness of action becomes essential. As greater demands are made upon the organism to adjust itself to the outside world, it becomes more necessary that there should be a separation of acts which are directly concerned in the maintenance of life, such as respiration, digestion, and circulation, from those which are more particularly concerned in the performance of work, protection, flight, or in the enjoyment of beautiful surroundings. Therefore, the division of the muscular system (the system of action) into voluntary and involuntary, was gradually evolved as a necessity; and these two systems have likewise evolved two nervous systems, which while connected, are more or less independent.

The independence of the vegetative system has been shown by Langley, who severed the spinal connector neurons between the central nervous system and the motor ganglia; and by Cannon, who removed the gangliated cord of the entire sympathetic system and still the animals lived and carried on the functions necessary to life.

As the cells of the vegetative system drifted away from the central nervous system, they continued their connection with it through fibers, which Gaskell has termed "connector fibers," to indicate their function. We must look upon all the fibers of the vegetative system which connect the central nervous system with the motor cells in the ganglia of the thoracicolumbar system, and also the cells which lie in the walls of the organs innervated, as "connector fibers" only, and not as an integral part of the vegetative system. Thus, the vagus fibers are not in reality a part of the vegetative system, but instead furnish the link which binds the motor cells of the vegetative neurons which lie in the walls of the organs with the nuclei in the bulb.

RESPONSE IN VOLUNTARY AND IN VEGETATIVE SYSTEMS COMPARED

The response to sensory stimuli in the voluntary system is immediate. The stimulus is received by the receptor neurons, and carried to the higher centers where it produces reflex action or is converted into action by the will in a fraction of a second. The sensory impulse carried centralward over somatic neurons calls for a definite and immediate action in definite and limited structures.

In the vegetative system, the response is slower and less definite, and varies in the two divisions of the system.

The nonmedullated fibers of the thoracicolumbar segments give off many branches which go to supply tissues in widely separated structures; therefore stimulation of a "connector neuron" of the sympathetic system which takes its origin in a single segment of the cord, may express action in many widely separated and different structures. Each sympathetic ganglion must be looked upon as a relay station where the impulses which are transmitted to its motor cells are divided and transferred to many fibers to go to many structures.

The craniosacral outflow is far more selective than the sympathetic in its action as may be inferred from the fact that no ganglion is imposed between its origin and its distribution in the organ. A stimulus which starts peripheralward over a definite neuron in the parasympathetic system is not changed in its course, but goes directly to the motor cells in the structure to be innervated, and the only spreading of the action that can take place is through the plexuses which lie in the walls of the tissues themselves. This is evident from the fact that the true cells of the parasympathetics are in the tissues of the organ innervated. This is also true of certain sympathetic neurons found in the genitourinary tract.

Distribution of the Neurons of the Thoracicolumbar and Craniosacral Outflows

If we consider the body as a tube, with the skin and superficial tissues as the outside of the tube, and the gastrointestinal tract and the structures which belong to it embryologically (the bronchi and lungs, liver, pancreas, and bladder) as the inside of the tube, then we have two particular groups of structures which are *activated,* one by the thoracicolumbar outflow, and the other by the craniosacral outflow.

These structures are very different. The outside of the tube is formed from the epiblast, the inside of the tube from the hypoblast. From the former are developed the epidermal tissues, the pilomotor muscles and muscles of the sweat glands which are innervated by the sympathetics. From the latter are developed the smooth musculature and secretory glands of the gastrointestinal tract, and the glands which open into it, the musculature and epithelium of the respiratory system, the bladder except the trigone, and the musculature of the prostate which is developed from the cloaca. These structures make up what Gaskell terms the ''enteral system'' of smooth musculature. They are all activated by the craniosacral outflow (parasympathetics) and receive inhibitory fibers from the thoracicolumbar outflow (sympathetics). The male urethra, except possibly the prostatic portion, and the female urethra are activated by the sympathetics.

The structures between the epiblastic tissues or the epidermal, and the hypoblastic tissues or endodermal, are derived from the mesoblast. These include the vascular system, the muscles, and other skeletal tissues, the generative and excretory organs, the trigone of the bladder, and that part of the prostate which is derived from the musculature surrounding the Wolffian and Müllerian ducts. The muscles and other skeletal tissues are innervated by the voluntary nervous system, while the vascular system supplying them is innervated by the thoracicolumbar outflow.

There are certain other structures, those belonging to the sphincter system, which are innervated by the thoracicolumbar outflow, and seem to be an exception to this division; yet instead of being an exception it may point to the fact, as Gaskell states, that the sphincters are really an infolding of the epidermal tissues. This can be readily understood as far as the internal anal sphincter and the sphincter of the urinary bladder are concerned, but it is more difficult to explain in case of the ileocecal sphincter; yet when we consider that the length of the entire gastrointestinal tube in the lower forms of life is very short and that it lengthens as the body increases in size, and the nutritional needs become greater, we can readily understand Gaskell's suggestion of the displacement of this one-time dermal tissue.

Another peculiarity of vegetative innervation is that while each division of the thoracicolumbar and the craniosacral outflows furnishes motor or activating fibers for certain definite tissues, as just mentioned, they also both send inhibitory fibers to certain other structures; and when this occurs, the fibers of one system prove to be activating fibers, the others inhibiting fibers.

ACTIVITY IN VEGETATIVE STRUCTURES

There has been considerable antagonism between the adherents of the myogenic and neurogenic theories of tissue activity, but the question is practically settled in favor of the former. Experiments, in which all nerves leading to organs have been severed, show the organs still able to function. If this were true only of such organs as the intestinal tube in which we have the intimate distribution of the nerve plexuses of Auerbach and Meissner, it would prove nothing, but it is also true of the blood vessels and other structures which are supplied by neurons without nerve nets, but whose cell bodies end in ganglia without the organ; and also in the intestinal tract after the plexuses of Auerbach and Meissner have been removed. It is evident, therefore, that function can be carried on by cells and organs independently of nerves.

In order to explain function in vegetative structures we must inquire into the physics and chemistry of the cells themselves. We must understand the colloidal nature of the cells and the relation of this colloidal mass to electrolytes, to circulating chemical substances, such as oxygen, carbon dioxide, the various products of anabolism and catabolism and the hormones, and further, its relation to the nervous system.

We cannot at this time offer full explanation of these relationships, but we have valuable data from which we are able to direct future investigation. There are three subjects the discussion of which will particularly clarify many of the physiologic principles involved in vegetative action, viz., *tonus, rhythmic action of tissues, the relationship of the sympathetic and parasympathetic systems of nerves to the function of organs,* and *their relationship to each other.* These we shall now proceed to discuss. Much interesting data bearing upon these subjects may be gathered from the works of Gaskell,[1] Langley,[2] Lilly,[3] Müller,[4] Zondek,[5] Schade,[6] and Schiff.[7]

TONUS

Every organ possesses a certain *tonus;* that is, a certain degree of tension. This differs in the striated muscle of the voluntary system and in the striated muscle of the heart and the smooth muscle of the vegetative structures. In the voluntary muscle, tonus is a contraction or tension dependent on nerve impulses sent to it from higher centers. It disappears when the nerves supplying it are divided. In the heart muscle and in smooth muscle generally, tonus is a property which does not depend on nerve impulses for its existence, though it is influenced by them. When nerves going to an organ are divided, tonus is not destroyed, although it is temporarily lessened.

When vasoconstrictors going to blood vessels are destroyed, there is a temporary reduction but not complete obliteration of the tonicity of the vessel walls; and, after a few weeks, tonicity is restored to something near its former state. Anderson[8] cut the oculomotor nerve and noted that although its power to respond to electric stimulation failed to return, yet contraction of the pupil took place. He explained the phenomenon as being due to a regeneration of supposedly trophic fibers while the motor fibers remained functionless; but with present knowledge this experiment could probably better be interpreted as indicating a tonicity in the muscle independent of nerve connection, as suggested by Schiff.

Tonicity in smooth muscle is never so great as in skeletal muscle, but it has one remarkable property—that of accommodating itself to the load which it must carry. The stomach adjusts itself readily and automatically to emptiness at one time and to a load of two or three pounds a few minutes later. The circumference of the intestine may be several times greater at one time than at another and yet its tonus remain practically unchanged; the heart accommodates itself equally well to sending out from three to five liters of blood per minute when the individual is at rest and twenty or more during heavy work. Bainbridge[9] has shown that the output per beat is doubled in the heart of the trained man during heavy muscular work. The bladder contracts on a few ounces of urine the same as when it is filled to capacity. These accommodations are all made without the intervention of nerves or the will.

Changes in tonicity and function are apparently identical. Increased function is accompanied by increased tonus and decreased function by decreased tonus. Body cells must be looked upon as being colloidal systems which take up food and give off products of metabolism; take up electrolytes and give off electrolytes, according to the phase of activity in which they are at the particular time. They are subject to the stimulation of nerves and of hormones. Zondek says that tonus is a function of the electrolytes.

RHYTHM

A second very important function of vegetative structures is that of rhythmic action. *Rhythm,* the same as *tonus,* is a fundamental property of vegetative organs. While it may be altered, either increased or decreased by appropriate nerve stimulation, it is primarily independent of nerves. Like tonus, it is a property of colloidal cells and aggregates of cells as found in the vegetative organs to act rhythmically. The rhythmic action, like tonus, is connected with the taking up and giving off of electrolytes. When potassium is added to the cell in excess of calcium, its tonus and rhythm are increased. When calcium is added in excess of potassium, both tonus and rhythm are decreased.

There is no such thing as a resting condition of a vegetative organ, only a condition of increased or decreased *tonus* and *rhythm.*

In harmony with recent knowledge of the physics and chemistry of body cells, all of the important organs have been restudied, and it has been found that *rhythm is of myogenic rather than neurogenic origin.* Even in the intestinal tract where the neurogenic basis seemed to be particularly well established because of the plexuses of Auerbach and Meissner, and, in the ureter and blood vessels, which were thought to offer special evidence for the neurogenic theory, the myogenic theory has come to be accepted because it has been shown that rhythm persists even after the organs are stripped of all intrinsic or extrinsic nerves, and even after removal from the body, if kept in proper solutions.

While rhythm is a property of the organs themselves independent of the nerves, yet it is altered, either increased or inhibited, by nerve stimulation. It is also affected by hormones, adrenalin having a particular effect whenever the sympathetic system generally is stimulated. The complete inhibition of gastrointestinal motility during the fright and anger of the male cat, as described by Cannon,[10] well illustrates this fact.

ACTIVATION AND INHIBITION IN VEGETATIVE STRUCTURES

Two forces are always present in living vegetative structures: one, activating, the other, inhibiting; one increasing tonus, the other decreasing it. Upon the relative strength of these forces depends the physiologic stability of the structure. There are three prominent factors which enter into structure or organ equilibrium. The first is the *electrolytic* content of the cells or the electrolytic content of the medium in which the cells are bathed, for activity and inhibition of activity are altered by the relative amount of potassium and calcium present at a given time, potassium increasing and calcium inhibiting activity. Likewise, the relative concentration of H or OH ions in the cells is of importance. A preponderance of OH ions causes the same condition as a preponderance of K, or as stimulating the parasympathetics. A preponderance of H ions, on the other hand, acts as a preponderance of Ca, the administration of adrenalin, or sympathetic stimulation. It is likewise known that *hormones* also alter activity. There is a further factor which must be considered, and that is the physical state of the colloidal cell mass; but this will require further investigation before it can be readily applied to our physiologic problems.

Activation and inhibition, as produced by stimulation of *vegetative nerves*, are especially well established, as will appear in the discussion of individual organs.

ANTAGONISM OF THE SYMPATHETICS AND PARASYMPATHETICS

Many vegetative structures are supplied by nerves belonging to both the sympathetic and parasympathetic systems. In such cases the principal function of the one is to activate and of the other to inhibit action. In other words, where the two systems meet, their stimulation roughly may be said to cause antagonistic effects. However, there are also antagonistic effects produced by neurones of the same system.

Reciprocal action is a necessary part of the physiology of motion in many of the somatic structures and in the physiology of tonus or rhythmic action in vegetative structures. In voluntary structures, for example the elbow, it would not be sufficient for an impulse to be sent out to the biceps calling on it to contract; there must also be a reciprocal impulse calling on the triceps to relax. So in vegetative structures with double innervation we have a similar reciprocal relationship, but the nerves governing action and inhibition usually belong to distinct and different groups, and equilibrium is maintained until the stimulation of one is able to overcome the other. There is some evidence that nerves belonging to one component of the vegetative system possess not only the power to produce their particular effect when stimulated, but also the power to counteract the effect of the opposing system. There is evidence which has been interpreted by Brücke,[11] in case of the heart, to show that the sympathetic fibers carry not only accelerator fibers but also depressor fibers. The experiment here referred to consisted of a slowing of the pulse when both vagi were cut, but only so long as the cardiac sympathetics were intact. The chief action of sympathetic stimulation, however, is to accelerate the heartbeat while that of the vagus is to slow it. The effect of such experiments as those of Brücke is to show that physiologic control of doubly innervated organs is more complicated than that of simple antagonistic action; but it does not destroy the principle, which is well established.

It is entirely probable that a different result obtains in organs according to the state of activity or rest when the nerve is stimulated.

The antagonism of the sympathetic and parasympathetic systems is shown in the following important organs: pupil, salivary glands, heart, bronchi, stomach, intestines, and bladder.

Stimulation of one system of nerves in organs which are doubly innervated has a tendency to upset the normal tonus and rhythm. But just as the heart possesses a considerable degree of reserve force, so each organ possesses a physiologic balance which permits it to receive a certain amount of stimulation having a tendency to upset its equilibrium, either of a chemical or of a nervous character, without having its tonus or rhythm thrown into an unbalanced state; in other words, without the appearance of symptoms.

We assume that vegetative organs are more or less continuously receiving stimuli either of central origin or of a reflex nature which affect their tonus and rhythm. When the stimuli become too great, the normal rhythm is broken and evidence of illness manifests itself.

The effect of nerve stimulation on a cell is to change its physical and chemical state. The antagonism of the sympathetics and para-sympathetics is shown by each one producing a different effect. Stimulation of the sympathetics is associated with an increase in calcium and stimulation of the parasympathetics, with an increase in potassium. This is particularly significant since these two elec-trolytes are antagonistic in their effect on tonus and rhythm. The real change produced by nerve stimulation is that of causing a new or different distribution of the appropriate electrolyte at the cell boundary.

Recently, Berg, Hess and Sherman[12] proved the relationship of the sympathetic and vagus nerves to serum calcium by severing the splanchnics and abdominal branches of the vagus. When the splanchnics were severed, the serum calcium fell markedly and when the vagus was severed, it rose.

This shows that, whereas it is generally recognized that stimulation of the sympathetics increases the serum calcium, these observers have shown a corollary to this, that removal of the sympathetic action causes a decrease in serum calcium, and removal of para-sympathetic action causes an increase in serium calcium. It would be interesting to know the reaction of potassium to the same experiments.

It seems that there is a reciprocal relationship between the vege-tative nerves and the electrolytes of the cells. Not only do nerves act upon electrolytes, but electrolytes act upon nerves, and always in the same manner. While the cells can act without nerves, nerves cannot act without the necessary electrolytes.

A very important reciprocal relationship exists in certain viscera whose outlets are guarded by sphincters, such as the urinary bladder. The body of the bladder is activated by the sacral nerve of the parasympathetics and is inhibited by the sympathetics. The sphincter, on the other hand, is activated by the sympathetics and is inhibited by the sacral nerve of the parasympathetics. When the bladder is to be emptied, parasympathetic action predominates. The musculature of the body of the bladder contracts and that of the sphincter relaxes. On the other hand, when urine is to be retained, sympathetic action predominates; the body of the bladder relaxes and the sphincter contracts. This reciprocal relationship, such as is seen between the bladder and its sphincter, is a necessary arrangement to insure retention or expulsion of the contents of a hollow viscus. The same mechanism governs defecation, and the emptying of the stomach, the ileum, and the gall bladder.

It seems that the normal stability of physiologic function in doubly innervated organs permits of a fairly wide range of action without equilibrium being destroyed. What influence the antagonistic action of the sympathetic and parasympathetic nerves have in maintaining the balance within normal limits can only be conjectured. Their influence in destroying equilibrium and producing symptoms of deranged function is much better recognized. Visceral reflexes may be recognized as arising in areas of inflammation in any important viscus and as expressing themselves in other viscera. They also may be produced from central stimuli, as for example when one set of vegetative nerves is markedly stimulated in comparison with the other.

Those phenomena which are recognized as reflex symptoms in disease are simply phenomena which result from stimuli in excess of those which are regularly carried by the same nerves. For a nerve stimulus to produce symptoms in a doubly innervated organ it must be sufficient to overcome the action of its antagonistic nerve and also to neutralize the influence of any electrolytes which oppose its action.

The antagonistic action of the two divisions of the vegetative system becomes a very important force in visceral disease. Harmful impulses which influence the vegetative nerves *centrally* are more or less selective in their action and express themselves usually in one division more than in the other or to the exclusion of the other, as is illustrated in the action of toxins through the sympathetics and anaphylactic substance through the parasympathetics. We are also led to believe that the various internal secretions and all physiologic as well as pathologic chemical substances are somewhat selective in their action.

Carbon dioxide acts through the vagus in controlling respiration, while adrenalin produces the same action as stimulation of the sympathetics. The toxins (Vaughan) derived from protein produce a train of symptoms which is characteristic of general sympathetic stimulation as described in Chapter IX.

While toxins influence nerve cells generally, yet the peripheral expression of toxemia in visceral structures is that of sympathetic stimulation. The most prominent symptoms, varying according to the degree of toxemia present, are: malaise, aching, chilliness or rigor, nerve instability, lack of appetite, digestive disturbances (hypomotility and hyposecretion), constipation, loss of weight, rapid pulse, vasoconstriction, particularly of the superficial blood vessels; increased blood pressure, sweats, rise in temperature, blood changes (leucocytosis in which polynuclears predominate), lack of endurance, loss of strength. If the toxemia becomes very severe, vasodilatation, sweating, subnormal temperature and collapse may appear.

The substances derived from the sensitizing or anaphylactic producing molecules (Vaughan) on the other hand, produce symptoms which indicate a predominance of stimulation in the craniosacral system.

METHODS AND RESULTS OF STUDYING THORACICOLUMBAR CONTROL OF BODY STRUCTURES

There are several ways in which the nerves have been studied; one by severing the fiber from its nutrient center and following out the degeneration according to the law of Waller; another by stimulating the end of a severed fiber and studying the parts activated. These methods have been used in studying the white rami communicantes and have shown that the sympathetic system is in connection only with that portion of the cord between the Ist thoracic and IIIrd lumbar segments. It has also shown that no white rami are given off from the cord in those segments which give origin to the nerves in the fore and hind limbs—the lower cervical and the lower lumbar and upper sacral segments; and further that all true vegetative motor (nonmedullated) fibers arise in ganglia without the cord.

It readily can be seen, however, that a study of the true sympathetic fibers cannot be made by observing the effects of stimulation of the white rami after *degeneration* has taken place; because they are only connector fibers. The true sympathetic fibers are the nonmedullated fibers which arise from the motor cells which lie in the various lateral, collateral, and terminal ganglia. It would be necessary to cut or stimulate the fibers after they emerge from their nutrient cells in the ganglia in order to determine the structures innervated by them; and further, it is impossible to observe the degenerative changes in them because they are nonmedullated, and degeneration shows in changes in the medullary sheath.

Langley devised the method of employing *nicotine* for the study of the sympathetics. He showed that nicotine either paralyzes the motor cells in the ganglion or interferes with the synapse; and that, whereas a ganglion so treated fails to transmit stimuli which are applied to the fibers proximal to the ganglion, stimuli applied to the fibers distal to the ganglion are transmitted to the end structures.

By the employment of nicotine Langley was able to trace the connector fibers from the cord to the ganglion in which they end, and then follow the nonmedullated sympathetic fibers to the structures innervated by them. He termed the fibers proximal to the ganglion in which they end (connector fibers of Gaskell) "preganglionic;" and the nonmedullated fibers which arise in the ganglion, "postganglionic;" and was able to show that all "preganglionic" fibers end in ganglia and that none of them go to the tissues direct. The connector fibers to the medulla of the adrenals might be considered as an exception to this, because the fibers do not end in a ganglion prior to entering the gland; but the cells of the medulla themselves are sympathetic cells and must be considered the same as other groups of sympathetic motor cells (ganglia). Langley further showed that many fibers which enter a ganglion are not influenced by the application of nicotine to that ganglion, but that they go on and end in a more distally situated ganglion. In this manner it was shown that all "preganglionic" or connector fibers of the sympathetic system which innervate *internal viscera,* pass through more than one ganglion before ending in the true motor cells of the sympathetic system. By this method it has been shown how far the sympathetic motor cells have traveled from their original place in the spinal cord. While motor fibers going to skeletal muscles pass directly to the muscle fibers from the motor cells in the cord, every efferent sympathetic connector fiber arising from the cord is interrupted by *one* (and only one) ganglion. It may send off many collateral branches to cells in other ganglia on its way, *but no fiber is ever interrupted by ganglion cells more than once before reaching the end organ supplied by it.* The collateral branches, therefore, which are responsible for the wide distribution of the sympathetic impulses are all given off from the "preganglionic" fibers. The collateral ganglia supply the viscera only and send no fibers to the spinal nerves to be distributed to such structures as the pilomotor muscles, muscles of the sweat glands and the blood vessels of the skeletal structures. The fibers supplying these structures arise from motor cells in the lateral ganglia.

The great majority of the nonmedullated fibers from the lateral ganglia, run back as *gray rami* to the corresponding spinal nerves or to the spinal nerves next higher or next lower. They then follow the spinal nerves to their destination and are distributed to the dermal tissues, pilomotor muscles, and muscles of the sweat glands. In the neck and trunk the dermal tissues supplied by the gray rami overlap very little, the segmental relationship of the spinal nerves being preserved. In the fore and hind limbs, however, the segmental relationships are not preserved.

The ganglia of the sympathetics have no special arrangement according to the function of the tissues innervated by them. The cells of a ganglion send out their nonmedullated fibers to take care of all the tissues supplied by the sympathetics in a certain region, no matter what their character, whether muscular or secretory.

SENSORY, SYMPATHETIC AND CRANIOSACRAL NERVES

Visceral tissues are comparatively insensitive to pain, yet they are supplied by afferent neurons whose function it is to carry stimuli centralward. The former belief that these afferent nerves belonged to the vegetative system is now called into question. Schiff[7] says: "As yet there is no adequate proof that there are afferent vegetative nerves. So far as we know the afferent fibers here in question act like somatic fibers."

We must conceive of a more or less continuous flow of sensory impulses traveling centralward from tissues supplied by the vegetative system, the same as from the voluntary system. *Sensory impulses whether from internal viscera or from skeletal structures innervated by sympathetic neurons are conveyed centralward by afferent spinal neurons which accompany the sympathetic nerves into the tissues.* The internal viscera contain so-called "Pacinian corpuscles'' which have the function of sensory end-organs. A sensory stimulus arising in a viscus may be transmitted to the cord and then expressed as pain through the spinal sensory nerves upon the surface of the body. This is spoken of as referred pain. Such referred sensory impulses are segmental in character. As ''viscerosensory'' reflexes (the term being used in a clinical but not physiologic sense) they are very important in the study of visceral disease. (See Chapters XII and XIII.)   There are other sensory stimuli passing centralwards from the viscera which do not evoke pain. Some produce a soreness or discomfort; others result only in reflex action. They are not sufficient to awaken consciousness. In fact, the viscera normally carry on their function without their action coming within the field of consciousness. Most visceral impulses on reaching the cord are transferred to motor neurons. The result is a ''visceromotor'' reflex (see page 197). Like the ''viscerosensory'' and ''viscerotrophic'' reflexes (pages 199 and 200) this is segmental in character, and of great value in the study of visceral diseases. These are fully discussed in the clinical chapters.

The transmission of sensory impulses in the thoracicolumbar outflow and the craniosacral outflow differs in several important particulars.

1. The craniosacral outflow supplies *all* structures innervated by it with both afferent and efferent fibers. As previously mentioned, the *viscera* and the vessels going to them are supplied by efferent thoracicolumbar nerves, while the afferent neurons supplying them are of somatic origin. Afferent fibers from peripheral vessels and dermal structures course through the spinal nerves.

2. Afferent fibers which carry impulses from those viscera supplied by both thoracicolumbar and craniosacral outflows, and which form reflexes with the skeletal structures exclusive of those of the head, most commonly, possibly always, accompany the thoracicolumbar outflow.

3. Sensory impulses which travel centralward in the craniobulbar outflow, confine their resultant reflexes for the most part to other organs supplied by the same outflow and other cranial nerves. Especial importance is attached to the sensory portion of the Vth cranial nerve which stands in much the same relationship to the parasympathetics as the spinal sensory nerves do to the sympathetics.

4. The reflexes caused by sacral afferent impulses are shown for the most part in efferent effects through the sacral spinal nerves.

From this discussion it can be seen that many visceral reflexes caused by stimuli which arise in sympathetically innervated structures will be expressed in the skeletal structures. All sympathetic reflexes, however, are not expressed in skeletal tissues. Possibly there are many disturbances in viscera and many somatic vasomotor disturbances in which the impulse is carried over the afferent neurons which course with the sympathetics and the efferent impulse is likewise carried over sympathetics.

The important reflexes produced by stimuli from tissues supplied by the craniobulbar and sacral outflows, on the other hand, frequently will be expressed in other internal viscera rather than in the skeletal structures. This is a very important fact because of its bearing on the study of the symptomatology of inflammation of internal viscera. Evident exceptions to this are (1) the spasm of the trapezius and sternocleidomastoideus muscles in which a "visceromotor" reflex is caused through afferent fibers in the vagus and efferent motor fibers in the spinal accessory; (2) the many visceral sensory reflexes (headaches) caused by afferent parasympathetic impulses from the viscera expressing themselves peripherally. through the sensory fibers of the Vth cranial nerve; (3) motor and trophic reflexes in the facial muscles, the afferent impulse being carried through the vagus and the efferent through the motor fibers of the facial and trigeminus nerves described in connection with the lung on page 328; (4) spasm and atrophy of the tongue through the vagus and facial and hypoglossus as described in connection with the lung on page 330, and (5) the sensory reflexes in the sacral spinal nerves which result from inflammation of viscera supplied by the pelvic nerve.

FUNCTION OF THE SYMPATHETIC GANGLIA

From the preceding discussion some of the functions of the sympathetic ganglia are evident. There is one very important relationship, however, which requires discussion at this time—that of the true relationship between the peripheral ganglia and the central nervous system.

If the ganglia are cell masses which have traveled out from the central nervous system, do they still retain the characteristics and

have the function of the cells of the central nervous system? Do
the cells within them have the power of mediating reflexes without
the impulse going back to the cord?

From physiologic data which have been obtained so far, it seems
that this question can be answered almost without doubt in the
negative; yet there are observers who take the opposite view.

Gaskell[13] says of these afferent fibers:

"All the afferent fibers have their nutrient centers in the posterior
root ganglia. No peculiarities, therefore, exist on the afferent side;
the course of the sensory fibers is the same in all sensory nerves, viz:
direct to the cells of the posterior root ganglia with *no connection
with any cells in sympathetic ganglia.* Seeing then that all the fibers
entering into the posterior root ganglia are medullated, it follows that
all nonmedullated fibers are efferent, none afferent, and that *the so-
called sympathetic system is not a complete central nervous system,
but consists purely of excitor neurons.*" [Italics not in original.]

Langley discusses the phenomena which seem to support the theory
of the ganglia being true reflex centers but comes to the conclusion
that they are due not to the impulse being transmitted from a sensory
sympathetic fiber to a motor sympathetic fiber through the mediation
of the ganglion cells, but to branches which are given off from the
medullated fibers prior to the time that they end in the ganglion cells.

This opinion of Langley is discussed so well by Luciani[14] that I
shall quote it extensively:

"Are we to regard these masses of ganglion cells as portions of
the cerebrospinal axis which have been displaced to the periphery,
but are still endowed with the functions of the centers? The earlier
anatomists seemed to incline to this view when they gave the name
of *cerebrum abdominale* to the solar ganglion. We have learned that
the fundamental property of the central nervous system lies in its
capacity for subserving reflex acts, so in order to decide this question
we must ascertain whether the ganglia of the sympathetic system are
capable of subserving reflexes.

"From the above conclusions on the course of the afferent fibers
of the sympathetic, any such possibility must *a priori* be excluded,
seeing that all or nearly all the afferent paths run without interruption to the spinal ganglia, and never enter into direct relations with

the sympathetic ganglia. The excitations which they transmit must therefore reach the centers of the cerebrospinal axis before they can be reflected again to the periphery.

"This logical conclusion is apparently contradicted by a series of observations which seem to show that under certain conditions the spinal ganglia may function as true reflex centers. Claude Bernard (1864) was the first to describe these phenomena. After dividing the lingual nerve above the point at which it emerges from the chorda tympani, and thus cutting off all connection with the central nervous system, he artificially stimulated the peripheral end of the lingual nerve, and saw an abundant secretion from the submaxillary gland. We have already recorded the experiments of Sokowin who observed that after cutting off all direct communication with the spinal cord, stimulation of the central end of the hypogastric nerve induces contraction of the bladder on the opposite side. This observation, subsequently confirmed by Nussbaum, Nawrocki and Skabitschewski, and others, was interpreted to imply that the inferior mesenteric ganglion was able to function as a reflex center.

"Other similar facts were observed in the sympathetic nervous system by Langley and Anderson. They saw on repeating the experiment of Sokowin that stimulation of the hypogastric also produced contraction of the internal anal sphincters, ischemia of the rectal mucosa, slight pallor of the cervix and body of the uterus on the opposite side, etc. Langley (assisted partly by Anderson) obtained similar results for the pilomotor muscles and the cutaneous blood vessels in the thoracic and lumbar regions.

"But, according to Langley, none of these reactions, in which excitation of the central end of a sympathetic trunk after separation from the higher centers causes motor or secretory effects, are true reflexes. His arguments and interpretation will be better understood by giving a specific example:

"If the lateral strand of the sympathetic be cut in the cat immediately above the 7th lumbar ganglion, and the central (cranial) end stimulated, erection of the hairs with contraction of the blood vessels will be seen in the cutaneous regions innervated by the 4th and 5th lumbar roots. The same effects may be obtained many days after, when sufficient time has elapsed for the degeneration of afferent nerve fibers with trophic centers below the level of section. It follows that the excitation in this case is not conducted by fibers whose trophic centers lie in the lower portion of the sympathetic. If the nerve roots of the 4th or 5th lumbar ganglion are now cut, the reaction described disappears after five days. We must, therefore, conclude that the excitation was transmitted by preganglionic efferent fibers.

"This striking fact that the supposed reflex ceases on degeneration of the preganglionic fibers is, according to Langley, common to all so-called 'sympathetic reflexes' hitherto described.

"The only possible explanation he can find is that each preganglionic fiber divides into several collaterals, and sends branches to different ganglia. Stimulation of the central end of one of these fibers causes an excitation that is at first propagated backward along the cut fiber, and then to another twig, until it reaches the ganglion which gives origin to the postganglionic fibers that evoke reaction. In other words, this is a similar process to that described

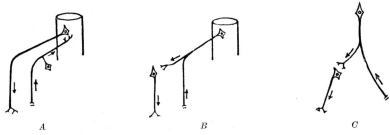

Fig. 14.—Mechanism of action in pseudo- or pre-ganglionic axonal, and true reflexes. (Langley.)
A, true reflex; B, pseudoreflex; C, common diagram for A and B.

by Kühne in his experiments on the conduction of motor nerve in both directions. Langley has proposed to call this special phenomenon by the name of *pseudoreflexes* or *preganglionic axon reflexes*. Fig. 198 [14 in this text] is a diagram of the course of the excitation as compared with a true reflex. Langley utilized these pseudoreflexes for the purpose of experimentally determining which preganglionic fibers are connected with different ganglia."

He concludes: "In my opinion none of the 'apparent' reflexes of the autonomic ganglia depend on a reflex mechanism similar to that which subserves reflexes in which the central nervous system is concerned, as in no case is an afferent fiber concerned in the process."

Bechterew[15] takes the opposite view from Gaskell and Langley, and considers the sympathetic ganglia as having the functions of true reflex centers. He considers that when these ganglion cells migrated outward from the cord, they carried with them the true functions of the cells of the spinal cord. On this point he says:

"The functions of the sympathetic nervous system are divided, as is well known, into sensory, motor, secretory, and trophic. The sensory sympathetic fibers transmit impressions to the spinal cord and brain; the motor, supply the involuntary or unstriped musculature. Aside from this, there are mixed fibers *which establish a connection between neighboring sympathetic ganglia.* The tonus of unstriped muscle fibers is reflexly maintained through sympathetic ganglia. The sympathetic system is also, without doubt, operative in *originating many reflexes in the sphere of the internal organs.*

"*There is lacking today scarcely a single proof of the fact that cellular interruption of nerve fibers takes place in the sympathetic ganglia. With this fact established these ganglia assume at once the rôle of true nerve centers.** It follows as a consequence from the proof of interruption as produced by Ramon Y. Cajal that the nature and manner of the relationship between nerve fibers and nerve cells in the sphere of the sympathetic system is in reality the same as in the spinal and cerebral portions of the central nervous system.

Ganglia are centers in which impulses coming from the central nervous system are relayed for the purpose of distributing their action widely. It has been shown that the number of fibers leaving a ganglion is always greater than the number of those which enter it. Therefore, ganglia may be looked upon as distributing centers for impulses. As yet, however, there is little, if any, evidence that they mediate reflexes.

Probably no one has given us so valuable a conception of the vegetative nervous system in all its physiologic relationships as Cannon.[16] His work is particularly valuable in that it shows its correlating function. He has pointed out how the two components —the sympathetic and parasympathetic—differ in the service that they render the organism. He has particularly emphasized that if the effects of harmful forces which are directed against the organism are to be overcome, they must be overcome through the nerves which supply visceral structures; and furthermore, that if good

---

*Italics in this quotation not in original.

effects from the forces which affect the organism are to be utilized for the benefit of the organism, it must also be done through these same visceral nerves.

References

1. Gaskell, Wm. H.: The Involuntary Nervous System, New York, 1916, Longmans, Green & Co.
2. Langley, J. N.: Autonomic Nervous System, Brain XXVI, 1903, and The Autonomic Nervous System, Part I, Cambridge, 1921, W. Heffer & Sons, Ltd.
3. Lilly, Ralph S.: Protoplasmic Action and Nervous Action, Chicago, 1924, University of Chicago Press.
4. Müller, L. R.: Das Vegetative Nervensystem, ed. 2, Berlin, 1924, Verlag von Julius Springer.
5. Zondek, S. G.: Die Elektrolyte, Ihre Bedeutung für Physiologie, Pathologie, und Therapie, Berlin, 1927, Verlag von Julius Springer.
6. Schade, H.: Die Physikalische Chemie in der Inneren Medezin, Dresden, 1923, Verlag von Theodor Steinkopf.
7. Schilf, Erich: Das Autonome Nervensystem, Leipzig, 1926, Verlag von Georg Thieme.
8. Anderson, H. K.: J. Physiol. 33: 414, 1905.
9. Bainbridge, F. A.: The Physiology of Muscular Exercise, London, 1919, Longmans, Green & Co.
10. Cannon, W. B.: Bodily Changes in Pain, Hunger, Fear, and Rage, New York, 1915, D. Appleton & Company.
11. Brücke: Ztschr. f. Biol. 67: 507, 1917.
12. Berg, B. N., Hess, Alfred F., Sherman, Elizabeth: Changes in the Percentage of Calcium and Phosphorus of the Blood Following Section of the Sympathetic and Vagus Nerves, J. Exper. Med. 47: 105, 1928.
13. Gaskell, Wm. H.: loc. cit., p. 17.
14. Luciana, L.: Human Physiology, London, 1917, Macmillan Co., Vol. III, p. 373.
15. Bechterew, W. V.: Die Funktionen der Nervencentra, Jena, 1908, Gustav Fischer, pp. 59-60.
16. Cannon, Walter B.: The Linacre Lecture on the Autonomic Nervous System: An Interpretation, Delivered at Cambridge on May 6, 1930. The Lancet, May 24, 1930, p. 1109.

CHAPTER VI

PHARMACOLOGIC DIFFERENTIATION BETWEEN NEURONS OF THE THORACICOLUMBAR AND CRANIOSACRAL OUTFLOW

While fibers from the thoracicolumbar and craniosacral systems both supply practically all of the important internal viscera belonging to the enteral system, their action is different. The fibers of these two systems are so closely connected in their distribution in these organs that it is impossible to differentiate them anatomically. Fortunately certain pharmacologic remedies have been found, some of which act upon the tissues activated by the sympathetic system, others of which act upon those tissues supplied by the craniosacral system. These substances have made it possible for us to obtain a fair working knowledge of the vegetative system. It is necessary for one to acquaint himself with the pharmacologic substances which have proved of greatest value in differentiating tissues activated by these systems, if he would study the action of the vegetative nervous system.

1. **Adrenalin.**—This substance is a product of the chromaffin tissue which has been deposited in the medulla of the suprarenal bodies. These chromaffin cells in the suprarenal body and the motor cells in the sympathetic ganglia are embryologically related (page 55). They belong to the same thoracicolumbar outflow from the spinal cord. Bailey and Miller[1] thus describe the formation of the medulla of the suprarenal body:

"A little later than the appearance of the cortical anlage, the cells of some of the developing sympathetic ganglia become differentiated into two types (1) the so-called *sympathoblasts,* which develop into sympathetic ganglion cells, and (2), *phaeochromoblasts,* which are destined to give rise to the phaeochrome or chromaffin cells (Fig. 387 [Fig. 15 in this text]). Hence the chromaffin cells are derivatives of the ectoderm, since the ganglia are of ectodermal origin."

Gaskell in his study of the origin of vertebrates, finds that adrenalin makes its appearance with the development of a contractile vascular system and suggests that the chromaffin nerve cells of the invertebrate are the ancestors of the adrenalin secreting cells and the sympathetic ganglion cells of the vertebrate.

Elliott[2] pointed out that the fibers which connect with the cells of the medulla of the suprarenal body are "connector," medullated fibers. They have not previously connected with any cells of the sympathetic ganglion system but come directly from the cells in the lateral horn of the cord, the same as all the connector fibers. From this it is but natural to conclude that these cells and the sympathetic ganglion cells are of the same system and same nature.

The particular value which adrenalin has in facilitating the study of the sympathetic nervous system, comes from the fact that central stimulation of the sympathetic nervous system and intravenous em-

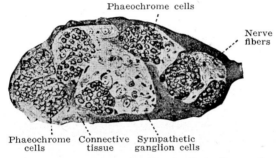

Fig. 15.—Section of a sympathetic ganglion in the celiac region of a frog (*Rana esculenta*), showing differentiating phaeochrome cells. (Giacomini, from Bailey and Miller.)

ployment of adrenalin, produce practically the same effects throughout the body tissues. Adrenalin acts peripherally; in the lateral and collateral ganglia for blood control (Hartman) and at the point where the sympathetic nerve fibers come in contact with the muscle cells —the myoneural junction—in other structures. It produces the same effect as though the sympathetic system were centrally stimulated. The only notable exception to this is found in the sweat glands. Stimulation of the sympathetics will cause a flow of sweat, whether this is due to the contraction of the muscles about the gland squeezing the secretion out, or to a true stimulus to secretion, is not yet known. Adrenalin, however, will not cause sweating.

By employing adrenalin and observing its effect upon the various smooth muscles and secretory glands of the body, physiologists have been able to work out the action of the sympathetic nervous system with a large degree of accuracy, and to put in the hands of the clinician a basis for understanding many clinical symptoms.

2. **Acetylcholine** is a substance derived from ergot. When injected into the blood in minute doses, for the most part it stimulates the nerve endings of the cranial and sacral divisions of the vegetative system, although certain effects are characteristic of sympathetic stimulation as noted on page 46. In minute doses it produces vaso-dilation, and in the strength of 1:100,000,000 produces inhibition in the frog's heart. In the gastrointestinal tract it usually produces the same effect as that produced by stimulation of the bulbar and sacral vegetative fibers. It produces vascular dilation. Reid Hunt[3] draws the following conclusions as to the vasodilator effect of acetylcholine:

"It has been shown in the above that acetylcholine has an intense vasodilator action on the vessels of the skin and of the ear; the action on the skeletal muscles is slight. It dilates the vessels of the penis, of the submaxillary gland and of the spleen; it seems also to dilate the vessels of the intestines and liver. Only slight evidence of a dilator action was found in the case of the kidney and none in that of the lung. The nasal mucosa seemed relatively less sensitive to the vasodilator action of acetylcholine than many other vascular areas. The vasodilation in all of these cases was diminished or prevented by atropine.

"As little as 0.000,000,002,4 mgm. acetylcholine per K. caused a pronounced fall of blood pressure.

"Acetylcholine injected into the trachea or applied to the surface of the lung, kidney, liver, adrenal and various muscles was very active in causing a fall of blood pressure; similar doses applied to the surface of the stomach, spleen and small intestine had no effect on the blood pressure.

"The mechanism involved in the vasodilator action of acetylcholine and related bodies is different from that involved in the action of any of the nerves (posterior root, parasympathetic and sympathetic) to which vasodilator functions have been attributed. It is also different from that involved in the depressor action of epinephrine.

"This mechanism, although capable of more energetic response than any hitherto described, is not involved in the action of the depressor or of other afferent nerves causing a fall of blood pressure.

"The only substances found having the same type of vasodilator action as acetylcholine were a limited number of compounds derived from, or closely related to, choline and pilocarpine and colchicine.

"Atropine and closely related substances were the only compounds found having a pronounced antagonistic action to the vasodilator action of acetylcholine. Pilocarpine diminished the action slightly. Physostigmine intensified all of the actions of acetylcholine."

3. **Ergotoxine** is a substance derived from ergot. It is of special interest in the study of the vegetative nervous system, because of a peculiarly selective action which it exercises on the sympathetic system alone. In small doses it stimulates, and in large doses paralyzes the activating fibers of the sympathetics, but seems to exert little or no effect on their inhibiting fibers. Thus ergotoxine in paralyzing doses causes dilatation of the blood vessels and inhibition of the heart, but leaves the sympathetic fibers in the respiratory and gastrointestinal systems unhindered in their opposition to the vagus and sacral nerves.

Thus in small doses, ergotoxine acts like adrenalin upon the vasodermal structures supplied by it; but unlike it on the endodermal structures. While adrenalin causes inhibition in the gastrointestinal and respiratory systems, ergotoxine fails to do this.

Ergotoxine causes contraction of the pregnant uterus.

4. **Atropine** is of the greatest importance in its relationship to the vegetative nervous system. While ergotoxine in large doses paralyzes all structures which are activated by the sympathetic system, atropine antagonizes the action of those vegetative fibers which come from the cranial, bulbar, and sacral portions of the cord—the parasympathetic fibers. Atropine does not act with the same degree of intensity upon all craniosacral fibers.

Atropine paralyzes the vegetative fibers in the IIIrd nerve which supply the pupil and allows the sympathetic fibers unopposed to dilate the pupil. It also paralyzes the ciliary muscle and destroys the power of accommodation.

Atropine opposes the action of the vegetative fibers which course in the VIIth, IXth, and Xth cranial and sacral nerves; hence reduces the irritability of the nasal mucous membrane and dries the nasal secretion; checks the salivary secretion; reduces the secretion of the glands of the bronchi, pharynx, stomach, intestines, liver, and pancreas; reduces the motility of the musculature of the respiratory and digestive systems; opposes the inhibiting action of the vagus on the heart. Atropine paralyzes the endings of the pelvic nerve in the lower colon, rectum, and cervix uteri.

From the action of atropine upon the sweat glands, we are left in doubt as to their innervation. These subdermal structures, as previously discussed, seem to be activated only by the sympathetic system; yet the fact that adrenalin does not stimulate the production of sweat, and further that the secretion is checked by atropine, leads some observers to the opinion that the sweat glands must be innervated by parasympathetic fibers. This same innervation is further indicated by their reaction toward pilocarpine although physiologic evidence is against it. Sweating is produced by acetylcholine.

5. **Pilocarpine** holds a similar relationship to the craniosacral outflow or parasympathetic nerve endings as adrenalin holds to the thoracicolumbar outflow or sympathetic nerve endings.

Pilocarpine shows a particularly strong action upon the secretory glands activated by the parasympathetic system, causing a flow of saliva; an increase in mucus in the bronchi; an increase in the flow of tears, and an increase in the secretions of the gastrointestinal canal.

It also acts on all smooth muscles supplied by the craniobulbar system in the same manner as though the nerves themselves were stimulated.

Contrary to what would be expected from our general knowledge of the sweat glands, pilocarpine stimulates them and causes profuse secretion.

By the employment of these pharmacologic remedies, important advances have been made in our knowledge of the vegetative system. Eppinger and Hess[4] have utilized these remedies in the study of groups of people and have been able to show that there is a tendency on the part of many individuals to have an unbalanced condition in the vegetative system, so that there is an abnormal irritability in the cell bodies of the neurons belonging to the craniosacral division. They have suggested the term ''vagotonia'' to describe this condition. Their discussion of the relative value of these various pharmacologic remedies and their relationships to the vegetative system deserves careful consideration.

It seems to the writer that these authors lay too much stress on the value of these remedies in differentiating between a condition of vagotonia and sympathicotonia. I have not been able to find that patients with vagotonia always react as readily to atropine and pilocarpine as would be indicated in their writings. It seems more rational to accept these remedies as having certain definite action, and if the patient responds to them, to accept the information as positive; if not, to rely on our clinical judgment. Their position regarding these various pharmacologic remedies in diagnosing or in studying the relative irritability of the nerve cells of the two components of the vegetative system is well expressed in the following quotation from *Vagotonia:*

"Electrical investigations have already shown that in many organs the manifestations caused by stimulation of the fibers of one system may be abolished when stimulation is applied to the fibers of the other.

"These reactions show that many physiologic antagonists may be demonstrated in the two systems. But the fact that the different nerves of the two systems may be commingled on their way to their end-organs makes anatomic differentiation impossible and physiologic testing extremely difficult.

"In certain pharmacologic substances, on the contrary, a means of getting at this differentiation is found. Adrenalin is known to be a substance which acts solely upon the 'sympathetic' nervous system. Its action is similar to that of electrical stimulation of the sympathetic fibers (Table III, page 225). One may, therefore, always regard a manifestation of the action of adrenalin as equivalent to that of stimulation of 'sympathetic' fibers.

"The 'autonomic' nervous system can also be influenced exclusively by certain drugs. The most important of these are atropine, pilocarpine, physostigmine, and muscarine. Following the use of muscarine, pilocarpine, or physostigmine, the same effects may be produced as are obtained by stimulation of autonomic (parasympathetic) fibers. Atropine, on the other hand, prevents many of the effects which are caused by stimulation of the autonomic (parasympathetic) fibers. It is to be expected, therefore, that atropine would be able to counteract, to a certain degree, the effects produced by pilocarpine, muscarine, and physostigmine. Experimentally this may be shown to be the case.

"The parallelism between physiological stimulation and the pharmacological action of these selectively acting drugs seems to be broken by the peculiar behavior of the sweat glands. While the results of anatomical and physiological investigations make it seem probable that these glands are innervated by the sympathetic, yet they react to autonomic (parasympathetic) poisons, whereas the sympathetic tonic adrenalin is able to abolish the secretion of the sweat glands.

"Since pharmacological tests seem to be the most decisive, the innervation of the sweat glands must be regarded as of autonomic (parasympathetic) origin.

"Before proceeding further, a tabular résumé of the antagonism of the action between adrenalin, on the one hand, and atropine and pilocarpine, on the other, is here presented.

"A detailed review of the literature cannot be given here owing to the great abundance of facts. This table has been partly taken from the works of Froehlich and Loewi, in part from the work on *Internal Secretions* by Arthur Biedl.*

"These tables are chiefly of service in showing that pharmacological investigations particularly have confirmed the idea that the two nervous systems, sympathetic and autonomic, are antagonistic in their action. While adrenalin exerts equal action upon nearly all organs with sympathetic innervation, it may be seen, however, that pilocarpine has more action on some parts of the autonomic system than on others. From this it may be seen that its effects cannot be contrasted with the universal effects of the action of adrenalin. Atropine also shows a gradual differentiation in its action, since it has practically no action upon the pelvic nerve, while it exerts a powerful influence upon the cranial portion of the autonomic system. Other drugs are known which also have a powerful action upon the autonomic, more in some of its branches than in others. Pilocarpine itself acts particularly upon secretory autonomic fibers, while its action upon the heart is much less potent. This gradual differentiation is very evident if one compares the action of pilocarpine upon the heart with that of muscarine. What is emphasized in considering these two autonomic stimulants, muscarine and pilocarpine, is that their selectivity differs. In the case of the heart, for example, muscarine may cause cessation of its action, while pilocarpine and physostigmine, with the exception of a transitory slowing of the

---

*This table modified appears on page 225.

pulse, have no noteworthy effect. That these drugs do influence the cardiac branches of the vagus, however, is shown by stimulating that nerve. Thus the effect of a stimulus applied to the heart is enormously increased after the administration of physostigmine, so much so that even a mild stimulation may cause the heart to stop beating.

"These few examples serve to show that the various autonomic stimulants do not have precisely similar effects, but have greater affinities for certain branches than for others, and furthermore, it is worth noting that some autonomic poisons affect the central more than the peripheral endings. Picrotoxin is an example. Finally a differentiation must be made between drugs which act as direct stimulants and those which act by increasing the irritability, i.e., the reactibility to other stimuli. Of the latter, physostigmine is an example."

TESTS FOR SYMPATHICOTONIA

Adrenalin Test.—One-tenth milligram of adrenalin intravenously, or 1.0 gm., injected subcutaneously, may be used to differentiate sympathicotonics from individuals with normal balance, or from those who belong to the parasympathicotonic group. If the pulse rate increases more than one-third above its usual rate, and if there is an increase in systolic pressure of from 30 to 40 mg., it is evidence of a sympathicotonia throughout the cardiovascular system and may usually be taken as meaning that the patient himself is a sympathicotonic. There is also likely to be a doubling of the amount of urine voided during the twenty-four hours following the test. In those who are markedly sympathicotonic, noticeable pallor may appear, with muscular tremors and feelings of fatigability and anxiety.

Ergotamine Test.—Ergotamine, when injected, produces just the opposite effect to that of adrenalin.

Ergotoxine exercises an action on the sympathetic system alone, in small doses stimulating and in large doses paralyzing the activating fibers. No effect on the inhibiting fibers is recognized. Ergotoxin, in paralyzing doses, produces dilatation of the blood vessels and inhibition of the heart, without effect upon the respiratory and gastrointestinal systems.

Löwi's Pupillary Reflex.—Löwi noted that a few drops of 1:1000 solution of adrenalin, instilled into the conjunctival sac, produces mydriasis in those who belong to the sympathicotonic group.

Sergent's White Line.—Sergent's White Line, produced by a light stroke drawn in the median line from above downward over the abdominal wall, is taken as being indicative of increased sympathetic tonus, or hyperadrenia.

Dermographia.—There are many dermographic phenomena, such as the white line, the red line, the red flush, and urticarial wheals, which must be considered in relationship to the vegetative system. These are discussed more fully in Chapter XXXIV.

Pende's Pilomotor Reflex.—Pende has shown that in patients who are distinctly sympathicotonic, stroking of the skin may produce goose flesh.

Ruggeri's Test consists of an acceleration of the pulse, following convergence of the eyeballs, produced by fixing the attention upon an object which is brought very close to the eyes.

TESTS FOR PARASYMPATHICOTONIA

Pilocarpine Test.—One centigram of pilocarpine hydrochloride, subcutaneously, provides varying degrees of salivation, perspiration, lacrimation, vomiting, diarrhea, reddening of the skin, asthmatic type of breathing, and a rectal and vesical tenesmus. The more marked these symptoms appear, the higher the degree of parasympathicotonia.

Eserine Test.—Eserine hydrobromide, subcutaneously, is also used as a test for parasympathicotonia. It produces the same group of symptoms as those produced by pilocarpine, only more marked.

Histamine Test.—When histamine is injected subcutaneously in doses of 2 to 3 mg., it produces vasodilatations and decreases blood pressure, even as much as 50 mm. having been noted. The degree of vasodilatation and hypotension increases in proportion to the degree of parasympathicotonia present.

Insulin Test.—Inasmuch as parasympathicotonics often show hypoglycemia it has been found that insulin is more active in this group of cases than in the sympathicotonic type. So if marked hypoglycemia follows injections of small doses of insulin, after from 50 to 100 grams of glucose have been administered by mouth, this fact may be taken as indicative of parasympathicotonia.

Atropine Test.—Atropine has much the same effect as adrenalin, but instead of stimulating the sympathetics as adrenalin does, it inhibits or paralyzes the parasympathetics. As a result it produces acceleration of the pulse, with rapid dilatation of the pupil and dryness of the mouth, the character of the effect depending upon the degree of sympathicotonia or parasympathicotonia present. In people who are already distinctly sympathicotonic the effect is much greater than in those who are parasympathicotonic.

Acetylcholine.—Acetylcholine when injected in the blood in minute doses, even in dilutions of 1:100,000,000 (in the frog), produces marked parasympathicotonic effects: slowing the heart, producing vasodilatation and lower blood pressure. It acts through both the cranial and sacral parasympathetic nerves, producing parasympathetic action for the most part but in certain cases acting as a sympathetic stimulant.

Oculocardiac Reflex.—Compression of the eyeballs for about thirty seconds, without producing pain, while the patient is in the recumbent position, may produce slowing of the heart. In people who are distinctly vagotonic it has been found that this slowing may amount to ten or twelve beats. Under conditions of excessive pressure, in marked parasympathicotonics, the heart has often been temporarily inhibited. In people of stable nerve balance, inclined to neither sympathicotonia nor parasympathicotonia, the slowing is usually less than twelve beats; in fact, in sympathicotonics no slowing may occur. This reflex is caused by stimulating the ocular fibers of the trigeminus, through which the impulse is transmitted to the cardiac inhibitory fibers. In individuals who are distinctly parasympathicotonic the reflex may also show itself in the gastrointestinal tract.

Erben's Reflex.—This consists of a slowing of the pulse when the head is bent strongly forward. It is most marked in those who are distinctly parasympathicotonic.

References

1. Bailey, Frederick R., and Miller, Adam M.: Text Book of Embryology, ed. 3, Baltimore, 1916, Wm. Wood & Co., p. 427.
2. Elliott, T. R.: Ductless Glands and the Nervous System, Brain, **35**: 306-321, 1913.
3. Hunt, Reid: Am. J. Physiol. **45**: 197, 231.
4. Eppinger, H., and Hess, Leo: Vagotonia, New York, 1915, Nervous and Mental Disease Pub. Co., pp. 4-7.

CHAPTER VII

THE RELATION OF THE IONIC CONTENT AND PHYSICAL STATE OF THE CELL TO CELL ACTIVITY AND NERVE STIMULATION

NEUROGENIC VERSUS MYOGENIC THEORY OF MUSCLE ACTIVITY

Colloid Structure of Cell and Action of Electrolytes Upon It

The myogenic theory of tissue activity requires a comprehension of the structure of the cell and its relationship to the body fluids. Strictly speaking, the cells are in a fluid state and we should speak of the more and less liquid portions of the organism, instead of the liquid and solid portions.

The body cells present a colloidochemical system, which is in a constant state of change during life. The change consists of alterations in phase of the colloidal systems and in exchange of electrolytes.

The basis of every cell consists of protein molecules and lipoids. The protein in the cell is of an entirely different nature from that in the body fluids, and this offers the basis for activity between the cell and the plasma. The cell contains nucleoproteins while the plasma proteins are of the albumin and globulin type. The latter are never found in the cell, although they come in contact with its external structure.

The changes which take place in cells consist of an action followed by a reversal to the former condition. This presupposes not only changes in the taking up and giving off of electrolytes but also changes in the relationship between the colloidal masses and the medium in which they are dispersed.

Activity is brought about most readily by electrolytes and less so by such substances as sugar, amino acids, and salts. The difference is partly a quantitative one and partly due to the difference in their ability to penetrate the cells. Narcotics have the greatest power of all substances to penetrate cells, and it is supposed that their action is based somewhat on that property. Cellular changes also depend upon the H and the OH content of the tissues, as mentioned in Chapter V.

Body fluids contain comparatively large quantities of chlorides, carbonates, and sodium, and small quantities of phosphates, magnesium, calcium, and potassium, while the cells contain only potassium and phosphates in considerable quantity, and traces of sodium, calcium, and chlorides. Potassium is anchored to the protein molecule of the cell and also exists in small quantities as potassium ions in the serum, while calcium exists mostly in the serum of the blood in the form of protein salts. Sodium is found mostly in the serum in the form of the inorganic salt, NaCl.

Ca is essential to the formation and maintenance of the cell membrane. Na, on the other hand, has a tendency to dissolve the cell membrane and allow the protoplasm within the cell to escape. Na and K exert an influence upon the internal cell protoplasm similar to that which they exert on the cell membrane. $CaCl_2$ and $MgCl_2$, on the other hand, exert a coagulating effect. Thus, it will be seen that there is an antagonistic action between the monovalent cations of Na and K, on the one hand, and the bivalent cations of $CaCl_2$ and $MgCl_2$, on the other, which is exerted on both the cell membrane and the internal cell protoplasm. Equilibrium is maintained by the presence of both in the proper quantities. (Chambers.[1])

Just as an antagonistic relationship exists between the electrolytes K and Ca, so does an antagonism exist between H and OH ions in the tissues. K and OH ions work in harmony with parasympathetic stimulation while Ca and H ions work in harmony with sympathetic stimulation.

Not only is a certain physical and chemical condition of all the cells which compose the neurocellular mechanism necessary to the production of normal nerve reaction, but also modifications of usual nerve reactions are brought about by variations in the chemical and physical state of the cells which make up both the neuron itself and the tissue acted upon (Bayliss,[2] Burns[3]). Our knowledge in this field of study is ever growing and is now sufficient to show that clinical reactions cannot be understood unless the entire neurocellular mechanism is taken into account.

The neurogenic theory of muscular activity has gradually given way to its rival, the myogenic theory, and it is now recognized that the power to act lies within the cell itself, and is independent of nerve stimulation except that action is modified by stimuli which are transmitted through nerves. (Engelmann,[4] Gaskell,[5] Parker,[6] Schade[7] and Zondek.[8])

The myogenic theory is based on numerous observations, such as the following: the heart functions in early life before it has nerve connection; if the nerve supplying certain tissues is cut, after a temporary depression or loss of power to act, function is again resumed, though it may be less perfect than previously; when the plexus of Auerbach and Meissner are removed, the intestine still has the power to act. (Magnus,[9-16] Gunn and Underhill,[17] and Alvarez.[18])

Action in tissues and organs is a result of changes in cells which follow chemical and physical laws. Nerve stimulation is not necessary to action, but is a potent factor in modifying it.

Although the myogenic theory of automaticity of cells is now accepted by most students of the subject, yet the importance of nerve influence on cell activity and the function of nerves in correlating action and converting the organism into a unified whole becomes more accentuated with greater knowledge.

NATURE OF CELL AND CELLULAR ACTIVITY

It is necessary for us to study the nature and function of the cell carefully in order to understand what it is that gives it the power of action. For the purpose of studying function it is of little value to know that the cell is made up of cytoplasm and a nucleus. We must go further and study the cell as a physical and chemical reacting entity. Cells consist of colloidal systems made up of solutions of protein in water and lipoids which hold electrolytes in labile form (Moore,[19] Bayliss,[20] Burns,[3] Höber[21]). They are surrounded by a membrane which varies in permeability and in which the sign of charge varies under different conditions. Stimulation or injury causes the cells at the point of application to assume a negative charge.

Proteins are neutral or isoelectric at a given degree of hydrogen ion concentration (pH 4.7). They form salts with acids when the solution reaches a hydrogen ion concentration below this point and with alkalies when it reaches a concentration above this point

(Hardy,[22] Loeb[23]). While this pH concentration is outside the range of colloidal reactions which are consistent with cellular life in the human being, yet it is an important fact to be considered in colloidal study. The tissues during life never become acid; only less alkaline.

Even though power of action lies within the cell itself, the part of the nervous system in cellular action and organic function is still a very important one. Without nerves the finer correlation and integration of action which is everywhere present in the body and which particularly characterizes man and higher animals as compared with lower types of beings, could not take place. Chemical change would go on, but only such influencing of distant cells could take place as was dependent upon the blood stream. All reflex stimuli would be cut off and the power of the will to direct would be eliminated. Purposeful action would be abolished, and the power to meet rapidly the requirements of the physical body and to adapt it to surroundings would be totally lost.

In discussing normal and abnormal action of body cells psychic influences likewise must be considered. One must always bear in mind that emotional and psychic stimuli influence cellular action the same as physical stimuli. This receives far too little attention in our study of pathologic-physiologic states. In our study of reflexes it has a very important bearing, because reflexes can be both discharged and modified by stimuli of psychic origin.

The importance of reckoning with the psychic state in physiologic and pathologic studies should be evident when we recall how important this side of man is, and how his every function in life has a psychic bearing.

WHAT CAUSES CELLULAR ACTIVITY

Cellular activity as we have seen consists of chemical and physical change, of a rearrangement of colloids and crystalloids so as to form new aggregates, of changes in osmosis, of alteration in cell permeability, and of changes in electrical charge. The stimuli which are normally responsible for such disturbances in physical and chemical equilibrium arise from three sources: (1) the advent in the cell of oxygen, electrolytes formed from food, inorganic salts introduced with food and water, and the products formed within the cell as a result of its activity; (2) nerve irritation, of either central or reflex origin; and (3) the action of hormones. The actual cellular changes follow chemical and physical laws and take place according to principles governing electrical reactions (Moore,[19] Mathews,[24] Lilly[25, 26]).

Nerve action, whether it be due to central or peripheral stimulation, causes change in electrical potential followed by changes in colloidal phases and in the ions in the cells. Howell[27] showed that vagus stimulation depended upon the presence of potassium in the cell stimulated, and Howell and Duke[28] have shown that stimulation of the vagus nerve going to a frog's heart which is being perfused causes an increase of potassium ions to be thrown into the perfusate. Otto Löwi[29] demonstrated that the perfusate contained different substances when the sympathetics and parasympathetics of the heart were stimulated. Zondek[30] has shown that stimulation of the sympathetic nerves going to an experimental frog's heart throws out into the perfusing fluid a substance which when perfused through another heart causes the same action as though its sympathetic nerves were stimulated, and that stimulating the vagus going to the first heart causes some substance to enter the perfusate which when perfused through the second heart causes the same action as though its vagus nerve were stimulated. These investigators show that nerve stimulation of the heart causes the heart cells to give up certain substances and presumably to take on others. Their work, together with that of others, some of whom are mentioned later in this discussion, shows that these substances themselves are an intimate part of the neurocellular reacting mechanism and that they of themselves without nerve action cause tissues to react; and, furthermore, that their ability to effect change is dependent upon the permeability of the cell membrane and the surface charge.

WHAT PART IN BODY CONTROL IS CARRIED OUT BY NERVES?

The fact that cells can act when nerve connection is severed does not lessen the importance of the effects which the nerves exert on body functions. It only robs the nerves of a prerogative which has long been assigned to them. There is a great difference in the distribution and in the function of the voluntary or somatic and the involuntary or vegetative nervous systems. While the voluntary system is confined in its distribution to the skeletal muscles and carries out only voluntary action, the vegetative nerves supply all smooth muscle and all secreting glands of the organism; and, supplying, as they do, all blood vessels throughout the body, influence every cell of both somatic and visceral tissues.

Our knowledge of the innervation of tissues is sufficiently advanced at this time so that we not only can assign to the voluntary and the vegetative systems the tissues which each system supplies but we can assign with a fair degree of accuracy to the two components of the vegetative system, the sympathetic and the parasympathetic, the usual part that each component plays in the function of many important tissues and organs of the body, as is evident from the discussions elsewhere in this book. Since the sympathetics and parasympathetics antagonize each other whenever they meet in the same organ; and since there are certain tissues which are innervated by one system alone, the activating and inhibiting fiber coursing in the same nerve, the difference in action depending upon differences in stimulation; and since the distribution of these nerves is now known for all important visceral structures, I can conceive of no better basis for studying the symptoms of visceral disease than that of classifying the disturbances in physiologic function as sympathetic or parasympathetic in nature in tissues with double innervation and as activation or inhibition of action in tissues with single innervation.

Many of the prominent symptoms of visceral disease may be readily classified as being due to predominantly sympathetic or predominantly parasympathetic action in the tissue or organ in which they take their origin; thus: the dry tongue, the lack of appetite, the reduced secretion and reduced mobility throughout the gastrointestinal tract during the toxic stage of infections show a predominance of sympathetic action, while the hypersecretion and hypermotility which are often present in the gastrointestinal canal as a result of such conditions as eyestrain, inflammation of the gall bladder, appendix, or pulmonary tissue are due to a preponderance of parasympathetic action. The same holds for other organs. Not only is it of value to classify symptoms according to the manner in which they affect the two components of the vegetative system, or effect action or inhibition of action in tissues innervated by one component alone but such a classification also affords a known measure whereby we may study the action of various hormones and drugs.

THE INTERDEPENDENCE OF THE VEGETATIVE NERVES AND THE IONIC CONTENT OF THE CELL

The basis for our knowledge of the relationship between the vegetative nerves and the ionic content of the cell was furnished by the experimental work of Sydney Ringer[31, 32, 33] which was carried on in 1880-1882, and which resulted in the production of the solution which bears his name. Ringer found that, while normal salt solution was suitable for transfusion and was a satisfactory solution in which to keep histologic specimens, it was not satisfactory for perfusing and studying a heart when disconnected from the circulation. He experimented by adding different salts until he produced Ringer's Solution. There are many formulas for this solution, but all contain the important elements, sodium, potassium, and calcium. A common formula for mammals is as follows:

NaCl	0.65	NaH_2PO_4	0.001
KCl	0.014	Glucose	0.2
$CaCl_2$	0.012	Water to	100.
$NaHCO_3$	0.02		

When the sodium chloride solution alone was used for perfusing the experimental heart, it soon ceased beating. By the addition of calcium, Ringer found that the heart would again respond to stimuli and continue beating for some time. He noted that the systolic action was strong, but that diastole was weak. He then found that the further addition of potassium caused an efficient diastole. He then added sodium bicarbonate and noted that it improved the beat but acted particularly on the diastole. He thought that its action was partly due to its influence in alkalinizing the solution. We now know further that sodium is an important factor in increasing the permeability of the cell membrane.

If we analyze the action of these salts upon the heart with reference to sympathetic and vagus action, we note that calcium acts much the same as stimulation of the sympathetic nerves while potassium and sodium produce a vagus (parasympathetic) effect. The sympathetic nerve is the activator, or accelerator, of the heart and is often called the nerve of systole, while the vagus is the inhibitor, often called the nerve of diastole.

Practically nothing was known of visceral neurology at the time that Ringer made his observations so the meaning of this discovery remained hidden. Only now are we able to follow up this work and fortify it with results of recent investigation and show its clinical importance (Gaskell,[5] Langley,[34] Bayliss,[2] Burns,[3] Higier,[35] Müller,[36] Pottenger,[37] Zondek,[38] Schilf,[39] Schade[40]).

As a result of the work of these and other investigators in the field of visceral neurology and biochemistry, such as Ringer,[31, 32, 33] Howell,[27] Howell and Duke,[28] Löwi,[29] Zondek,[30, 38] Kraus and Zondek,[41] Abderhalden,[42] Daly and Clark,[43] Kolm and Pick,[44] Carter and Andrus,[45] Sollmann[46] and Burridge,[47] we are able to say that normal control of the heart muscle depends upon a certain equilibrium between the action of the sympathetic and the vagus nerves supplying the heart and a relative proportion between the ions, particularly the calcium and potassium in the cells. If there is present in the cells of the heart muscle a relative increase in calcium over potassium $\frac{Ca}{K}$ increased sympathetic effects are shown; while, if there is relative increase in potassium over calcium $\frac{K}{Ca}$, increased vagus action results.

What was found in the heart has proved to be true also in other tissues, such as the bronchi (Kayser,[48] Pottenger[49, 50]), the gastrointestinal tract, the skin and nasal passages (Pottenger[51]), and the eye (Auer and Meltzer[53]).

The work of Berg, Hess, and Sherman,[54] as previously cited, is most convincing. By sectioning the splanchnics the serum calcium dropped, and by sectioning the vagus, it rose; thus showing the definite relationship between nerve and electrolytes.

Important discussions of the calcium content of the blood are given by Jansen,[55] Peterson,[56] and Kylin;[57] however, it is necessary to emphasize the point that it is not alone the ion content of the blood but of the tissues that must be studied.

Not only are we able to classify the action of calcium and potassium in their relationship to the sympathetics and parasym-

pathetics, but we are now able to say that the predominant action
of magnesium and sodium, like potassium, harmonizes with action
on the part of the parasympathetic component of the vegetative
system. Sodium and calcium are antagonists throughout cell life.
The antagonistic action of magnesium and calcium is shown in the
case of paralysis of the respiratory muscles as a result of an over-
dose of magnesium. The administration of calcium intravenously
will relieve the paralysis immediately.

SOME FACTS ABOUT POTASSIUM IN THE CELL

Potassium is present in every cell of the body. In the frog's heart
its withdrawal from the perfusing Ringer's solution is followed by
a stoppage of the heart after a brief period. The peripheral vessels
may be perfused for hours with Ringer's solution and functionate
normally, but if the potassium is withdrawn, edema at once appears.

An interesting fact has developed in studying radioactive substances. Potassium is radioactive, and is the only element of the
body that is. It emits only β rays. It is a point of importance that
certain other radioactive substances, rubidium and caesium, may
be substituted for potassium in the perfusing Ringer's solution and
maintain normal function. On the other hand, no nonradioactive
substance has been found which can take its place; nor can its
place be taken by radioactive substances emitting α rays. Perfu-
sions of the frog's heart have been performed with potassium-free
solutions when a substance emitting β rays was within effective
distance of the heart. Potassium is a thousand times weaker than
uranium and a billion times weaker than radium in its radioac-
tivity. (Zwaardemaker.[58])

The emanations from potassium are negatively charged electrons
which travel through the colloidal aggregates with their content
in ions and on account of their velocity, accelerate the rate of migration of gaseous ions in a way similar to ultraviolet light and cause
them to become electrical conductors. On account of their negative
charge they distort all systems which are in electric equilibrium
through which they pass. In summer smaller amounts of radioactive substances are needed than in winter, so the relative amount
of potassium as compared with calcium is found to be less in sum-

mer and greater in winter. Potassium and sodium increase the permeability of the cell membrane, while calcium decreases it (Burns[3]).

VAGOTONIA AND SYMPATHICOTONIA

Eppinger and Hess,[59] as mentioned on page 107, suggested in 1910 that there was a large group of individuals which shows a hyperirritability of the parasympathetic system, which is manifested by a predominance of parasympathetic action even in conditions of health. They called these *vagotonics*. They also drew attention to others who show an overbalance of the vegetative equilibrium on the side of the sympathetic system. These they named *sympathicotonics*. This clinical grouping has not received the favorable reception that it deserves, largely because of a lack of knowledge on the part of clinical workers of the vegetative nervous system on which the classification is based; but also because vagotonia, as a rule, is limited to certain structures rather than affecting parasympathetic structures generally; and further because the distinction was probably too closely drawn, particularly as far as the diagnosis depends upon the patient's reaction to certain pharmacologic substances, such as atropine, pilocarpine, adrenalin, ergotoxin and acetylcholine. Nevertheless, this grouping is of great clinical importance, because it classifies the reaction tendencies of those belonging to the groups and helps in understanding some of the vagaries met in the symptomatology of visceral disease. It stands to reason that a sympathicotonic individual will react to stimuli which are distinctly sympathicotropic or distinctly vagotropic in a different manner than a vagotonic individual and vice versa.

WHAT IS THE CAUSE OF DISTURBED EQUILIBRIUM IN THE VEGETATIVE NERVOUS SYSTEM?

As to the cause of the disturbance in equilibrium in the vegetative structures, we can only speculate; but the recognition of the effect of the ion content of the cell upon nerve activity and the dependence of the ions upon the permeability of the cell membrane and its electrical charge show that the entire neurocellular mechanism must be taken into consideration in explaining nerve response and further suggest the necessity of studying the metabolism of the important salts which enter the body, particularly calcium, potassium, sodium, and magnesium. The fact that an increase in H ions is followed by the same effects as an increase in calcium, and an increase in OH ions by the same effect as an increase in potassium makes it necessary to take into consideration the pH of the tissue.

From the influence of certain hormones upon calcium metabolism, notably that of the parathyroids, thyroid, pituitary, and the gonads, we cannot help wondering whether an alteration in calcium metabolism which results in a disturbance in the relative amount of calcium salts found in the tissues might not be caused by abnormalities in internal secretions and whether the basis of abnormal nerve irritability and the conditions of vagotonia and sympathicotonia might not thus be bound up intimately with the endocrines. At least, I believe it will be profitable to study the neurocellular mechanism from all of these standpoints; nerve, cell chemistry, cell physics, and the endocrines. This point of view is supported by a recent study of Engelbach and McMahon[60] on the osseous system in endocrine disorders. It is now recognized that the calcium content of the tissues, the body fluids, and bones are all influenced by the endocrines.

CLINICAL CONFIRMATION OF INTERDEPENDENCE OF VEGETATIVE NERVES AND IONIC CONTENT OF CELL

I have recently tested the synergism between calcium and sympathetic nerve stimulation in a variety of vagotonic syndromes. Such syndromes on the part of organs which have both sympathetic and parasympathetic innervation should be relieved could we directly depress the reacting mechanism of the parasympathetics sufficiently, or increase the reacting mechanism of the sympathetics to such a degree that it would equal or overbalance the action of the parasympathetics. This we have found to be the case in a sufficiently large number of conditions to give us hope for an improvement in therapy in many visceral syndromes.

As one becomes familiar with vegetative neurology and accustomed to think of disturbed function in terms of sympathetic and parasympathetic action, he will see a gradual simplification of the symptomatology of disease. Instead of there being a large group of disconnected and incoordinated symptoms attached to each visceral disease, there will be a logical grouping into those denoting either action or inhibition of action in one or the other component of the vegetative system as discussed in Chapter VIII.

This classification being a physiologic one offers a basis for a more rational therapy, especially since certain drugs and physiologic remedies may also be classified according to whether their action is upon one or the other division of the vegetative system. Adrenalin and calcium are among the substances which produce inhibition of action similar to that caused by stimulation of the sympathetics themselves in such structures as the pupil, the bronchi, the gastrointestinal tract, and the body of the bladder in which a sympathetic stimulation inhibits action; ergotoxin has the property of stimulating in small doses and paralyzing in large doses the activating sympathetic fibers without influencing the inhibiting fibers; and the phosphates in certain structures also fortify the action of calcium which seems to be necessary to sympathetic nerve action. On the other hand, pilocarpine produces stimulation and atropine inhibition of the parasympathetics; while potassium, magnesium, and sodium all produce parasympathetic action in visceral structures. A further explanation of the action of calcium in all of these instances is furnished by its action in decreasing the permeability of the cell membrane, hence reducing cell activity. (Lilly.[25])

Based upon these facts, we find a rational method of relieving many disturbing symptoms and syndromes met in disease, a few of which will be enumerated. Others will readily occur to the observing clinician.

1. **Anaphylaxis.**—Anaphylaxis is a condition which resolves itself into a more simple group of phenomena when analyzed from the standpoint of the neurocellular mechanism than when approached in any other manner. In the first place, the cells under anaphylaxis show increased activity from which we would draw the conclusion that their cell membranes are in a state of increased permeability which may be interpreted to mean that the membrane contains a relative deficiency of calcium. In this connection it must be remembered that the anions of the sodium salts precipitate calcium (Lilly[26]). The phenomena appear primarily and predominantly as parasympathetic hyperirritability whether they affect the respiratory, the gastrointestinal or other systems of the body. The symptoms may be reduced in severity or even prevented by inhibiting the parasympathetics through the previous administration of atropine,

and they may be lessened in severity or relieved by adrenalin and calcium. In states of anaphylaxis the cells affected by the reaction are hyperactive and this is reduced by calcium, which decreases the permeability of the cell membrane.

2. **Serum Disease.**—Serum reaction is a hypersensitive phenomenon and as such is a parasympathetic syndrome. It can be partially or wholly prevented by administering atropine prior to the injection of the serum and when established may be partially or wholly relieved by the same remedy, adrenalin or calcium. I have seen symptoms disappear quickly following the hypodermic use of adrenalin and the intravenous administration of calcium chloride.

3. **Urticaria.**—Urticaria is another hypersensitive phenomenon of parasympathetic origin and may be relieved by adrenalin and calcium.

4. **Asthma.**—One of the most interesting and instructive subjects for investigation bearing out the facts cited in this chapter is asthma. From the standpoint of visceral neurology, the essential conditions in asthma are bronchial spasm and increased bronchial secretion, both of which may be caused by overaction on the part of the bronchial branches of the vagus nerve. From the standpoint of the cell there is increased permeability of the plasma membrane, an increase of electric potential (an increased negativity), and an increased electric conductivity of the tissues. The action of sodium and potassium ions predominates over that of calcium and the tissues show an increased alkalinity. Action of the sympathetics is for the time being overcome, the normal equilibrium between them and the vagus is destroyed, and hyperactivity of the vagus is established. To be sure, there are other symptoms present, such as rapid heart, heart strain, dyspnea, cyanosis, increased bronchial secretion, and emphysema; but these are secondary to the heightened vagus action.

There is much evidence, as I have discussed elsewhere,[49, 50, 51, 52] that asthma is not primarily a condition of anaphylaxis to pollens, foods and other proteins, nor a primary vagus reflex from a stimulus arising in some other organ, nor a condition produced primarily by changes in weather or climate or dust or other inhaled irritants, but a condition incited by these various factors in a susceptible individual whose bronchial neurocellular mechanism, either because of inherited or acquired factors, is out of equilibrium and in whom vagus action predominates. The real seat of the disturbance may be in the chemical composition of the cell or in its physical and electric state or in altered adrenal secretion. The same seems to be true of many other parasympathetic, as well as sympathetic, syndromes.

In the treatment of asthma, aside from sedatives which relieve the irritability of the nerves in general, and desensitization or withdrawal of determined sensitizing substances, we find that relief may come from any one of four physiologic methods of attack: (1) by direct inhibitory action on the vagus by atropine, or by stimulating the sympathetics so that they are able to overcome the hyperactivity of the vagus, as I have seen occur as a result of toxins during the toxic period of acute infections, such as tonsillitis, influenza, pneumonia, and typhoid fever; (2) by increasing the relative calcium as compared with potassium content of the bronchial cells, thus lowering their permeability; (3) by employing various hormones, such as adrenalin, which produce the same action on the bronchial musculature as is produced by stimulating the sympathetics, by the use of the cortical hormone either alone or in conjunction with adrenalin which produces similar but a more sustained effect than the latter, and such other products as parathyroid, thyroid, and pituitary, which are intimately connected with calcium metabolism; and (4) by increasing the H of the tissues, because lessened alkalinity accompanies sympathetic action. This may be done by a high protein high fat diet. The employment of hydrochloric acid after meals has theory to recommend it.

Asthma thus well illustrates and emphasizes the interdependence of the visceral nerves, the endocrine secretions and the ionic content of the body cells, and shows how necessary it is to take into consideration all parts of the neurocellular mechanism and all substances which may influence it if we would understand disturbances in function.

5. **Hay Fever.**—Hay fever is a condition of hypersensitiveness closely related to asthma. Its relation to the parasympathetic neurocellular mechanism is emphasized by the fact that it may be relieved or alleviated by desensitization or by the use of atropine, adrenalin, calcium, and hydrochloric acid.

6. **Bronchitis.**—The increase in bronchial secretion which accompanies asthma is reduced by atropine, adrenalin, and calcium. This

should be expected, because it is primarily due to increase in vagus action. These measures, while less valuable in the bronchitis which is due to chronic infections, will at times even in them effect a diminution in the cough and secretion.

7. **Affections of the Gastrointestinal Tract.**—While there are many interesting syndromes in the gastrointestinal tract expressed on the part of both the sympathetic and parasympathetic systems, yet I shall refer to only a few. Any condition found, however, should be considered from the standpoint of action or inhibition of action and classed according to whether such activity coincides with action of the sympathetic or parasympathetic neurocellular mechanism.

It can be seen that all symptoms which represent increased muscular or secretory activity in the gut proper (excluding the sphincters which bear opposite innervation), or those organs, such as the liver, pancreas, and body of the bladder, which are derived from the gut and bear the same innervation, are due to a predominance of parasympathetic activity. Among such may be mentioned *hypersecretion* in the stomach (hyperchlorhydria) or intestinal tract; *hypermotility* in these organs, leading to such conditions as *diarrhea, mucous colitis,* colicky pains, and *spastic conditions* of the intestinal tract. Such conditions may be influenced through the inhibitory action of atropine upon the vagus, or through stimulation of the sympathetic neuromuscular mechanism by adrenalin or by calcium which has a tendency to increase the action of the sympathetics so that they may depress the heightened vagus action to such a point that equilibrium may be again restored.

There are also certain sympathetic syndromes on the part of these structures which need to be considered, such as the *hyposecretion* and *hypomotility* represented by the s*low digestion* and *constipation* which accompany the acute toxic stage of infections. This is explained by the fact that the toxins act upon the sympathetics and overbalance the action of the parasympathetics represented by the vagus and pelvic nerve, destroying the nerve equilibrium and producing a predominant sympathetic effect. The same neurocellular condition exists in chronic hyposecretion and hypomotility and likewise results in relaxation of the bowel and *constipation.*

These conditions may be improved, at least temporarily, by the administration of sodium or magnesium salts, particularly the sulfates, which stimulate the vagus mechanism and cause an increase in glandular secretion and an increase in muscular contraction. Such conditions may also be influenced at times by general stimulants for the parasympathetic systems, such as pilocarpine.

Spasm of the various sphincters, as a rule, is a condition of hyperactivity of the sympathetics, although, as mentioned elsewhere, Carlson[61] believes cardiospasm may be due to either increased sympathetic or increased parasympathetic action. The relief for such conditions consists in general sedative measures, but should be aided by substances which are distinctly inhibitory to the sympathetics, such as ergotoxin in rather large doses, or substances which raise the action of the vagus to the point of restoring nerve equilibrium in the part affected. We must not forget pilocarpine and the salts of sodium and magnesium in this connection. We must also remember the possibility of the spasm being due at times to vagus action, as suggested by Carlson.

Gall bladder drainage, as carried out by the Lyon[62] method, was designed for the purpose of effecting action in the neuromuscular mechanism which maintains equilibrium in the common duct and its sphincter, the gall bladder and the gall ducts in such a way as to cause them to pour forth the pathologic secretion which they hold. The sympathetics innervate the sphincter at the ampulla of Vater and probably the common duct and inhibit muscular action in the gall bladder. The parasympathetics oppose this action and when stimulated dilate the sphincter and possibly contract the musculature of the gall bladder, although this musculature is very weak and there is some question as to how much force could be exerted by its contraction. They also activate the ducts in the liver and cause them to contract when stimulated. In the presence of infection and stasis it is desirable to empty the gall bladder and the ducts of the liver and drain them. This has been successfully done by introducing magnesium sulfate into the duodenum where it exerts its influence upon the vagus neuromuscular mechanism, stimulating it and producing conditions which favor the emptying of the gall bladder and the liver ducts. See Chapter XX. Other parasympathicotropic drugs might act in the same way, but magnesium sulfate in 25 to 35 per cent solutions introduced through the duodenal tube has acted best. There are reported many failures where this method is employed, the same as there are in all procedures which are instituted for the relief of disturbed physiologic conditions in the human organism, but it should not be abandoned without thorough investigation, for it does seem to be based on sound physiologic principles.

Eczema.—One must not forget the importance of the sympathetic nerves and the thyroid hormone in their relationship to all dermal and subdermal structures. As far as we know, there is no physiologic connection between these structures and the parasympathetic system, therefore eczema, dry skin, ichthyosis and other affections of the skin accompanied by dryness and itching should be considered in their relationship to the sympathetic neurocellular mechanism and the thyroid gland.

For a long time, itching of the skin has been treated empirically by calcium. The rationale of its action may be based on its effect on the physics of the cell in reducing cell permeability, for in all irritative conditions there is an increased activity of the cells, hence an increased permeability of the cell membranes. This is reduced by calcium.

We have tried its effect upon ichthyosis and very severe eczemas. We have employed thyroid substance in connection with the calcium in both instances. In patients suffering from eczema, we have seen marked thickening of the skin over the hands, arms, thighs, and face, severe cracking of the skin over the palms, splitting of the nails and dryness of the hair yield to these measures. In one case the arms showed long deep scars where the flesh had been torn by the nails during sleep. The patient had tried so many things without relief that she was hopelessly pessimistic as to obtaining benefit. By the use of calcium intravenously and thyroid for many months we not only brought about a cessation of the itching but a satisfactory reduction in induration and a favorable result which has shown no exacerbation in more than ten years.

DISCUSSION

Calcium must not be put forward as a cure-all; otherwise its very important function will be lost sight of through disappointment. I have used it sufficiently in parasympathetic syndromes to demon-

strate beyond question that we are able to antagonize many pathologic parasympathetic syndromes.   It has influenced favorably
eczema and ichthyosis, conditions of extreme hyperirritability of the
dermal cells.   Its effect is partly due to decreasing cell permeability.

These facts of themselves are of utmost importance to clinical
medicine. Its employment is surrounded by many difficulties which
must yet be overcome. Its relationship to other ions must be more
carefully worked out; its effects upon the physical reactions of the
cell must be studied; so must its relationship to the sympathetic
nerves and the various hormones. One must not expect it to bring
about a cessation of all symptoms in these conditions mentioned.
At present it must simply be looked upon as an aid. In the future
we hope that we may understand the entire neurocellular mechanism sufficiently so that the action of calcium may be definitely
known.

While I have published in previous papers the method of using
calcium, it might be well to repeat it here. We usually employ a
5 per cent solution of calcium chloride, put up in sterilized ampules.
Of this we have used most commonly 5 c.c. at an injection—sometimes 10 c.c., and sometimes a much larger dose of a higher dilu-
tion—the same to be repeated at intervals of from one to two days
or a week. The remedy must be injected very slowly. We usually
take from five to ten minutes to inject 5 and 10 c.c. I am of the
opinion that larger doses of the salt more highly diluted and administered less frequently are preferable. During its administration, unless injected slowly, the patient may complain of a sensation
of warmth or intense heat; constriction in the throat; sometimes
nausea; sometimes burning in the rectum; but all of these symptoms are evanescent, passing away in a few minutes.

One should never forget that the employment of intravenous
therapy is a serious matter, and that it must be surrounded by
every precaution. Personally, I think it is better that the patients
be in bed, although we have treated quite a number as ambulatory
patients.

References

1. Chambers, Robert: The Nature of the Living Cell as Revealed by Microdis-
       section, Harvey Lectures 1926-27, Baltimore, Williams and Wilkins Co.
2. Bayliss, William M.:   Interfacial Forces and Phenomena in Physiology, Her-
       ter Lectures, 1922, London, Methuen & Co., Ltd.

130   SYMPTOMS OF VISCERAL DISEASE

3. Burns, David: An Introduction to Biophysics, New York, 1921, The Macmillan Co.
4. Engelmann, J.: Das Herz, Leipzig, 1904.
5. Gaskell, W. H.: The Involuntary Nervous System, London, 1916, Longmans, Green & Co.
6. Parker, G. H.: The Elementary Nervous System, Philadelphia, 1919, J. B. Lippincott Co.
7. Schade, H.: Die Physikalische Chemie in der Inneren Medizin, Dresden und Leipzig, 1923, Verlag von Theodor Steinkopff.
8. Zondek, S. G.: Die Elektrolyte, Ihre Bedeutung für Physiologie, Pathologie und Therapie, Berlin, 1927, Verlag von Julius Springer.
9. Magnus, R.: I. Mitteil. Versuche am überlebenden Dünndarm von Säugetieren, Arch. f. d. ges. Physiol. 102: 123-151, 1904.
10. Magnus, R.: II. Mitteil. Die Beziehungen des Darmnervensystems zur automatischen Darmbewegung, Arch. f. d. ges. Physiol. 102: 349, 363, 1904.
11. Magnus, R.: III. Mitteil. Die Erregungsleitung, Arch. f. d. ges. Physiol. 103: 515-524, 1904.
12. Magnus, R.: IV. Mitteil. Rhythmizität und refraktäre Periode, Arch. f. d. ges. Physiol. 103: 525-540, 1904.
13. Magnus, R.: V. Mitteil. Wirkungsweise und Angriffspunkt einiger Gifte am Katzendarm, Arch. f. d. ges. Physiol. 108: 1-71, 1905.
14. Magnus, R.: VI. Mitteil. Versuche am überlebenden Dünndarm von Säugetieren, Arch. f. d. ges. Physiol. 111: 152-160, 1906.
15. Magnus, R.: Die Bewegungen des Verdauungskanals, Ergebn. d. Physiol. 7: 27-64, 1908.
16. Magnus, R.: Die Bewegungen des Verdauungsrohres. Tigerstedt's Handbuch der physiologischen Methodik. Leipzig, 1911, ii, zw. Abth., 99-149.
17. Gunn, James A., and Underhill, S. W. F.: Experiments on the Surviving Mammalian Intestine, Quart. J. Exper. Physiol. 8: 275, 1914.
18. Alvarez, Walter C.: The Mechanics of the Digestive Tract, ed. 2, New York, 1928, Paul B. Hoeber.
19. Moore, Benjamin: Biochemistry, London, 1921, Edward Arnold.
20. Bayliss, William M.: The Colloidal State, London, 1922, Henry Froude & Hodder & Stoughton.
21. Höber, Rudolf: Physikalische Chemie der Zelle und der Gewebe, ed. 5, Leipzig, 1922, Wilhelm Engelmann.
22. Hardy, W. B.: Colloidal Solution, J. Physiol. 33: 251, 1905.
23. Loeb, Jacques: Proteins and the Theory of Colloidal Behavior, New York, 1922, McGraw-Hill Book Co.
24. Mathews, A. P.: Some General Aspects of the Chemistry of Cells. General Cytology, edited by E. V. Cowdry, University of Chicago Press, Chicago, 1924.
25. Lilly, Ralph S.: Protoplasmic Action and Nervous Action, University of Chicago Press, Chicago, 1924.
26. Lilly, Ralph S.: Reactivity of the Cell, General Cytology, edited by E. V. Cowdry, University of Chicago Press, Chicago, 1924.
27. Howell, W. H.: Vagus Inhibition of the Heart in Its Relation to the Inorganic Salts of the Blood, Am. J. Physiol. 15: 280, 1906.
28. Howell, W. H., and Duke, W. W.: The Effects of Vagus Inhibition on the Output of Potassium From the Heart, Am. J. Physiol. 21: 51-63, 1908.
29. Löwi, Otto: Humoral Transmissibility of Cardiac Nerve Activity, Arch. f. d. ges. Physiol. 193: 201, 1921.
30. Zondek, S. G.: Untersuchungen über das Wesen der Vagus und Sympathikus reizung, Berl. klin. Wchnschr. 58: 1893, 1921; and Deutsche med. Wchnschr. 47: 1520, 1541, 1921.
31. Ringer, Sydney: Concerning the Influence Exerted by Each of the Constituents of the Blood on the Contraction of the Ventricle, J. Physiol. 3: 380.

32. Ringer, Sydney: A Further Contribution Regarding the Influence of the Different Constituents of the Blood on the Contraction of the Heart, J. Physiol. **4:** 29-42.
33. Ringer, Sydney: A Third Contribution Regarding the Influence of the Inorganic Constituents of the Blood on the Ventricular Contraction, J. Physiol. **4:** 222-225.
34. Langley, J. N.:   The Autonomic Nervous System, Brain **26:** 1, 1903.
35. Higier, Heinreich: Vegetative or Visceral Neurologie, Ergebnisse der Neurologie und Psychiatrie **2:** No. 1, 1912.
36. Müller, L. R.:   Das Vegetative Nervensystem, Berlin, 1920, Verlag von Julius Springer.
37. Pottenger, F. M.:   Clinical Tuberculosis, Vol. II, St. Louis, 1922, The C. V. Mosby Co., p. 166.
38. Zondek, S. G.:   Die Elektrolyte, Ihre Bedeutung für Physiologie, Pathologie und Therapie, Berlin, 1927, Verlag von Julius Springer.
39. Schilf, Emil: Das Autonome Nervensystem, Leipzig, 1926, Verlag von Georg Thieme.
40. Schade, H.:   Die Physikalische Chemie in der Inneren Medizin, Leipzig, 1923, Verlag von Theodor Steinkopff.
41. Kraus, F., and Zondek, S. G.:   Preliminary Report on Experiments on the Rôle of Electrolytes in the Heart Beat, the Effect of Salt in Hemorrhage and the So-called Tonus Current, Klin. Wchnschr. **1:** 996, 1922.
42. Abderhalden, Emil: The Nature of Innervation and Its Relation to Internal Secretion, Klin. Wchnschr. **1:** 7, 1922.
43. Daly, I. de B., and Clark, A. J.:   Actions of Ions Upon Frogs' Hearts, J. Physiol. **54:** 367, 1921.
44. Kolm, R., and Pick, E. P.:   Ueber die Bedeutung des Calciums für die Erregbarkeit des Sympathischen Herz—Nervenendigungen, Arch. f. d. ges. Physiol. **189:** 137, 1921.
45. Carter, E. P., and Andrus, E. C.:   Effect Upon Cold-Blooded Heart of Changes in Ionic Content of Perfusate: I. Upon Normal Mechanism; II. Upon Arrhythmias, Am. J. Physiol. **59:** 227, 1922.
46. Sollmann, T.:   The Pharmacology of the Autonomic System, Physiol. Rev. **2:** 479, 1922.
47. Burridge, W.:   Researches on the Perfused Heart. The Effects of Inorganic Salts, Quart. J. Exper. Physiol. **5:** 347, 1912.
48. Kayser, Curt: Wratsch, Berlin, Oct. 15, 1922, ii, 453.
49. Pottenger, F. M.:   The Physiologic Basis for the Employment of Calcium in the Treatment of Asthmatic Paroxysms, California State J. Med. **21:** 293, 1923.
50. Pottenger, F. M.:   A Discussion of the Etiology of Asthma in Its Relationship to the Various Systems Composing the Pulmonary Neurocellular Mechanism, With the Physiologic Basis for the Employment of Calcium in Its Treatment, Am. J. M. Sc. **167:** 203-219, 1924.
51. Pottenger, F. M.:   The Relationship of the Ion Content of the Cell to Symptoms of Disease, With Special Reference to Calcium and Its Therapeutic Application, Ann. Clin. Med. **2:** 187, 1923.
52. Pottenger, F. M.:   The Potential Asthmatic, J. Lab. & Clin. Med. **13:** 913, 1928.
53. Auer, J., and Meltzer, S. G.:   The Influence of Calcium Upon the Pupil and the Pupillometer Fibers of the Sympathetic Nerves, Am. J. Physiol. **25:** 43-65, 1909.
54. Berg, B. N., and Hess, Alfred F., and Sherman, Elizabeth: Changes in the Percentages of Calcium and Phosphorus of the Blood Following Section of the Sympathetic and Vagus Nerves, Jour. Exper. Med., 1928, xlvii, 105.
55. Jansen, W. H.:   Der Kalkgehalt des Menschlichen Blutes, Deutsch. Arch. f. klin. Med., 1918, Leipzig, cxxv, 168.

132   SYMPTOMS OF VISCERAL DISEASE

56. Peterson, W. F., Levinson, S. A., and Arquin, Sergius: The Relation of the Reaction to the Epinephrine to the Potassium-Calcium Ratio and Other Ratios, Arch. Int. Med., 1928, xlii, 257-269.
57. Kylin, E.: Der Gehalt des Blutes an Calzium und Kalium, Acta med. Scandinav. (supp. No. 19), 1927, p. 1.
58. Zwaardemaker, J.: Archiv. ges. Physiol., 1918, clxxiii, 28.
59. Eppinger and Hess: Die Vagotonie, Sammlung klinischer Abhandlungen, von Noorden, Nos. 9 and 10, 1910.
60. Engelbach, Wm., and McMahon, Alphonse: Osseous Development in Endocrine Disorder. Endocrinology, 1924, viii, 1.
61. Carlson, H. J., Boyd, T. E., and Pearcy, J. F.: Studies of the Visceral Sensory Nervous System. XIV. The Reflex Control of the Cardia and Lower Esophagus, Arch. Int. Med., October, 1922, xxx, No. 4.
62. Lyon, B. B. Vincent: Nonsurgical Drainage of the Gall Tract, Lea & Febiger, Philadelphia, 1923.

PART II

THE RELATIONSHIP BETWEEN THE VEGETATIVE NERVOUS SYSTEM AND THE SYMPTOMS OF VISCERAL DISEASE

CHAPTER VIII

BASIS OF CLASSIFICATION OF SYMPTOMS OF DISEASE

Symptoms of disease are largely changes in physiologic equilibrium, which are expressed either subjectively or objectively, and which result either directly or indirectly from the presence and action of such disease.

Many classifications of symptoms may be offered, depending upon different points of view; but a rational classification of the symptoms of visceral disease must take into consideration the colloidal state and ionic content of the body cells and the nervous and endocrine systems through which cellular activity may be influenced, and the psychic as well as the physical state of the patient.

As previously stated all smooth muscle of the body, the striated heart muscle, and all secreting glands are subject to activation and inhibition through the vegetative nerves, and are supplied with afferent neurons, through which not only is their action correlated with the action of other structures, but also through which impulses course centralward to affect reflexly other structures. It must be evident, therefore, that this system of nerves is closely connected with symptoms arising in or expressed in visceral structures. Smooth muscle and secreting glands are also influenced by the products of the glands of internal secretion. The secretion of some of these glands is also dependent upon stimuli coursing in the vegetative nerves. It must be kept in mind that there is a third important factor in determining nerve and hormone action—the condition of the colloids of the body cells and their ionic content. The experiments of Zondek,[1] as previously cited, shows that stimu-

133

lation of the sympathetic nerves going to the heart throws out calcium into the perfusate, which when perfused through another heart causes the same action in it as though its sympathetic nerves were stimulated; and that stimulation of the vagus throws out potassium into the perfusate which when perfused through another heart causes the same action as though its vagus were stimulated. Daly and Clark[2] and Kolm and Pick draw the conclusion from much experimenting that calcium ions cause the same action as that which results from stimulating the sympathetic nerves or injecting adrenalin, while potassium ions act the same as stimulating the parasympathetic nerves. Neither calcium nor potassium can act except in the presence of sodium ions. So important is the ion content of the cells, that Pick[4] and Kolm and Pick[3] have shown that a hypersensitization of one component of the vegetative system, such as might be caused by an alteration in the calcium or potassium content of the cells, acts in the same manner as an excessive stimulation of the neurons and causes a reversal of action—that is, a parasympathetic effect in organs with double innervation when a sympathetic effect should have ordinarily occurred. These facts shed much light on variations in response to nerve and hormone action which result in symptoms of disease as well as on the pharmacologic action of those drugs and other substances, such as adrenalin and acetylcholine, which now and then produce an action the reverse of that which is expected.

Man is a dual being—physical and psychic. Stimuli arising in physical structures may produce symptoms confined to physical structures or which extend to the psychic being. So may stimuli of psychic origin affect both the psychic and physical. I can conceive of no marked physical or psychic stimulus, however, which confines its action to the system in which it arises.

Some physical and psychic stimuli show a preference for the sympathetic, others for the parasympathetic division of the vegetative nervous system. The major emotions, however, are expressed through the sympathetic system by way of the centers in the diencephalon. It is also self-evident that different endocrine glands react differently. Thus toxins of disease act upon the nervous system as a whole, but produce symptoms in visceral structures which are characteristic of stimulation of the sympathetic system. They stimulate the adrenals and thyroid and the resultant secretions become added factors in the production of symptoms. Such emotions as fear, anger, and pain act upon the sympathetics as shown by Cannon and his coworkers, while joy and happiness tend to preserve the normal physiologic nervous and endocrine equilibrium. Anaphylaxis expresses itself peripherally in the production of symptoms characteristic of parasympathetic stimulation, and the allergic reactions caused by parenteral digestion produce parasympathetic effects in tissues wherever affected.

It is evident that symptoms must necessarily vary according to the nature of the disease; whether inflammatory or not; according to the permeability of the cells; whether accompanied by toxic or antigen-tissue reaction; according to the character of the tissues involved; the pH of the tissues; the state of sensitivity of the nerves which come under the influence of the disease factors; the condition of the cellular colloids and their content in electrolytic ions; and according to the relationship which such tissues bear to other organs or structures through the nervous system, through the internal secretions, or other chemical substances. In this connection it must be borne in mind that many pathologic chemical products are produced under the influence of disease.

For inflammatory diseases of important internal viscera, I have suggested the following classification of symptoms, varying according to whether or not the process is infectious and accompanied by toxemia, and also according to the degree of toxemia: (1) symptoms due to toxemia (general symptoms) ; (2) symptoms due to reflex action; (3) symptoms due to the disease process itself; and another may be added (4) symptoms which appear after the disease has expressed itself markedly.[5, 6, 7] These include many changes in body function resulting from disturbances in electrolytic nervous and endocrine balance, such as respiratory, circulatory, and metabolic changes; mechanical disturbances; and disturbances in psychic equilibrium.

Another group of symptoms consists of those which accompany antigen-tissue reaction. These are not commonly found in the syndromes which accompany organic diseases of the viscera. It must be borne in mind, however, that a hyperirritable condition of the bronchial vagus, when the bronchial tissues have been aggravated by sensitization to certain specific proteins, may be precipitated into an attack of asthma by either direct or reflex stimulation, the cause of the stimulus being a disease process in other organs, such as the nasal mucous membrane, sinuses, ear, lung tissue, heart, stomach and intestinal tract, gall-bladder, appendix, genitals, and bladder. If we wish our classification to apply to all visceral diseases, we might use the term *general* or *constitutional symptoms* to cover all symptoms which are not of reflex origin or not due to the disease *per se* acting locally. In this classification, toxic reactions would be classed as general or constitutional symptoms, the tissue-antigen reactions as general or local according to circumstances.

The above classification was first suggested for pulmonary tuberculosis but will hold for all infections involving internal viscera.[8] Its advantage lies in the fact that the symptoms cease to be independent entities and fall into related groups which result from some definite acting cause. This grouping of symptoms emphasizes the unity of the human body, hence the unity of medicine. It points out the interrelationship of the various viscera and how a given stimulus simultaneously disturbs the normal equilibrium in many organs. It further suggests that symptoms are produced through a disturbance of the factors which normally influence the activity of these viscera; namely, visceral nerves and the products of the endocrine glands.

The important symptoms of early *tuberculosis* arranged according to this classification are shown in Table I.

TABLE I

GROUP I SYMPTOMS DUE TO TOXEMIA (GENERAL OR CONSTITUTIONAL)	GROUP II SYMPTOMS DUE TO REFLEX CAUSE	GROUP III SYMPTOMS DUE TO THE TUBERCULOUS PROCESS PER SE
Malaise. Lack of endurance. Loss of strength. Nerve instability. Digestive disturbances (hypomotility and hyposecretion). Metabolic disturbances resulting in loss of weight. Increased pulse rate. Night sweats. Elevation of temperature. Anemia. Changes in leucocytes. Increased sedimentation rate.	Hoarseness. Tickling in larynx. Cough. Digestive disturbances (hypermotility and hypersecretion), which may result in loss of weight. Circulatory disturbances. Chest and shoulder pains. Flushing of face. Spasm of muscles of shoulder girdle. Diminished motion of affected side.	Frequent and protracted colds (tuberculous bronchitis). Spitting of blood. Pleurisy (tuberculosis of pleura). Sputum.

In advanced tuberculosis these early symptoms are exaggerated and others of a reflex nature, such as anorexia and vomiting, appear, and symptoms of a fourth group present when the disease becomes more severe,[9] as follows:

SYMPTOMS RESULTING FROM MARKED EFFECTS OF PULMONARY TUBERCULOSIS

Respiratory changes.
Circulatory changes.
Changes on part of nervous system.
Changes in blood.
General metabolic changes.
Degenerative changes.
Menstrual irregularities.
Other changes in internal secretions.
Changes in the colloids of the cells and their electrolytic ionic content.

If we analyzed the symptoms of such diseases as *tonsillitis* and *whooping cough,* they would be grouped something like the following:

TONSILLITIS

Toxic.

Malaise; nervousness; headache; general aching; lessened appetite; deficient secretion and motility in the gastrointestinal canal (coated tongue, hypochlorhydria, constipation); increased pulse rate; rise in temperature; and later, anemia.

Reflex.

The symptoms of this group are shown mainly in the pharynx and larynx: thus hoarseness, laryngeal irritation, cough; increased mucous secretion; increased salivary secretion; pain; spasm in muscles of deglutition.

Symptoms Due to the Disease Per Se.

Difficulty of, and pain on swallowing; obstruction to upper air passages; pressure on Eustachian tube.

WHOOPING COUGH

Toxic.

Malaise; nervousness; aching; lessened appetite; deficient motility and secretion in gastrointestinal tract (coated tongue, hypochlorhydria, constipation); rapid heart; rise in temperature.

Reflex.

Increased secretory activity in bronchi (bronchitis) and upper respiratory passages; laryngeal spasm; cough and vomiting.

Symptoms Due to the Disease Per Se.

The microorganisms which cause whooping cough readily pass through the bronchial mucous membranes and pass to the bronchial glands which enlarge greatly, producing reflex symptoms through the pulmonary and laryngeal vagus, and at times cause pressure symptoms.

CAUSE OF THE VARIABILITY OF SYMPTOMS

One of the most confusing facts met in the diagnosis of clinical disease is the *variability of symptoms*. The same symptoms are not always present in the same disease. This variability does not only apply to the same disease in different individuals, but may also be noticed in a given disease as it affects the same individual at different times. This is explained by the facts (1) that in the healthy, the relative stability or excitability of the nerve cells in general, and of the sympathetic and parasympathetic systems in particular, differs in different individuals; (2) the relative stability or excitability of nerve cells of different divisions of the sympathetics and parasympathetics often differs in the same as well as in different individuals; and as shown by Kolm and Pick[3] the cells which result in the ultimate reaction vary under different conditions produced by disease both in their colloidal characteristics and in their ionic content, which in turn alters and may even reverse an expected reaction. For example: the injured part of a cell becomes more acid and electronegative than the rest; so do injured cells as a whole (Burns[10]).

Reversal of action may now and then show itself when one or the other components of the vegetative system is stimulated, or when the Ca/K ratio or the H/OH ion ratio is disturbed. (Kraus,[11] Zondek.[12])

Calcium increases the heartbeat regularly, but if present in excess, it slows it. An excess of calcium can overcome the action of potassium and the reverse; so here is a basis for a reversal of action when the sympathetic or parasympathetic nerves are stimulated. The same can be interfered with by an excess of the H or OH ions in the blood, for they too exert similar action to the Ca and K as previously mentioned.

In experiments on the heart and intestine, if Ca is omitted from the solution in which they are bathed, there is no response to either adrenalin or sympathetic stimulation, and parasympathetic stimulation is much weakened. Neither is there a parasympathetic response if Na and K are omitted from the solution.

When Ca is in excess, if the vagus is stimulated, instead of slowing the heart it sometimes increases its rapidity.

Most symptoms, as mentioned above, are departures from normal function. Normal visceral function depends upon a certain normal condition of the body cells as to both their colloidal phases and ionic content, and a degree of stability of the nerves in which they will withstand a given stimulus without producing action, and the presence of chemical substances (internal secretions, electrolytes and metabolic products) circulating in the blood which are necessary to meet metabolic requirements. Inasmuch as internal secretions act in harmony with the nerves, either sympathetics or parasympathetics, in their influence on body functions; we can say, if not expressing the whole truth, yet furnishing a working truth, that a symptom of a disease of an internal viscus is the particular disturbed function which results from all the forces which are acting upon or with the nerves which supply it; or to put it in another way, it is the manner in which the individual is able to carry on a given function in the presence of a given disease process.

This may be illustrated by a condition which we meet every day in such affections as appendicitis. One patient will have during the acute attack, much more vomiting than another, and also other severe symptoms on the part of the gastrointestinal canal. Some will have so few symptoms that the disease may not be suspected until it is well marked. One patient will have a chronically inflamed appendix for years and not suspect it until acute symptoms appear; while another will have distressing reflex symptoms which cause serious invalidism. Another example is furnished by tuberculosis of the lungs, a disease which is accompanied by many reflex symptoms on the part of the gastrointestinal canal, as described in Chapter XXIII. Many of these result from vagus stimulation—hyperacidity, hypermotility, spastic constipation, intestinal stasis, colicky pains, and occasionally mushy and frequent stools. These symptoms are usually more marked when the disease is not accompanied by severe toxemia, because toxins stimulate the sympathetic nerves and, in the gastrointestinal canal, this produces an inhibition in the action of the vagus. Thus there are two opposing forces acting upon the gastrointestinal structures; one, reflexly through the vagus, attempting to increase muscular contraction and stimulate secretory activity, the other acting centrally upon the sympathetics attempting to inhibit muscular contraction and secretory activity. The same opposing forces are seen in the heart; the vagus, reflexly trying to slow the contractions; the sympathetics, centrally stimulated during toxemia, attempting to increase the rapidity of contraction. At times the influence of the sympathetics prevails, and at times that of the parasympathetics. So we may have any degree of muscular activity and any degree of secretory activity present in the intestinal canal from a marked hypomotility and hyposecretion to a marked hypermotility and hypersecretion; and a pulse rate in excess of normal or below normal. Further, as the relative influences upon the sympathetics and vagus are not the same in the same individual from time to time, but change with the inflammatory process in the lung and the various requirements of the body, the gastrointestinal symptoms and the pulse rate may change from day to day. The influence of psychic stimuli upon symptoms must always be kept in mind, for they are capable of disturbing and altering the symptoms which would naturally be produced by given physical stimuli.

Variability of symptoms is the rule in clinical medicine, a fact which can be readily appreciated by understanding the nerve and chemical control of physiologic function and the factors which influence them, both physical and psychic.

It is not only necessary to understand that symptoms produced by a given disease may differ in different individuals and in the same individual at different times, but it is equally necessary to bear in mind that while the stimulus which would be expected to produce a given symptom is present, the symptom may not appear or its reverse may appear if the stimulus to the nerve is excessive, or the neuron itself is hyperexcitable or a certain ionic concentration exists in the body cells. It is necessary, therefore, always to bear in mind that *inflammation in organs gives origin to stimuli which have a tendency to produce such and such symptoms, although the symptoms themselves may not materialize.*

Many of the most important symptoms arising from diseases of internal viscera are reflex in nature. In order to understand these symptoms, one must study the innervation of the various viscera and the interrelationship which exists between them, also the interrelationship which exists between the viscera and the skeletal structures. In the following pages will be found discussions of both physiologic principles and clinical observations, dealing particularly with symptoms of a reflex nature which result from inflammation of internal viscera.

References

1. Zondek, S. G.: Untersuchungen über des Wesen der Vagus und Sympathicusreizung, Berlin klin. Wchnschr. **58**: 1393, 1921; also Deutsche med. Wchnschr. **67**: 1520-1522, 1591, 1921.
2. Daly, I. de Burgh, and Clark, A. J.: The Action of Ions Upon the Frog's Heart, Jour. Physiol. **54**: 367, 1921.
3. Kolm, R., and Pick, E. P.: Ueber die Bedeuting des Calciums für die erregbarketit des sympathetischen Herz-nerven endigungen, Arch. f. d. ges. Physiol. **189**: 137, 1921.
4. Pick, E. P.: Wien. klin. Wchnschr., 1920, No. 50.
5. Pottenger: Some Practical Points in the Diagnosis of Active Tuberculosis, read before the 21st Annual Meeting of Idaho State Medical Assn., Pocatello, Idaho, October, 1913. Northwest Med., January, 1914.
6. Pottenger: Clinical Tuberculosis, St. Louis, 1917, The C. V. Mosby Co., Vol. I, p. 366.
7. Pottenger: The Relationship of Pulmonary Tuberculosis to the Vegetative Nervous System, Transactions of the Section on Practice of Medicine, J. A. M. A., 1917, pp. 173-186.
8. Pottenger: The Importance of the Study of Pathological Physiology in Internal Medicine; Illustrated by the Analysis of the Symptomatology of Tuberculosis, Mississippi Valley M. J., June, 1917.
9. Pottenger: Clinical Tuberculosis, St. Louis, 1917, The C. V. Mosby Co., Vol. I, p. 437.
10. Burns, David: An Introduction to Biophysics, New York, 1921, The Macmillan Co., p. 134.
11. Kraus, F.: Deutsche med. Wchnschr., 1920, No. 8.
12. Zondek, S. G.: Arch. f. Exper. Pharmacol. **87**: 342, 1920. (Cited in Die Elektrolyte, Ihre Bedeutung für Physiologie, Pathologie, und Therapie, Berlin, 1927, p. 108.)

CHAPTER IX

SYMPTOMS DUE TO TOXEMIA

A study of the symptoms due to toxemia given in Table II will reveal the fact that this same group of symptoms is produced no matter what the nature of the toxemia or what tissue is involved:

TABLE II

SYMPTOMS DUE TO TOXEMIA

CAUSED BY HARMFUL STIMULATION OF	SYMPTOMS
I. Body Cells Generally	1. Malaise
II. Nervous System Generally	2. Lack of endurance
III. Endocrine System Generally	3. Loss of strength
	4. Nerve instability
IV. Sympathetic Nervous System	5. Diminished digestive activity
	6. Incresed metabolic rate
V. Sympathicotropic Endocrines,	7. Loss of weight
particularly adrenals	8. Increased pulse rate
and thyroid	9. Night sweats
	10. Elevation of temperature
	11. Anemia
	12. Leucocytosis
	13. Increased sedimentation rate

These symptoms naturally divide into two groups:[1-2] 1, those due to disturbed function in the body cells and the nervous and the endocrine systems as a whole, consisting of malaise, lack of endurance, loss of strength, and nerve instability; 2, those which are due to disturbed function in tissues activated by the sympathetic nervous system and sympathicotropic endocrine glands, consisting of digestive disturbances (hypomotility and hyposecretion), metabolic disturbances, increased pulse rate, night sweats, elevation of temperature, and blood changes. What part of the neurocellular mechanism is disturbed, and the manner in which the injury is produced is discussed in Chapter VII.

While the symptoms differ according to the degree of the toxemia present, yet some symptoms of this group will be found no matter what the cause, whether typhoid fever, whooping cough, bronchitis, an infected tonsil or gall bladder, tuberculosis, or syphilis.

This is in accordance with the studies of Vaughan,[3] who has shown that the toxic molecule is the same in all protein. Toxins may act

142

directly on body cells probably changing their physical and chemical nature and producing in them a state of fatigue; but an important effect is unquestionably produced through the nervous system. The action as well as the nutrition of cells is influenced greatly by the nerves supplying them; so it seems rational to assume that stimuli affecting cellular activity do so partly through nerve control without implying that this is the only control.

Toxemia causes an increase in the normal excitability of nerve cells, lowering the threshold of response, thus making the individual more susceptible to harmful stimuli. The entire nervous system is influenced by toxemia, but that particular group of nerves which shows the greatest degree of peripheral stimulation, as indicated by disturbed organic function, belongs to the sympathetic system. This manifests itself in a particularly striking manner as a depressed function of all organs belonging to or derived from the gastrointestinal tract, except the sphincters; a rapidity of heart action; and a vasoconstriction in the cutaneous blood vessels. Toxemia thus causes a dry tongue, a deficient motility and deficient secretory activity in the stomach and intestines, increased rapidity of heart action and a widespread constriction of superficial blood vessels interfering with the dissipation of heat. Heat being augmented for the time being by increased chemical activity attendant upon the inflammation, the interference with dissipation results in a rise of temperature.[4, 5]

The malaise and general nerve instability resulting in loss of endurance and strength, is caused by stimulation of nerve cells and centers in the central nervous system as well.

Unfortunately we cannot differentiate the effects of toxemia as it expresses itself in the endocrine glands from that expressed through the nervous system. There are important endocrine glands, however, which are stimulated by it, particularly the adrenals and thyroid. These derive their activating nerve supply from the sympathetics, hence are stimulated to increased activity by toxins. The result is increased metabolic activity. One can readily understand then that toxemia exerts a multiple influence which favors loss of weight, a depressed function of the gastrointestinal organs which fail to provide sufficient pabulum, an increased metabolic activity which hastens the breaking down of the body tissues and an injury to cells which interferes with assimilation.

When toxemia is prolonged, a loss of body bases occurs which results in a shifting of the acid alkali balance of the tissues toward the acid side. This has an important bearing on the production and prolongation of toxic symptoms. This condition calls for the administration of alkalies, either in the form of alkaline foods or alkaline salts. This is more marked in some diseases than in others.

References

1. Pottenger, F. M.: The Syndrome of Toxemia, an Expression of General Nervous Discharge Through the Sympathetic System, J. A. M. A., January, 1916.
2. Pottenger, F. M.: The Importance of the Study of Symptoms With a Discussion of MacKenzie's Law Governing Their Production, Tr. Sect. Practice Med., A. M. A., 1921.
3. Vaughan: Protein Split Products in Relation to Immunity and Disease, Philadelphia, 1913, Lea & Febiger.
4. Pottenger, F. M.: Fever, a Part of the Syndrome of Toxemia, New York M. J., August, 1916.
5. Pottenger, F. M.: Clinical Tuberculosis, St. Louis, 1917, The C. V. Mosby Co., Vol. II, p. 108.

CHAPTER X

SEGMENTATION OF THE BODY

In order to understand the synaptic relationships which exist between the sympathetic and the spinal nerves; and further, in order to understand the effects which are manifested in visceromotor, viscerosensory (referred pain), and viscerotrophic reflexes when viscera are the seat of inflammation, as described in the following chapters, it is necessary to study the segmentation of the body.

Segmentation is most evident in those lower forms of life where each segment is provided with a more or less complete nervous mechanism. Fig. 16 is a diagrammatic representation of a primitive vertebrate—the amphioxus. The structures of each segment, both somatic and visceral, are innervated by neurons which arise within that segment. The viscera thus receive their nerve supply from the same part of the spinal cord as the skin and muscles over them. The human body shows the same segmentation, but it is more irregular. It is shown in the embryo more clearly than in the adult, as illustrated in Fig. 17.

A study of Figs. 18 to 21 will show that there is a somewhat segmental regularity in the innervation of the adult man, but it is necessary to understand developmental processes in order fully to appreciate it.

The human vertebral column consists of thirty-three or thirty-four vertebrae—7 cervical, 12 dorsal or thoracic, 5 lumbar, 5 sacral, and 4 or 5 coccygeal. The latter two groups are fused together in the adult to make the two bones, sacrum and coccyx. The spinal cord is made of segments from which arise spinal nerves, one nerve from each segment. These segments correspond in number with the divisions of the vertebral column above the coccyx, except in the cervical region, there being 8 cervical segments, 12 thoracic or dorsal, 5 lumbar, and 5 sacral.

While the segments closely correspond to the number of the vertebrae, they are not on the same level. The spinal cord is much shorter than the vertebral column; in fact, it ends in the adult in the upper lumbar region. The spinal nerves in the upper cervical region pass out horizontally, but become somewhat oblique in the lower cervical, and very oblique in the lumbar and sacral segments. In the lower cervical region the spinal nerves pass out one vertebra lower than their emergence from the cord. The upper thoracic

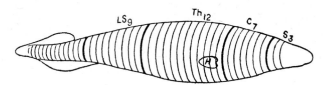

Fig. 16.—Diagrammatic representation of a primitive vertebrate animal—the Amphioxus—divided for convenience into three segments for the head, seven for the neck, twelve for the thorax, nine for the lumbosacral region, and an indefinite number for the coccygeal region. For clearness of comparison the heart (*H*) is represented as occupying the same position as in man, so that an adequate stimulus from the heart would cause pain in the distribution of the four upper thoracic nerves covering and protecting the heart. (After Ross and Mackenzie.)

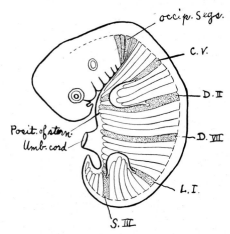

Fig. 17.—Diagram of a human embryo, fifth week, showing the arrangement and extension of the mesoblastic segments. The first and last of each segment entering into the formation of the limbs is stippled (*C. V.* and *D. II* and *L. I* and *S. III*). The position is indicated in which the sternum is formed. (A. M. Patterson.)

nerves, Ist to VIIth, pass out one vertebra lower than their emergence from the cord. The lower thoracic, lumbar, and sacral nerves run down for a considerable distance, within the dura mater (forming the cauda equina) before emerging between the vertebrae. As a result of this arrangement, the lower cutaneous segments are not on the same level with their respective segments of the cord or their respective vertebrae, but are lower on the surface than either. The Xth thoracic cutaneous segment is on a level with the Ist lumbar vertebra; and the XIIth with the IVth lumbar. This accounts for the fact that the areas of reflex cutaneous pain which result from inflammation of viscera innervated by the lower thoracic segments, such as the kidney, ureter, and uterus, are found in the lumbar instead of the lower thoracic region. This relationship may be understood by a study of Figs. 18, 19, and 20.

While considerable differentiation has taken place in some of the segments of the more advanced vertebrates, such as man, and while some of the viscera are markedly displaced from the segments in relation to which they originally developed, they still preserve more or less accurately their primitive nerve connection. A study of this will greatly aid the interpretation of symptoms of visceral disease.

There is a true segmentation of the body surface, which is shown in both the skin and the muscles. Definite skin areas and definite groups of muscles are (in the same species) innervated by the same spinal nerves. The segmentation of the skin is more regular than that of the muscles. This may be inferred by comparing Figs. 19 and 20, wherein it is shown that the motor and sensory nerves supplying the muscles do not at all correspond in areas of distribution to the corresponding sensory nerves supplying the cutaneous surface. This is well illustrated in the spinal nerves originating from the cervical portion of the cord. The posterior or sensory cervical nerves are limited in their skin distribution to the head, neck and arms, and that portion of the chest above the second rib anteriorly, and the spine of the scapula posteriorly; while the motor and deep sensory nerves from the cervical portion of the cord supply such accessory muscles of respiration as the sternocleidomastoideus, scaleni, pectoralis, trapezius, levator anguli scapulae, rhomboidei and diaphragm which are far removed from these areas. The clinical importance of this will be seen in the study of superficial and deep sensation.

There is a certain amount of overlapping in the skin areas which belong to each spinal segment, because while each nerve supplies its corresponding zone completely, it also sends some filaments to the zones above and below.

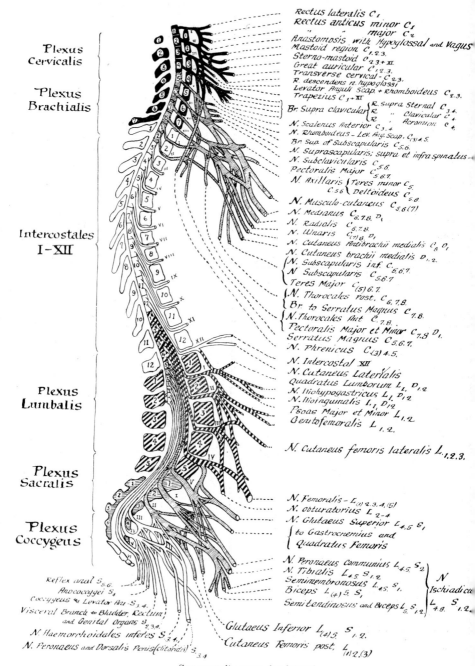

Plexus
Cervicalis

Plexus
Brachialis

Intercostales
I–XII

Plexus
Lumbalis

Plexus
Sacralis

Plexus
Coccygeus

Rectus lateralis C_1
Rectus anticus minor C_1
    "   major C_2
Anastomosis with Hypoglossal and Vagus
Mastoid region $C_{1,2,3}$
Sterno-mastoid $C_{2,3+XI}$
Great auricular $C_{1,2,3}$
Transverse cervical - $C_{2,3}$
R. descendens n. hypoglossi
Levator Anguli Scap. + Rhomboideus $C_{2,3}$
Trapezius C_{1+XI}
Br. Supra clavicular { R. supra sternal $C_{3,4}$
     R   "   Clavicular C_4
     R   "   Acromion C_4
N. Scalenus Anterior $C_{3,4}$
N. Rhomboideus - Lev. Ang. Scap. $C_{(3)4,5}$
Br. Sup. of Subscapularis $C_{5,6}$
N. Suprascapularis; supra et infra spinatus -
N. Subclavicularis $C_{5,6}$
Pectoralis Major $C_{5,6,7}$
N. Axillaris { Teres minor C_5
    $C_{5,6}$ { Deltoideus $C_{5,6}$
N. Musculo-cutaneus $C_{5,6(7)}$
N. Medianus $C_{6,7,8}$ D_1
N. Radialis $C_{6,7,8}$ D_1
N. Ulnaris $C_{7,8}$ D_1
N. Cutaneus Antibrachii medialis C_8 D_1
N. Cutaneus brachii medialis $D_{1,2}$
{ N. Subscapularis inf. $C_{5,6,7}$
{ N Subscapularis $C_{5,6,7}$
{ Teres Major $C_{(5)6,7}$
{ N. Thorocales Post. $C_{6,7,8}$
{ Br. to Serratus Magnus $C_{7,8}$
{ N. Thorocales Ant. $C_{7,8}$
Pectoralis Major et Minor $C_{7,8}$ D_1
Serratus Magnus $C_{5,6,7}$
N. Phrenicus $C_{(3)4,5}$
N. Intercostal XII
N. Cutaneus Lateralis
Quadratus Lumborum L_1, D_{12}
N. Iliohypogastricus L_1, D_{12}
N. Ilioinguinalis L_1, D_{12}
Psoas Major et Minor $L_{1,2}$
Genitofemoralis $L_{1,2}$

N. Cutaneus femoris lateralis $L_{1,2,3}$

N. Femoralis - $L_{(1)2,3,4,(5)}$
N. obturatorius L_{2-4}
N. Glutaeus Superior $L_{4,5}$ S_1
{ to Gastrocnemius and
{ Quadratus Femoris

N. Peronaeus Communis $L_{4,5}$ S_2
N. Tibialis $L_{4,5}$ $S_{1,2}$
Semimembronosus $L_{4,5}$ S_1 } N
Biceps $L_{(4)5}$ S_1 } Ischiadicus
Semitendinosus and Biceps L_5 $S_{1,2}$ $L_{4,8}$ $S_{1,2}$

Glutaeus Inferior $L_{(4)5}$ $S_{1,2}$
Cutaneus Femoris post. $L_{(1)2,(3)}$

Reflex anal $S_{5,6}$
Anococcygei S_4
Coccygeus & Levator Ani - $S_{3,4}$
Visceral Branch to Bladder, Rectum
    and Genital Organs $S_{2,3,4}$
N. Haemorrhoidales inferes $S_{3,4}$
N. Peronaeus and Dorsalis Penis (clitoris) $S_{3,4}$

See opposite page for legend.

There is more variation in the segmentation of the muscles than in the skin. This is seen particularly in the extremities where the muscles have become somewhat displaced. The sensory innervation of the muscle follows that of the muscle segments and not that of the skin. This affords a physiologic basis for a difference in location of hyperalgesia of the skin and of the muscles when certain viscera are involved in disease processes. The serial segmentation of the pilomotor muscles as well as that of the vasomotor control of the skin corresponds closely to the sensory segmentation of the skin. These segments may be studied from Fig. 21, in which Luciani has diagrammatically represented the results of Bolk's studies of cutaneous metamerism. This diagram shows the arms and legs in the position of their embryonic growth, and emphasizes the manner in which the innervation of the limbs followed their pushing away from the body.

The spinal segments between the IVth and Vth cervical and Ist dorsal anteriorly, and the VIth cervical and Ist dorsal posteriorly, are not represented in the median line of the body, these nerves having slipped out with the developing anterior extremity to supply it. Neither are the segments below the Ist lumbar anteriorly and the IIIrd lumbar posteriorly represented in the median line, for the nerves belonging to these segments have traveled out with the posterior extremity to innervate it.

This irregularity in cutaneous segmentation accounts for sensory symptoms which are at times found in the arms and finger tips in pulmonary inflammation as mentioned on page 313, and which appear in the arm in angina; and also occasionally in pleurisy, simulating the pain of cardiac origin.

It has been my observation that sensory disturbances in the neck, shoulders and arms, are common in chronic pulmonary tuberculosis,

Fig. 18.—Showing the relationship of the segments of the spinal cord to the spinal nerves which emerge from them and to the bodies and spines of the vertebrae. (After Dejerine.)
It will be noted that all the cervical and first two thoracic spinal nerves emerge from the cord on practically the same level as the bodies of the corresponding vertebrae. The spinal nerves emerging from the thoracic segments, third to seventh inclusive, emerge from the spinal column about one vertebra below their origin in the cord. From the eighth downward, the nerves emerge gradually farther and farther below the point of origin in the cord in such a manner that the fifth lumbar nerve emerges four vertebrae below its origin and the sixth sacral nerve, which originates in the cord on a level with the body of the third lumbar vertebra emerges from the spinal column at the coccyx.

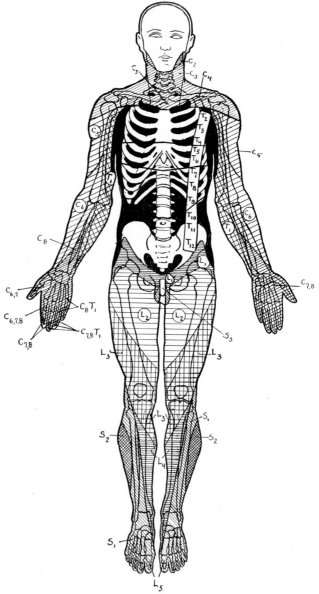

Fig. 19A.—Illustrating the cutaneous sensory zones of the anterior surface of the body. The pilomotor muscles and sweat glands follow the cutaneous innervation; consequently, each segment indicates the area of altered sensation and the changes in the pilomotor muscles and the sweat glands which are affected when innervation of the respective segment is disturbed. Compare with Fig. 19B which shows the innervation of the muscles. (After Dejerine.)

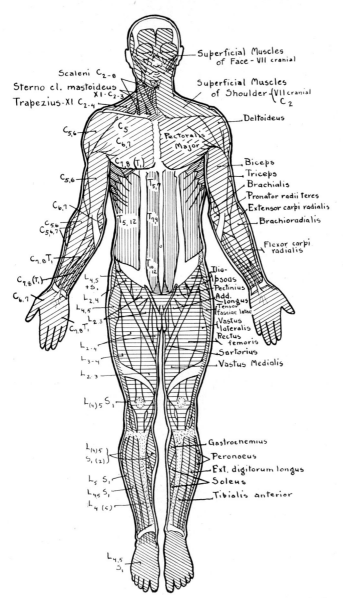

Fig. 19B.—Illustrating the innervation of the muscles of the anterior surface of the body. It will be noted that the distribution of the motor nerves from the various segments does not coincide with the distribution of the cutaneous nerves, as shown in Fig. 19A. Sensation is supplied to the muscles by sensory nerves which correspond in origin with their motor nerves. (After Dejerine.)

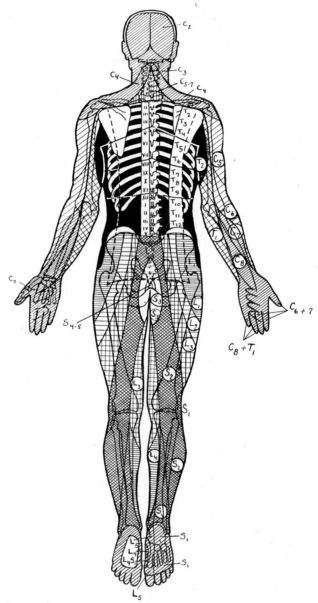

Fig. 20A.—Illustrating the cutaneous sensory zones of the posterior surface of the body. The pilomotor muscles and sweat glands follow the cutaneous innervation; consequently, each segment indicates the area of altered sensation and the changes in the pilomotor muscles and the sweat glands which are affected when innervation of the respective segment is disturbed. Compare with Fig. 20B which shows the innervation of the muscles. (After Dejerine.)

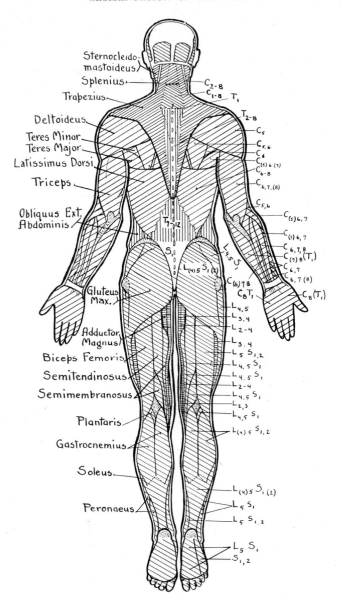

Fig. 20B.—Illustrating the innervation of the muscles of the posterior surface of the body. It will be noted that the distribution of the motor nerves from the various segments does not coincide with the distribution of the cutaneous nerves, as shown in Fig. 20A. Sensation is supplied to the muscles by sensory nerves which correspond in origin with their motor nerves. (After Dejerine.)

and that intestinal disturbances are sometimes accompanied by pains in the legs. In the presence of diseases in the lungs and intestines (particularly the lower portion) the cell bodies which give origin to the spinal nerves supplying the neck, shoulders, and arms in the former, and the legs in the latter, sometimes become hypersensitive; and if states of toxemia appear, aching in the corresponding structures is prone to manifest itself.

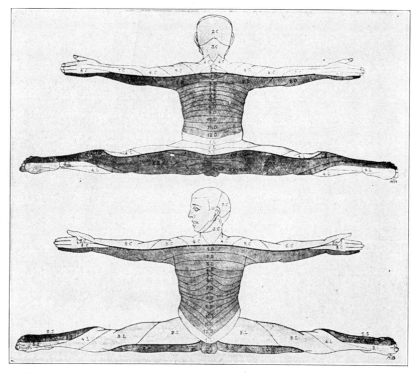

Fig. 21.—Diagrammatic representation of cutaneous areas of sensibility. (After Bolk.)

Metameric distribution or transverse segmentation of cutaneous areas of sensibility of human body, drawn with the limbs in the position of their embryonic growth. (Diagram constructed by Luciani from Bolk's data.) The series of dermatomes which successively correspond to the cervical, lumbar, and sacral roots is indicated by different degrees of shading.

This figure is particularly valuable in showing how the sensory zones extend from the body to the arms and legs, and plainly shows the regularity of what under ordinary circumstances might seem to be gross irregularity in innervation.

It is necessary to understand the relationship of the various viscera to the skin segments. This relationship can best be studied in the embryo before the organs migrate. When they migrate, however, they retain their nerve connection with the spinal segments through the sympathetic connector neurons as shown in Fig. 22, from which we may judge of the original positions of the organ in the body thus:

The diaphragm arises from that portion of the gastrointestinal canal which is near the pharynx and maintains its principal connection with the cord through the phrenics which originate from the IIIrd and IVth or IVth and Vth cervical segments. The lungs are supplied with sympathetics whose connector neurons arise from

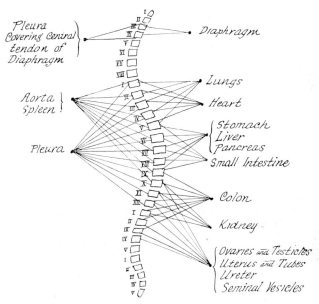

Fig. 22.—The connector neurons for the important thoracic, abdominal, and pelvic viscera.

In the figure the connecting neurons are those which belong to the thoracicolumbar outflow; except those going to the diaphragm, which are spinal nerves (phrenics). The motor cells for the viscera are found in the various collateral ganglia.

The figure shows that the innervation of the various viscera may be divided into groups. The heart and lungs are innervated from practically the same segments, the upper Ist to VIth thoracic. The stomach, liver, and pancreas from the same segments, Vth to IXth thoracic. The colon, kidney, and pelvic viscera from practically the same segments, IXth and Xth thoracic to IIIrd and IVth lumbar.

In spite of this grouping in innervation, each organ is brought in reflex connection with efferent neurons, both sensory and motor, which are more or less definite, in such a way that the motor and sensory reflexes do not overlap as much as might be indicated. This is illustrated in Part III.

the Ist to the VIth or VIIth thoracic segments but on account of their developmental relationships, are in reflex connection with structures which are innervated by the midcervical segments of the cord. The pleura is supplied by the thoracic sympathetics Ist to XIIth, the intercostals Ist to XIIth, and the phrenics. Reflexes produced by stimuli over the sympathetics and intercostals take place in the thoracic sensory zones, and from the phrenics in the IIIrd, IVth, and Vth cervical sensory zones. The heart arises immediately below and is in connection with the cord through the Ist to VIIth thoracic segments and causes reflexes regularly down the inner aspect of the left arm and over the upper portions of the left chest, the ventricle over the upper and the auricles over the lower portion.

The aorta is supplied by sympathetics arising largely from the upper five or six thoracic segments. The spleen is innervated by sympathetics arising from thoracic segments from the IIIrd to the Xth.

Next come the stomach, pancreas, and liver. These are connected with the cord through connector neurons coming from the thoracic segments Vth to IXth and reflecting strongest in the VIth and VIIth segments. The stomach and pancreas reflect in the left side of the body, and the liver in the right, but all apparently in the same segments.

The small intestines follow next in order with their connector fibers arising in the Vth to IXth thoracic segments, and reflecting strongest in the VIIIth and IXth segments. The small intestine is followed by the colon which reflects strongest in the lowest thoracic and Ist to IIIrd lumbar segments, having its connection in the cord through the neurons arising from the lower thoracic and upper lumbar segments.

The kidney receives innervation from the lower thoracic and Ist lumbar segments but reflects strongest in the XIth and XIIth thoracic and Ist lumbar segments.

The ovary, testicle, uterus, Fallopian tubes, ureter, and seminal vesicles are innervated by the Xth to XIIth thoracic, and Ist to IVth lumbar segments.

CHAPTER XI
VISCEROGENIC REFLEX

We now come to one of the most important subjects in our discussion, the "viscerogenic reflex." No observing clinician can fail to note the importance of this as a factor in the production of symptoms of disease. As clinical observation develops and becomes more accurate, the interdependence of organs is emphasized. No organ is free from the influence of other organs, and every organ influences other organs and structures. The property of viscera to influence other viscera, and in turn to be influenced by them, lies at the basis of normal physiologic integration. This same property under the stimulus of diseased conditions lies at the bottom of one of our most important groups of symptoms, the group which results from reflex action.

The burden of the study before us is the visceral reflex, the reflex which arises in some internal tissue or organ and expresses itself in the same or in some other tissue or organ. These reflexes are a clinical expression of a stimulus which is carried centralward by some afferent nerve and expressed in action by an efferent nerve which mediates with it in the central nervous system. The resultant reflex may be either visceral or somatic.

DEFINITION OF TERMS

Although an entire section of this monograph, Part I, is devoted to a discussion of the visceral or vegetative nervous system, I deem it wise to define briefly the terms used at this point, so that those who do not care to study the more technical subject may still understand my meaning. This is all the more necessary because of the multiplication of terms used to designate the same structures by different writers as described in Chapter II.

I shall employ the term *vegetative nervous system* to designate those nerves which supply the smooth muscle, the heart, and the secretory glands of the body. This term will be used to designate all nerves which do not belong to the voluntary system. The vegetative system supplies all structures which carry on those acts, such as initiating respiratory movements, digestion, and the circulation of the blood, without which the animal cannot exist. Every bit of unstriated muscle and every secreting gland of the body is under the control of this system of nerves.

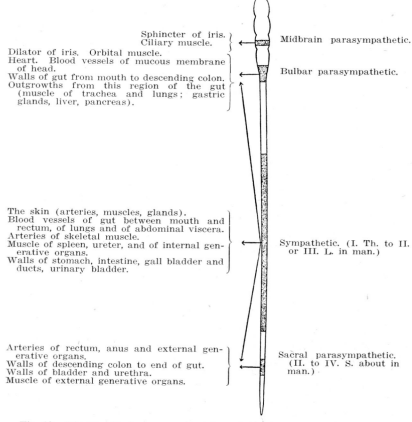

Sphincter of iris.
Ciliary muscle. } ← Midbrain parasympathetic.
Dilator of iris. Orbital muscle.
Heart. Blood vessels of mucous membrane
  of head.
Walls of gut from mouth to descending colon.   ← Bulbar parasympathetic.
Outgrowths from this region of the gut
  (muscle of trachea and lungs; gastric
  glands, liver, pancreas).

The skin (arteries, muscles, glands).
Blood vessels of gut between mouth and
  rectum, of lungs and of abdominal viscera.
Arteries of skeletal muscle.
Muscle of spleen, ureter, and of internal gen-   ← Sympathetic. (I. Th. to II.
  erative organs.   or III. L. in man.)
Walls of stomach, intestine, gall bladder and
  ducts, urinary bladder.

Arteries of rectum, anus and external gen-
  erative organs.   Sacral parasympathetic.
Walls of descending colon to end of gut.   (II. to IV. S. about in
Walls of bladder and urethra.   man.)
Muscle of external generative organs.

Fig. 23.—Diagram to show general origin and distribution of efferent vegetative fibers. By "muscle" is, of course, meant unstriated muscle only. By the "walls" of a structure is meant all the unstriated muscle in it. The innervation in some cases is still a matter of controversy (gastric glands, liver and pancreas; vessels of lungs; small arteries of skeletal muscles and arteries of the central nervous system). (Langley.)

Since this figure was drawn, the controversy on most of these structures has been fairly definitely settled, as will appear in the text.

The vegetative nervous system is made up of two separate components, one of which takes its origin from the thoracic and upper lumbar segments of the cord, called the *sympathetic* system; the other arising from two widely separated segments of the central nervous system, the midbrain and medulla on the one hand and the sacral segments of the cord on the other, called by various names, but which I shall call throughout this work the *parasympathetic* system, Plates I and V, pages 46 and 160.

A study of Plate I will acquaint the reader with the innervation of the principal structures supplied by the vegetative nerves. That portion of the central nervous system which is represented in blue, including the solid blue lines running from it, represents the parasympathetic system; that portion of the central nervous system which is indicated in red, represents the thoracicolumbar portion of the cord, from which areas the sympathetic fibers, which are indicated in the illustration by red lines, take their origin. This plate shows the double innervation of the structures of the head, the heart, and all of the organs of the enteral system. It also indicates the single innervation of the pilomotor muscles and the sweat glands.

From the fact that both sympathetic and parasympathetic fibers are indicated as supplying the blood vessels of the head, it must not be concluded that parasympathetic fibers supply all vessels. This is only true in the case of part of them. Other blood vessels of the body with possibly a few exceptions are innervated only by the sympathetics.

Fig. 23, from Langley, shows the nerve connection between the midbrain, medulla, and various segments of the cord and the unstriated muscle of the various parts of the body.

TWO DISTINCT GROUPS OF VISCERAL REFLEXES

Some structures are innervated by one of these systems alone. Such is the case with the pilomotor muscles, sweat glands, most of the blood vessels, many of the genitourinary structures, and the ciliary body. Other structures receive fibers from both divisions. This is particularly true of those structures which make up the enteral system—the gastrointestinal tract and those organs developmentally derived from it, such as the respirtaory system, liver, gall bladder, pancreas, and body of the bladder; also certain portions of the eye and other structures about the head. Formerly it was taught that the cardiac end of the stomach and the esophagus were innervated only by the parasympathetics, but now a scanty sympathetic supply has also been proved for these structures. Where the same structure receives both sympathetic and parasympathetic fibers, roughly speaking they oppose each other, one activating and the other inhibiting action. In other structures both activating and inhibiting fibers are found in the same system as described in Chapter V.

From clinical observation it is evident that there are two definite groups of visceral symptoms, depending upon two definite groups of visceral nerves. It is further evident that reflexes occur between the sympathetics and spinal nerves, not only in the segment of the cord which receives the afferent, sensory impulse from the viscus, but also in segments removed, the cell bodies receiving the impulse and those causing the reflex action being connected either by collateral branches of the afferent fiber or by *intercalated neurons*. This is true of the pulmonary reflex in which the afferent impulse enters the cord by way of the posterior roots of the upper six thoracic nerves, but the reflex is mediated in the midcervical segments of the cord.

Similar connections are found in the divisions of the parasympathetic system. Afferent neurons carry impulses centralward where they mediate with efferent neurons to cause reflex action. This connection is particularly close between the sensory neurons of the vagus and the motor neurons of the various branches of the same nerve. We also see it between the sensory fibers of the Vth cranial nerve and the vagus, as shown by asthma resulting from pressure in the nose. We also assume it to exist between the pelvic nerve and the vagus as shown in the character of digestive disturbances which sometimes occur, when the rectal tissues and those structures belonging to the urogenital system which are supplied by the pelvic nerve are inflamed.

An important physiologic fact with reference to visceral innervation may be inferred by studying the viscerogenic reflexes, particularly those arising in the lungs. It will be noted that the reflex muscle spasm which is indicative of acute pulmonary inflammation, Fig. 50, p. 309, likewise, the reflex trophic changes which are indicative of old or chronic pulmonary inflammation, see Fig. 55 *A* and *B*, pp. 318 and 319, may be present either anteriorly or posteriorly without being present both anteriorly and posteriorly. It is further evident that when the changes in the pulmonary tissue involve the anterior portion of the lung, the reflexes are expressed at least for the

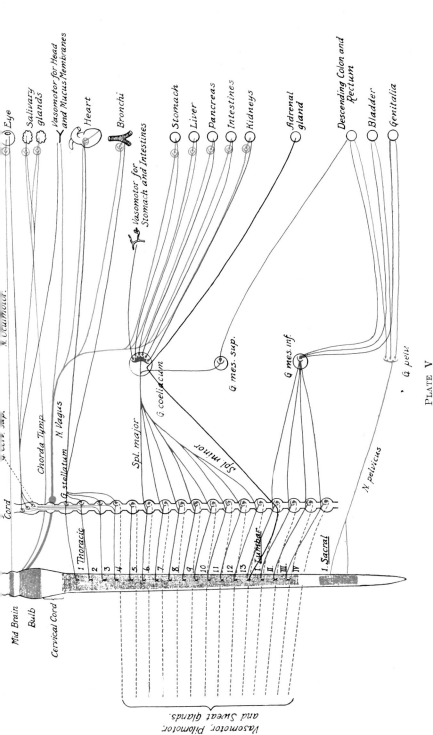

PLATE V

SCHEMATIC ILLUSTRATION OF THE VEGETATIVE NERVOUS SYSTEM. (FROM HIGIER, AFTER MEYER AND GOTTLIEB).
Sympathetic fibers are shown in red; the parasympathetic in blue.

most part in the anterior muscles of the shoulder girdle and in the subcutaneous tissue and skin over the anterior surface of the neck and chest above the second rib; and, when the changes are in the posterior portion of the lung, the reflexes are expressed in the posterior muscles of the shoulder girdle and in the subcutaneous tissue and skin over the posterior portion of the neck and shoulders above the spine of the scapula.

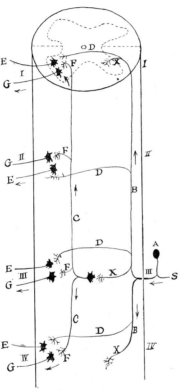

Fig. 24.—Showing schematically the paths through which intrasegmental and intersegmental reflexes are produced. The impulse is transmitted to the posterior root ganglion, *A*, over the afferent fiber *S*. From the ganglion, *A*, root fibers, *B*, enter the cord which divide into ascending and descending branches. From these branches collaterals, *D*, are given off which are transferred to the gray matter in the anterior horn and form synapses with motor nerves, *E*, to produce reflexes. Such reflexes occurring in the segment of the cord into which the root fibers enter, as indicated in segment III, are called intrasegmental reflexes. Those occurring in segments I, II, and IV are intersegmental reflexes. Other collaterals, *X*, are given off from the posterior root fibers which form synapses with association fibers, *C*, which also divide into ascending and descending branches and give off collaterals, *F*, which form synapses in the anterior horn gray matter with motor neurons, *G*, to produce intersegmental reflexes.

From this clinical observation we infer that the afferent spinal nerves which carry impulses from the anterior portion of the lung, mediate with efferent spinal nerves which supply the soft structures which cover the anterior surface of the chest; and that those which carry impulses from the posterior portion, mediate with spinal efferent nerves which supply the posterior surface of the chest. The question naturally arises: are we further justified in assuming that the same differentiation in innervation obtains generally for the different viscera? It does for the pleura and peritoneum without doubt. If such is the case, reflexes which involve structures covering the anterior and posterior surfaces of the chest wall are produced by different afferent components which are more or less independent.

The importance of the *intercalated neuron* cannot be overestimated. It is, in fact, the one great nerve factor which makes the difference between the higher vertebrates and lower invertebrates. It is that which leads to integration of action and brings the entire physical being into a unity of action. It is natural as a developmental necessity that the various parts of the physiologic system should be connected by these intercalated neurons so as to integrate their action. The scheme of nerve control seems to require a more or less close connection, and clinical observation demonstrates its existence. These intercalated neurons are illustrated in Figs. 24 and 25, pages 161 and 163.

CONDITIONS UNDERLYING VISCERAL REFLEXES

It can be seen, then, that the number of reflexes which may originate in the various viscera is almost unlimited. In practice, however, while the number is somewhat confusing, those most evident are few, and can often be determined with comparative ease.

For the guidance of those who are not accustomed to think in terms of visceral neurology, it is necessary to emphasize one very important fact, viz.: an impulse may be started which, if it completes its action, will result in contraction of muscles, an increase or decrease in glandular secretion, or in pain; yet such a result may not occur because the impulse is not sufficient to overcome the resistance in the neurons involved in the reflex; or to put it in another common phrase in nerve physiology, the strength of the impulse is not sufficient to overcome the threshold resistance, and as a result the stimulation does not pass over to the activating com-

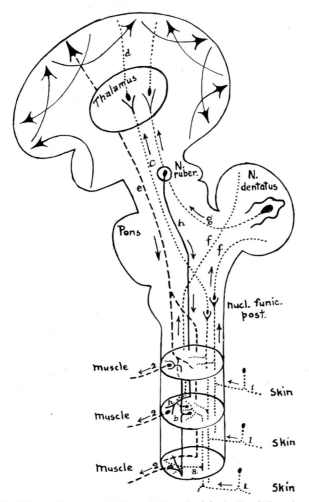

Fig. 25.—Schematic representation of the physiologically different conductions. Dotted line—afferent tracts. Broken line—efferent tracts. Solid line—intercentral tracts.

On entering the spinal cord the afferent fiber divides into ascending and descending branches. Before dividing into these branches the entering afferent fiber may give off a collateral branch which runs through to and ends in the anterior horn. Similar collateral branches are given off from the ascending and descending primary branches as shown in *a*. By means of these collateral branches, impulses are transferred to the cells in the anterior horn whence they are conveyed by the motor fibers to the muscles to produce reflex action. Instead of reflex collaterals, intercalated neurons may transfer the impulse from the sensory to the motor tracts in higher or lower segments. Such an intercalated neuron is shown in *b*. A third type of reflex may be produced by the impulse being conducted from the spinal cord to the medulla and thence to the nucleus ruber where it is transferred to motor paths. This is shown in the illustration by the solid line, *h*, running from the nucleus ruber to the motor neuron going to the muscles. (After Villiger.)

ponent of the reflex. *Because certain sensory impulses are traveling centralward is no guarantee that they are sufficiently strong to overcome the resistance between afferent and efferent neurons and to result in reflex action.* They may; and, again, they may not. One cannot understand the variability of reflex symptoms unless he understands this fact. Stimuli have a tendency to produce certain reflex acts, but may not be adequate and so the reflex may not be apparent. Individuals show varying degrees of nerve stability and their response to stimuli will differ accordingly. Another fact of importance is that reflexes differ according to the state of function of the organ in which they are expressed. We should not expect the same reflex response from an empty stomach as from one filled and functioning fully. We should never expect the same response in individuals who show different degrees of emotional, nervous, and physical equilibrium.

Adequate Stimulus.—One must always bear in mind the condition which is known as *adequate stimulus* when considering visceral reflexes. Stimuli are continuously passing centralward from the viscera, which neither produce recognizable reflexes nor disturb the consciousness of the patient, because the stimuli are not adequate. Every reflex that is registered indicates that a stimulus adequate to carry the nerve force through all components of the reflex is present. This is discussed more fully on page 57.

SIMPLE AND COMPLEX REFLEXES

Many neurons may take part in a reflex. A sensory impulse may start on the body surface or in some viscus. In order to reach the sensory areas in the cortex of the brain, so that the individual may become aware of the action of the stimulus, it passes through one neuron whose cells end in the ganglion of the posterior root; a second from the nuclei in the posterior root to the subcortical center in the thalamus; and a third, which arises in the thalamus and ends in the cerebral cortex. To complete this reflex act, the stimulus must be conveyed from the sensory to the motor nerve center. A neuron then extends from the motor cortical center in the brain to motor nuclei of cranial or spinal nerves where the impulse is transferred to the cells of the activating efferent motor neurons. Other neurons may intervene at any juncture and make the reflex still more complicated.

Many stimuli are not sufficiently strong to force the synapses between all of the neurons in the path between the end organ and the brain. These may result in reflex action without the subject being aware of the stimulus, the transfer to the motor neurons taking place in the subcortical and subthalmic areas, often in the segment or segments near to the one *receiving* the afferent impulse.

Other reflexes are liberated by means of reflex *collaterals*. The patella reflex is an example of this. By stroking the tendon of the quadriceps muscle below the patella when the knee is dependent, sensory stimuli pass to the spinal cord by way of the spinal ganglia. On entering the cord, the sensory fibers divide into ascending and descending branches which ultimately end in the gray matter of the cord. The ascending branch ends within nuclei of the posterior column. The entering sensory fibers before dividing and also their ascending branches, give off collateral branches to the motor cells in the anterior horn which convey the impulse through the motor neurons and cause the contraction of the muscle.

In other instances, other interposed neurons exist between the afferent and efferent neuron within the substance of the cord. In this manner impulses may be transmitted to efferent neurons at quite a distance from the segment which receives them. This is the character of the visceral reflexes from the lung. The impulses travel from the inflamed lung through the afferent neurons of the upper six thoracic segments, but express their motor and sensory action in the cervical spinal nerves whose segments are far higher in the cord. These fibers which connect the afferent and efferent neurons within the cord, are functionally only connector neurons.

In those acts which result from sensory impulses reaching the cerebral cortex, the paths of transfer from the sensory areas to the motor areas are very complex. These are well described by Tilney[1] and Ranson.[2]

Fig. 24 represents schematically the manner in which both *intrasegmental* and *intersegmental reflexes* are produced. The *intersegmental reflexes* may be produced in two ways. The stimulus enters the posterior root ganglion, *A*, over the sensory fibers, *S*. The dorsal root fibers from *A* enter the cord and divide into ascending and descending branches, *B*. From *B*, collaterals *D* are given off which go to the gray matter of the successive levels of the cord, and joining with motor nerves, *E*, produce reflexes. If the collateral, *D*, is given off in the same segment of the cord which the posterior root fibers enter, as shown in segment III, then there are produced *intrasegmental reflexes*. If *D* is given off in higher and lower levels, as shown in I, II, and IV, then there are produced *intersegmental reflexes*.

Again the dorsal root fibers send off collaterals, *X*, which form synapses in the gray matter and transfer impulses to association fibers, represented in the figure by *C*, which convey impulses to motor neurons, *G*, through collaterals, *F*, in the same segment and in segments both of higher and lower levels in the cord, producing *intersegmental reflexes*. The ascending and descending fibers of the dorsal root not only give off collaterals at various levels in the cord, but many of them reach the brain as seen in Fig. 25.

The cardiac, gastric, and gall bladder motor reflexes are examples of the intrasegmental type, while the pulmonary motor reflex is of the intersegmental type. Some of the best examples of the latter type are those in which an organ in one part of the body affects another in a distant part, like cardiospasm produced by irritation of the bladder.

In the production of the *intrasegmental* and *intersegmental* reflexes the afferent and efferent impulses usually course in the same side of the cord. There are some other reflexes produced in which the impulse crosses from one side of the cord to the other. Such a reflex may be either *intrasegmental* or *intersegmental*. Examples of this are found at times in severe cases of angina in which the muscles of the right side are involved in the spasm as well as those of the left.

The basis of reflex symptoms is the afferent neuron. Every organ contains afferent fibers, which carry impulses toward the higher centers usually found in the cord or medulla, which are then transferred to other cells, motor in character, to complete reflex action. Some of the internal viscera are supplied by only one division of the vegetative system, others by both. An organ supplied by one system will have reflex connection only through that one; while another, supplied by both, will have a double source of reflexes. In a few instances, such as the pleura, a third set of reflexes may arise through the spinal nerves.

A reflex, according to physiology, must be produced by an impulse traveling centralward over a sensory neuron where it is transferred to an efferent motor neuron. Therefore, sensory phenomena produced through efferent sensory neurons are not reflexes in the physiologic sense. Such pain and such trophic disturbances as result from afferent impulses being transferred to efferent sensory neurons must be caused by transference of stimuli in some other manner than by synapse. A stimulus arising in the viscera travels centralward over neurons which are of much lower sensibility than the sensory cerebrospinal nerves. Head assumes that this visceral stimulus is projected peripheralward over the neuron of greater sensibility which is the cerebrospinal nerve. See Head's law, page 183. Mackenzie suggests that the afferent stimuli which result in pain cause irritability of the neighboring sensory cells in the cord which causes them to be affected by the afferent impulse more readily. For this reason, pain arising in the viscera is referred to the surface of the body and called *referred pain*. In this work, therefore, I shall use the term *sensory reflex* rather than the usual term, *referred pain*, but only as a clinical convenience, not as a physiologic fact. Likewise I shall speak of the *trophic reflex* over the sensory neurons with the same understanding.

Under the discussion of reflexes, the complexity of some of them will be apparent. Simple reflexes require for their production a sensory and a motor neuron only, with facilities for mediation, and may take place in a single segment of the cord. Others are extremely complex; for example, the sensory neuron may enter a sacral segment of the cord and the efferent motor neuron to complete the reflex may be in the medulla. In this way we can account for the reflex vomiting which occurs when structures supplied by the pelvic nerve are inflamed. The intercalated neurons which course up and down the spinal cord, whose function it is to connect afferent impulses with efferent motor and sensory neurons to complete action, are of various lengths. These fibers are important factors in maintaining integration of action.

Different types of reflex paths are shown in Figs. 24 and 25.

In Fig. 25 the afferent impulse coming from the skin is conducted over a sensory neuron, *1*, to a nucleus in the posterior root ganglion (nucl. funic. post.), thence to the cord; and then to another neuron, *c*, which ends in the thalamus; and then over a third, *d*, to the cerebral cortex. The efferent neuron, *e*, conducts the impulse from the motor areas in the cortex to the cells in the anterior horn of the cord and transmits them to another motor neuron, 2, which supplies a muscle. These paths are called *projection paths*.

SEGMENTAL RELATIONSHIP BETWEEN THE SENSORY AND MOTOR NEURONS IN THE CENTRAL NERVOUS SYSTEM

While the reflexes which occur between afferent and efferent neurons may take place either in the same segments of the cord, as they do in simple reflexes, or in segments which are separated, as in complex reflexes; yet it is well for those particularly interested in the subject to know the relationship which may be found in the same segments; for reflexes from most organs are most apt to occur between sensory neurons entering and motor neurons leaving the same segment, according to the following law of Sherrington:[3]

"Broadly speaking, *the degree of reflex spinal intimacy between afferent and efferent spinal roots varies directly as their segmental proximity.* Thus excitation of the central side of a severed thoracic root, e.g., seventh, evokes with especial ease contraction of muscles or parts of muscles innervated by the corresponding motor roots, and next easily muscles innervated by the next adjacent motor roots. The spread of short spinal reflexes in many instances seems to be easier tailward than headward. This may be related with the oblique correlation that so largely holds between the distribution of the afferent root in the skin and the distribution of the efferent root in the underlying muscles.

"Taken generally, *for each afferent root there exists in immediate proximity to its own place of entrance in the cord (e.g., in its own segment) a reflex motor path of as low a threshold and of as high potency as any open to it anywhere.* Further, in response to excitation even approximately minimal in intensity a single afferent root, or a single filament of a single root, evokes a spinal discharge of centrifugal impulses through more than one efferent root, i.e., the discharge is plurisegmental. And this holds especially in the limb regions. In the limb region the nerve root is therefore a morphological aggregate of nerve-fibers, rather than a functionally determined assortment of impulse-paths. The view that the efferent spinal root is a functional assemblage of nerve-fibers is certainly erroneous. The formation of functional collections of nerve paths (peripheral nerve-trunks) out of morphological collections (nerve roots) seems to be the meaning of the limb-plexuses."

In order to make the above law enunciated by Sherrington complete, I would suggest the following modification: *Impulses arising from a given viscus are transferred centralward to those segments of the cord with which that particular viscus is related embryologically; and each afferent impulse finds in that particular segment to which it is finally transferred a reflex motor path of as low a threshold and of as high potency as any open to it anywhere.* This makes clear the exception to the above law, which is noted in reflexes of pulmonary origin described on page 303, in which the stimuli are regularly transmitted to a level in the cord higher than their entrance before they mediate with efferent nerves to complete reflex action. Fig. 22, page 155, shows the segmental origin of the nerves supplying most of the important viscera. It will be seen that Sherrington's law quoted above is borne out by all the reflexes there shown except those from the lung, and the exception of the lung is explained by its embryological segmental relationship.

Impulses originating in the lung return over afferent neurons to the upper five or six thoracic segments of the cord; but instead of producing reflexes in somatic tissues innervated by efferent fibers which originate in these segments, they mediate through intercalated neurons with spinal nerves arising from the midcervical segments, as described in Chapter XXIII.

Another very important fact which should be understood in the study of reflexes is the relationship of the strength of the stimulus to the reflex response. A given stimulus produces a given reflex response according to the "all or none" law of nerve action. If the stimulus is increased, it will not increase the response in the peripheral structures already affected, but the increased strength of stimulus is shown in the fact that more efferent neurons are involved and so the response spreads to adjacent tissues. This is illustrated by cardiac ventricular pain which ordinarily is confined to the inner aspect of the left arm and upper left chest, but when the stimulus is very severe the response may cross to the right side of the body or be reflected up into the neck, or, more rarely, downward in the adjoining segments of the cord.

LOCATION OF THE SEGMENTS FOR

Sensibility.　　　　　　　　　　　　　　Motility.

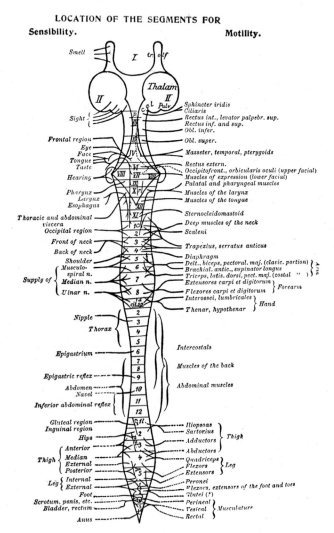

Fig. 26.—Diagrammatic illustration of the central nervous system and the tissues supplied with motor and sensory nerves from each area or segment of it. On the left of the figure are arranged the nerves of sensation; on the right, the motor nerves.

tr. olf., olfactory tract; *c.g.l.*, lateral geniculate body; *p. r. cr. pat.* indicates approximately the location of the reflex centers for the pupillary (*p*), the respiratory (*r*), cremasteric (*cr*), patellar (*pat*), and tendo Achillis (*A*) reflexes. (Jakob.)

Fig. 26 represents schematically segments in the central nervous system with the organs and tissues which take their sensory and motor innervation from them. Arranged as they are, the sensory on one side of the figure, and the motor on the other, their close relationship can readily be grasped.

THE RELATION BETWEEN THE VISCEROGENIC REFLEX AND VISCERAL INFLAMMATION

The manner in which reflexes arise is worthy of consideration. What is there in an inflammatory process which produces a stimulation of the nerve endings so as to result in reflex action? The answer to this is probably supplied by a study of the parenteral digestion of protein.

Parenteral digestion of foreign protein is accomplished by body cells and results in local inflammation and exudation, with accompanying changes in the electrolytes both of cell and body fluids and changes in electric potential of the cell.

In infection involving internal viscera, we have the same process except that we are dealing with both homologous and bacterial protein; the latter resulting in allergic inflammation. The breaking down of either native or foreign protein, however, is a matter of splitting up of the more complex protein molecules into less complex substances. The effect of cleavage of the protein of the patient's own tissues the same as that of foreign protein is expressed to a considerable extent upon the vegetative nervous system, although we assume that there is an absence of the necessity of the protective phenomena of sensitization which is so evident in cleavage of foreign protein. If the cleavage of either foreign or homologous protein is rapid, toxic molecules are liberated continuously and, if in large amounts, produce the syndrome of toxemia. Again, as a result of the chemical action, products are formed which irritate the nerve endings in the inflamed parts; and these, probably, in conjunction with other stimulating agencies, such as heat, pressure, and electrolytic change cause peripheral irritation of the receptors of the vegetative nervous system. The result of this stimulation is shown in reflexes through both the sympathetic and parasympathetic systems. Those through the sympathetic are commonly expressed in sensory, motor, and trophic disturbances in the skin, subcutaneous tissue, and muscles of those areas of the body surface which are in segmental relationship with the afferent fibers of the sympathetic system. Those of the parasympathetics show in tissues supplied by the vagus, pelvic, and certain cranial nerves. Aside from this there are reflexes in which both afferent and efferent neurons belong to the same component of the vegetative system and others in which the afferent belongs to one component and the efferent to the other.

This may be illustrated by inflammation in the lung, which shows reflex sensory, motor, and trophic changes in the skin, subcutaneous tissue, and muscles which receive their innervation from the mid-cervical segments of the cord, because the impulses from the inflamed pulmonary tissue are carried by the afferent fibers to the posterior root ganglia of the upper thoracic spinal nerves, and then transmitted through intercalated neurons to this portion of the cord and there re-flected through the cervical spinal nerves. The vagus reflexes, on the other hand, show in cough, disturbed innervation of the larynx through both superior and inferior laryngeal nerves, slowing of the pulse which is often quite evident, and commonly, increased secretion and increased motor irritation of the gastrointestinal canal, spastic constipation being particularly common, and nausea and vomiting being frequently met during the acute inflammation accompanying cavity formation. Headache and other sensory reflexes may also be produced through sensory neurons of the Vth cranial nerve. Other reflexes through cranial nerves, particularly the Vth, VIIth, IXth, XIth, and XIIth, are shown in Tables IV to VII, pages 306 and 307.

References

1. Tilney, Frederick, and Riley, Henry Alsop: The Form and Function of the Central Nervous System, New York, 1921, Paul B. Hoeber.
2. Ranson, Stephen Walter: The Anatomy of the Nervous System From the Standpoint of Development and Function, Philadelphia, 1921, W. B. Saunders Co.
3. Sherrington, Charles S.:   The Integrative Action of the Nervous System, New York, 1906, Charles Scribner & Sons, p. 158.

CHAPTER XII

VISCERAL PAIN

Pain is one of the most important protective phenomena possessed by man. In the voluntary nervous system it is developed to a high degree. The voluntary nervous system executes action in somatic structures and perceives and differentiates sensation with keen discrimination. The vegetative system, on the other hand, executes action in visceral tissues but perceives and differentiates sensation poorly.

Since the vegetative nervous system presides over all visceral structures, and since it cooperates closely with the voluntary system in the protection of the individual in the continuous reactions which must take place between him and his environment, it is necessary that these two systems be closely bound together.

The vegetative nervous system, strictly speaking, is a peripheral system of activating neurons, whose cell bodies lie without the central nervous system in ganglia and in the tissues innervated; but, it will be recalled, medullated fibers connect these peripheral cells with the central nervous system.

All afferent (sensory) nerves belong to one system—the somatic. Sensory nerves which supply somatic structures develop the power of perceiving and differentiating every important sensory impulse which impinges upon the exposed body surface in order to protect man and help him adjust to the forces which are present in his outside environment. The afferent visceral neurons are modified according to the functions which they subserve in supplying the sheltered and protected structures within the body which do not require discriminative sense but which are required to correlate activity in visceral structures. The cell bodies which give origin to the neurons of both systems, however, lie in the ganglia of the posterior spinal root. This arrangement defines the limits of reflex relationship, determines the somatic and visceral structures which are in reflex relationship with each other, and also the position of visceral pain.

Since the visceral afferent nerves do not have to adjust themselves to the many painful stimuli which are found in man's outward environment, they fail to develop a keen sense of pain. However, the juxtaposition and segmental relationship of the cell bodies of the visceral afferent neurons and the cell bodies of the skeletal sensory neurons in the central nervous system permit and facilitate the transfer of irritation from the less sensitive visceral to the more sensitive skeletal system. Thus the highly sensitive somatic system expresses pain which belongs to the visceral structures.

One of the first suggestions that pain is not found in the viscera themselves was made by Ross,[1] who believed that visceral sensation, if it reaches the plane on which pain should be felt, is expressed in somatic nerves, the location of which is determined by the segmental relationship between visceral and somatic afferent neurons.

Mackenzie[2, 3] was also convinced that injured viscera were not painful, and cited, in proof of his opinion, his experience in tearing and pinching various viscera in conscious patients without their experiencing pain. He accepted Ross's explanation of the surface pain being due to segmental irritation of the central cells of the somatic sensory neurons in response to the visceral stimulus.

Lennander's[4] name also enters all early discussion bearing upon the sensibility of viscera. He too declared that the viscera were insensitive, after much experimenting upon the conscious patient.

Head's[5] investigations clarified the subject of pain, both somatic and visceral. He recognized three types of sensibility:

"I. *Deep sensibility,* capable of answering to pressure and to the movement of parts, and even capable of producing pain under the influence of excessive pressure, or when the joint is injured. The fibers, subserving this form of sensation, run mainly with the motor nerves, and are not destroyed by division of all the sensory nerves to the skin.

"II. *Protopathic sensibility,* capable of responding to painful cutaneous stimuli, and to the extremes of heat and cold. This is the great reflex system, producing a rapid widely diffused response, unaccompanied by any definite appreciation of the locality of the spot stimulated.

"III. *Epicritic sensibility*, by which we gain the power of cutaneous localization, of the discrimination of two points, and of the finer grades of temperature, called cool and warm." Head recognized visceral pain as belonging to the protopathic type of sensibility, and spoke of the protopathic supply of internal viscera instead of the afferent system of the sympathetics. He believed that there was, under certain conditions, visceral pain which the patient was capable of discerning at the site of the diseased organ; but that the principal expression which attained the level of consciousness was expressed by transfer to sensory neurons of the voluntary system.

Davis, Pollock and Stone[6] have shown that there are two types of visceral pain: one at the site of the disease, the other referred. They have also shown that distention of any hollow viscus is capable of exerting painful sensation.

Davis and Weiss[7] abolished the pain in a case of hyperesthesia of the skin due to angina pectoris by infiltrating the area with novocaine.

It would seem from the experience of all of these investigators to be indicated at least, even proved, that the expression of pain when viscera are irritated is an incidental and not a primary function of visceral afferent nerves. The principal function of this system is that of intelligently directing or diffusing impulses so as to mediate reflexes which are required for the correlation of physiologic activity.

Heinbecker, Bishop, and O'Leary[8] have made a splendid contribution toward the differentiation of pain and touch fibers in peripheral nerves.

Variable Sensibility of Different Tissues.—There are certain visceral structures which are far more sensitive than others. The serous membranes in general are extremely sensitive when inflamed, the pleura for example.

Luciani[9] in discussing the observations and experiments which have been made up to the present time on the sensibility of internal organs, sums up the results as follows:

"(a) Only the tissues provided with nerves are sensitive to pain stimuli: the epidermis, the horny tissues in general, the cartilages and fibro-cartilages are totally insensitive, because they have no nerves.

"(b) The organs, tissues, and internal membranes innervated by the sensory roots of the nerves of the cerebrospinal axis are more or less sensitive to painful stimulation.

"(c) The organs and internal tissues innervated exclusively by the nerve-fibers of the sympathetic system are little sensitive to pain stimuli under normal anatomical and functional conditions, but in a state of inflammation they may acquire an exquisite sensibility to pain.

"There are no exceptions or comments for the first proposition; the second and third, on the contrary, must be examined. The connective tissues, ligaments, tendons, and aponeuroses have, under normal conditions, an indefinite sensibility to pain. The periosteum is very painful, as shown on scraping the bones in certain surgical operations; but bone itself, particularly the compact substance, is insensitive, as proved in amputation without chloroform. The pain sensibility of bone-marrow under physiologic conditions is doubtful.

"The muscles in the normal state are but little sensitive to pain. During amputations without anesthetics they give no pain. Strong compression gives rise to a specific dull pain; intense faradization is very painful. This sensitiveness to pain is not due to excitation of the cutaneous nerves, because Duchenne observed it with direct electrical stimulation of the pectoralis major muscle exposed during excision of the breast. The feeling of muscular fatigue presents every gradation from a simple sense of heaviness to acute pain, which may last twenty-four to forty-eight hours, and is accentuated on the slightest pressure. But in this case the state of the muscle is evidently altered, owing probably to the accumulation of fatigue products, which act as an irritant poison. Similar abnormal conditions underlie the muscular and articular pains of a rheumatic and gouty character. On the other hand, the sharp pain that accompanies the cramp caused by violent and involuntary contracture of the muscles is transitory. It has been attributed to the compression of the cutaneous sensory nerves that traverse the muscles, but this is a fallacy, because in that case, in accordance with the law of peripheral projection, the pain would be perceived in the skin and not in the contractured muscle.

"Serous membranes in general, as the peritoneum, pleura, cerebral and spinal dura mater, and the synovium, are believed to be sensitive to pain even under normal conditions, and when inflamed become much more so.

"The pain sensibility of the mucous membrane of the digestive tract is generally very acute near its junction with the skin (oral and pharyngeal cavities), but it diminishes in the esophagus. The painful sensation of choking produced when an alimentary bolus that is too large or too hard sticks near the cardiac aperture of the stomach is not due solely to the sensibility of the mucous membrane, but rather to the cramp that compresses the nerve fibers that surround the canal. The pain sensibility of the stomach is moderately acute, that of the intestine low, but it increases again in the rectum and at the anal orifice. Puncture, section, cauterization (as shown by experiments on rabbits and dogs, and surgical operations in man), do not produce true sensations of pain in any part of the intestinal canal under normal conditions. But in a pathological state, the intestine may become the seat of severe pains, such as those of colic.

"The mucous membrane of the respiratory apparatus is sensitive to pain in the nasal and laryngeal tracts, but insensitive throughout the bronchial ramifications.

"The mucous membrane of the uretogenital system is very sensitive along the urethral canal, particularly in the prostatic or membranous part; that of the bladder, on the contrary, has little sensibility. Even large calculi may remain unperceived for some time until inflammation sets in. The vulva is sensitive, but the vagina, cervix of the uterus, and the uterus itself are only moderately sensitive. As long as they are normal they can be cut or cauterized without producing pain. Pain in these parts undoubtedly depends on compression or traction of the sensory nerves that lie in the depth of the tissue, or in the uterine appendages and the vaginal canal.

"The excretory ducts of the glands are usually very sensitive to distention. The intense pain of hepatic and nephritic colic is well known.

"The heart, arteries, and veins are insensitive to pain in the normal state. The same may be said of the hepatic parenchyma, spleen, pancreas, kidneys, and lymphatic glands. The genital glands, the testicles, the ovaries and their appendages are, on the contrary, highly sensitive. Compression of these parts causes acute pain, and may even induce syncope.

"From all these facts it is clear that the internal tissues and organs have, as a rule, a lower sensibility to pain than the surface of the body; and that the deep organs innervated by the sympathetic normally feel little pain, but they have a very high latent pain sensibility which may become apparent under abnormal conditions, particularly in inflammation.''

Visceral Versus Somatic Pain.—*Visceral pain, at least that which is pronounced, is a pain caused by stimuli arising in an internal viscus which is referred and felt in the areas supplied by a skeletal (somatic) sensory nerve. The perception centers are made aware of it in the same manner as they are made aware of somatic pain, but instead of perceiving the pain as occurring in the viscus, they recognize it as being in the sensory skeletal nerve or nerves. The referred pain from the viscera is produced by transference of the sensory impulse from the afferent fibers of the sympathetic system to the spinal sensory neurons in the same segment; and from the vagus afferent neurons to the sensory neurons of the Vth cranial nerve (trigeminus).*

Visceral pain thus expresses itself in sensory spinal nerves and the Vth cranial nerve. The localization of visceral pain depends upon the fact of the segmentation of the body in early embryonic life, when the formation of the nervous system and the differentiation of the viscera are taking place; and explains the fact that pain which is caused by inflammation of a viscus expresses itself in definite skeletal zones but not always directly over that viscus.

This is well illustrated in the pain which arises from the various divisions of the gastrointestinal canal. The abdominal wall is supplied with sensory nerves from the lower six thoracic spinal segments. The stomach, small intestines and ascending and transverse colon are supplied with connector nerves from the Vth to XIIth thoracic and Ist to IIIrd lumbar segments. The innervation of these various intestinal segments is such that the supply for the upper portion of the gut comes mainly from the upper segments of the cord, the middle from the middle, and the lower portion from the lower. This determines the location of referred pain when different portions of the digestive tube are stimulated. When the stomach is inflamed, the pain is in the epigastrium; when the small intestine, the pain centers lower, about the umbilicus; and when the colon, the pain is still lower, between the umbilicus and pubis, as shown in Fig. 27.

Neither does this express all of the truth, for there are two types of pain to be considered: one, the superficial pain which follows the sensory skin zones (dermatomes) in its distribution, and, another the deep pain, a sense of pain or pressure which affects the deep structures, such as muscles and tendons, which follows the muscles (myotomes) in its distribution. These are often located in different areas. While each sensory spinal nerve supplies fibers to definite segmental

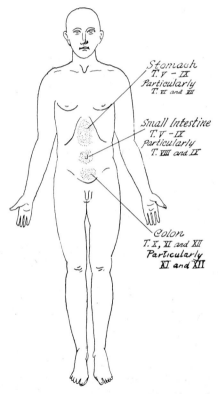

Fig. 27.—Diagrammatic illustration showing location of pain when different portions of the gastrointestinal tract are involved.

The stomach, VIth and VIIth thoracic zones; small intestine, VIIIth and IXth thoracic zones; colon, XIth and XIIth thoracic zones.

skin areas which are responsible for superficial pain, it also sends out fibers which join with the corresponding motor nerve and becomes responsible for the pain felt on pressure over deep structures. The difference in the areas of distribution of the superficial and deep pain is shown in Figs. 19-A and B and 20-A and B, pages 150 to 153.

One must understand that pain is due to stimuli which are more severe than those which are usually flowing centralward during normal conditions of activity. The afferent neurons coursing with the sympathetic system are continuously carrying stimuli to the cord which are transferred to the spinal sensory nerves, but are not of sufficient strength to cause the perceptive centers in the brain to take cognizance of them; consequently, no painful sensations are perceived. It is only under fairly strong stimulation or when the neurons are hyperirritable that the thalamic and cortical sensory centers are made aware and pain is felt.

Referred Character of Visceral Pain.—In considering pain as a symptom of disease of the internal viscera, it was formerly taken for granted that the chief seat of pain is the organ involved, just as pain is found at the seat of inflammation of structures on the surface of the body. That this cannot be true is clearly shown by a study of the innervation of those internal organs which have traveled far from the area in which they were found in early embryonic life, such as the heart, lungs, and diaphragm. When the pulmonary tissue is inflamed, disturbed sensation may be found over the neck and chest in the superficial tissues supplied by the IIIrd to Vth sensory cervical nerves or in the muscles supplied by nerves from the same segments. The diaphragm also reflects its pain in case of central diaphragmatic pleurisy in the IIIrd to Vth cervical sensory zones. Pain from the heart involves the Ist, IInd, and IIIrd thoracic zones, and is felt on the surface of the chest and down the inside surface of the arm.

The viscera are not endowed with epicritic sensibility, but only with deep and protopathic. By this fact Head[10] explains the referred nature of visceral pain, for when a part is once endowed with epicritic sensibility the pain is no longer referred. He says: ''We believe that this condition (protopathic sensibility) is due to the uncontrolled passage of a set of impulses, which normally undergo modification of inhibition before they reach the highest centers. This view is supported by the existence of a normal protopathic surface, such as that of the glans penis.

''Most of the characteristic reactions obtained from a part in a condition of protopathic sensibility undergo modification with the return of epicritic impulses; reference alone is completely abolished.

It may be asked why a function apparently so useless remains, though in a condition of permanent suppression. The answer to this question is given by the existence of referred pain in disease of the internal organs. These parts are probably innervated, like the glans penis, from the deep and protopathic systems. But, unlike the glans, their sensibility is extremely low; heat- and cold-spots must be scanty or even absent from most parts of the stomach and intestines. Moreover, pain cannot be produced by such stimuli as the prick of a pin, sufficient to evoke sensations from protopathic parts on the surface of the body. Internal surfaces cannot respond to artificial stimuli, to which they have never been exposed during the life of the individual or the race.

"Even if a stimulus is able to evoke impulses from these sheltered parts of defective sensibility, it does not usually produce a sensation, in consequence of the concurrent activity of the sensory organs of the skin. But a sensation may be produced, whenever these visceral impulses become sufficiently strong to overcome this inhibition, or when the central resistance to their passage is in any way lessened. Once the path has been opened, the resistance to potentially painful impulses is lowered, and a weaker visceral stimulus will evoke a sensation. To this diminished resistance is probably due the production of pain by otherwise inadequate stimuli in cases of long-continued visceral irritation.

"Since the internal organs are totally devoid of epicritic sensibility, a sensation produced within the visceral area will tend to show the same peculiarities as one evoked from a part supplied with deep and protopathic sensibility only. If the stimulus consists of pressure or of the movement of muscles, the patient will recognize to some extent its true locality, in proportion as the part is supplied with end-organs from the deep afferent system. When, however, the stimulus evokes pain the sensation will tend to be referred into remote parts.

"Now, just as one part of the affected area on H's hand seemed to be linked with some other remote portion, so visceral sensory surfaces seem to be closely associated with somatic segmental areas. When pain is evoked, it is not localized in the organ stimulated, but is referred to some area on the surface of the body.

"Thus, the retention, on the primary level, of afferent impulses, which if not inhibited, would lead to incorrect localization, has a protective object. To the normal organism they would be worse than useless, but in disease they underlie widespread pain and uncontrollable muscular reflexes."

Referred pains can only be understood when the organ is carefully studied with reference to its embryologic development, in which case it will be seen that the usual visceral pain follows the segmental relationship which determined the innervation in early developmental life as discussed in Chapter X. The cells of the visceral nerves originally were found in the neural canal; and, while during the development of the individual they wandered far from it, yet they have preserved their segmental relationships through the connector fibers which run from the spinal segments to the motor cells of the ganglia, lateral, collateral, and terminal, in case of the sympathetic system; and from the nuclei in the midbrain and bulb, and the cells in the sacral segments of the cord, to the motor cells in the organs themselves in case of the parasympathetics as shown in Chapter III. Visceral pain is expressed by afferent neurons coursing in the sympathetic and parasympathetic systems, transferring the impulse to sensory spinal nerves and the Vth cranial nerve; and the location of the pain depends upon the segments of the body with which they are in reflex relationship, because the pain is expressed in the peripheral distribution of those sensory nerves, either spinal or Vth cranial, whose cells lie adjacent to them.

Mackenzie[11] says with reference to the referred nature of visceral pain: "In putting forward the view that the pains arising from the viscera are not felt in the organ, but are referred to the peripheral distribution of cerebrospinal nerves in the external body wall, I have opposed to me the practically unanimous opinion of all people, whether they have studied the subject or not."

Mackenzie explains the fact that pain is often felt on pressure over an organ as being due to hyperalgesia which affects the soft tissues covering the surface of the body. He calls attention to the fact that the pain remains stationary though the organ shifts its position; and further, the pain often extends beyond the limit of the organ. This I have discussed above and illustrated by the pain in inflammation of the lungs, diaphragm, and heart.

HYPERALGESIA.—In considering so-called deep pain, it must be remembered that skeletal structures are supplied by the sensory spinal and sensory cranial nerves; and, while pain is most acutely developed in the skin, it is also present, though less acute, in subcutaneous tissue and muscle. Hyperalgesia of the soft tissues is not uncommon in the areas which have been the seat of reflex sensory pain. Mackenzie cites the severe pain felt by John Hunter in his arm after an attack of angina pectoris. Soreness of the shoulder and upper arm muscles is often complained of by patients who suffer from inflammatory diseases of the lungs.

Hyperalgesia of the skin is also common in visceral diseases. Not infrequently do we find tuberculous patients suffering from a complicating pleurisy in whom the skin becomes very sensitive, even a very slight stroke causing pain. In studying hyperalgesia of the muscles, it is important to bear in mind that the sensory innervation of the muscles follows their motor innervation and not that of the cutaneous zones. This is especially necessary in order to understand the pain in the muscles where the muscle and skin zones are not coextensive as in diseases of the lungs as noted on page 313.

No study of hyperalgesia and other forms of visceral pain can be complete without recognition of the great work done by Head. Head, contrary to Mackenzie, recognizes two types of sensation in internal viscera, one in the organ itself, which is more that of discomfort and uneasiness, and one on the surface of the body which is a true painful sensation. Head has formulated the following law of the location of visceral pain :[12]

"When a painful stimulus is applied to a part of low sensibility in close central connection with a part of much greater sensibility, the pain produced is felt in the part of higher sensibility rather than in the part of lower sensibility to which the stimulus was actually applied."

The fact that the internal viscera are less sensitive than the skin areas supplied by sensory nerve cells, which lie adjacent in the same segments of the cord, according to this rule, would account for the pain being felt in the more sensitive nerves of the skin. In the presence of disease of the internal viscera, where the sensory cell bodies in the cord become highly excitable, the mere touch or pinching of the cutaneous surface, or slight pressure over deeper struc-

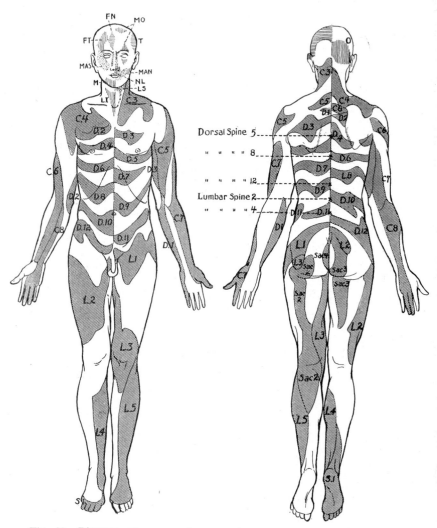

Fig. 28.—Diagram of zones and areas of hyperalgesia after the clinical researches of Head (anterior and posterior view). The eight cervical segments are indicated by *C1, C2-C8;* the twelve dorsal or thoracic segments by *D1, D2-D12;* the five lumbar segments by *L1, L2-L5;* and the four sacral segments by *Sac.1, Sac.2-Sac.4.*

The areas of the head are indicated as follows: *N*— nasal or rostral area; *FN*—frontonasal area; *MO*—medio-orbital area; *FT*—fronto-temporal area; *T*—temporal area; *V*—vertical area; *P*— parietal area · *O*—occipital area; *NL*—nasolabial area; *Max.*—maxillary area; *Man.*—Mandibular area; *M*—mental area; *LS*—superior laryngeal area; *LI*—inferior laryngeal area; *TO*—hyoid area. (Luciani.)

The position of the sensory zones on the surface of the body is lower than the emergence of the corresponding sensory nerves from the cord. In order to show this relationship the spinous processes of the fifth, eighth, and twelfth dorsal and the second and fourth lumbar vertebrae are shown in the figure.

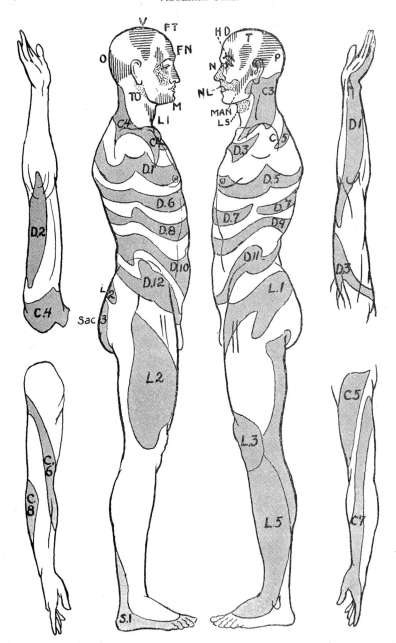

Fig. 29.—Diagram of zones and areas of hyperalgesia after the clinical researches of Head (lateral view). For description see Fig. 28.

tures gives evidence of pain, when the same degree of stimulation would not produce any sensation more than that of being touched, if the cell bodies in the cord had not been made hyperexcitable by stimuli coming from the viscera. After much careful study, Head mapped the body in zones which show hyperalgesia when internal viscera are inflamed. This is well presented by Luciani:[13]

"Head's clinical investigations have such great practical importance that it is desirable to reproduce the following diagram and table, which sum up his results.

AREA IN THE TRUNK AND LIMBS		AREA IN THE HEAD
Heart	C3, C4 —D2 —D8	{ Ventricles and aorta, N, FN, MO, FT { Auricles _____FT, T, V, P
Lungs	C3, C4 —D4 —D9	_____N, FN, MO, FT, T, V, P
Stomach	D7 —D9	_____FN, MO, T, V, P
Intestine	D9 —D12	_____V, P, O
Rectum	Sac. 2—Sac. 4	_____
Liver	C3, C4 —D7 —D10	_____FN, MO, T, V, P, O
Gallbladder	D8 —D9	_____T, V
Kidney and urethra____D11—L1		
Bladder (mucous membrane and neck)		
	Sac. 3—Sac. 4	
Detrusor vesicae	D11—L2	
Prostate_____D10—D12 Sac. 1—Sac. 3		
Epididymis_____D11—D12		
Testicle_____D10		O
Ovary_____D10		O
Ovarian appendix D11—L1		
Uterus_____D10—L1		
Neck of uterus_____Sac. 2—Sac. 4		
Mammae _____D4—D5		
Spleen (from Signorelli) D6		

Figs. 25 and 26 [28 and 29 in this text] show the segmental cutaneous areas of the trunk, extremities, and head. The form and extent of these were arrived at:

"(a) By mapping out the areas in a number of cases of cutaneous hyperesthesia with coincident visceral affections;

"(b) From the topography of the eruptions in 52 cases of *herpes zoster;*

"(c) By mapping out the analgesic areas in organic diseases of the spinal cord and roots.

"The 8 cervical segments are indicated by C1, C2 . . . C8; the 12 dorsal or thoracic segments by D1, D2 . . . D12; the 5 lumbar segments by L1, L2 . . . L 5; and the 4 sacral segments by Sac. 1, Sac. 2 . . . Sac. 4.

"The areas of the head are indicated as follows: N—nasal or rostral area; FN—fronto-nasal area; MO—medio-orbital area; FT —fronto-temporal area; T—temporal area; V—vertical area; P— parietal area; O—occipital area; NL—nasolabial area; Max.—maxillary area; Man.—mandibular area; M—mental area; LS—superior laryngeal area; LI—inferior laryngeal area; To—hyoid area.

"The accompanying table shows the relations between the cutaneous areas and the internal organs."

This table should be studied carefully by all students of visceral neurology.

Recurrent Pain in Sensory Spinal Nerves Resulting from Visceral Disease.—A troublesome symptom of chronic visceral disease is recurrent aching or pain expressed in those somatic sensory zones which are supplied by neurons whose cell bodies lie adjacent in the cord to the cell bodies of the afferent neurons from a viscus which is or has been the seat of disease. Its presence disturbs and discourages the patient and its explanation confuses the physician. This pain may come when there is no exacerbation of the disease. Different causes excite pains which are associated with different viscera. For example: A patient who has previously suffered from pulmonary tuberculosis experiences pain under many conditions in the zones in which the sensory reflex from the lung is expressed—the neck, shoulders, and muscles of the chest and shoulder girdle. These may appear at the time of changes in the weather, when tired, or when the patient is physically or nervously below par, regardless of whether the disease is active or not. They frequently come at the time of the menses. Pain arising from chronic inflammation of the pleura is influenced in the same manner. Pain arising from stomach and intestinal diseases will often appear when the patient is tired or nervously exhausted, or suffering from other depressive conditions without there being at the time activation of the disease in the organs. Pain from the kidney and uterus will be experienced by patients, who have previously suffered from chronic inflammation of these organs, when the patient tires or becomes depressed. And so it is with other important viscera. The neurons which carry the impulses which call forth the viscerosensory reflexes, become hypersensitive to such a degree that aching or pain is expressed in the respective sensory zones as a result of stimuli which probably would be insufficient to cause reflex action in normal nerve cells.

When a visceral impulse has once broken over to cause pain, thereafter pain may be elicited by a stimulus which is of much less intensity. Mackenzie speaks of this as being a persistent hyperirritability of the nerve cells in the areas of the cord which receive the impulses from the diseased organ.

The explanation of this pain is furnished by the fact that nerve cells under normal conditions will stand a certain amount of stimulation without producing action. Afferent stimuli continuously pass centralward from all viscera, but they only cause reflex action when the stimulus becomes *adequate* to overcome the resistance between the cell body which receives the impulse and the cell body which effects the action whether it be a contracture of muscle, a stimulation of secretory activity, or a change in sensation, such as is recognized as some form of sensory disturbance. When for a long time harmful afferent stimuli pass to the cord, the threshold of response for the nerve cells to which these stimuli are transferred is lowered, and they respond to a stimulus below that which they would withstand during normal conditions. In other words, these cells become hyperirritable and reach a state where a lesser stimulation produces an *adequate stimulus*. In case of the pain or aching which is often experienced by patients who have previously had an inflamed lung, pleura, intestinal tract, kidney or uterus, or other organ as mentioned above, the threshold of response in the cell bodies of the sensory spinal nerves becomes lowered to such a degree that when these patients experience any unusual condition which affects nerve cells generally those cells whose threshold of response has not been previously lowered withstand the stimulation, while those in which the threshold for stimuli has been lowered respond with pain.

This idea is expressed graphically in Fig. 30, in which AC, the distance between lines AB and CD, represents the strength of stimulus which can be withstood by the nerve cells of the body, generally, without discharging energy—producing pain, muscular contraction, or altered secretion. When inflammation is present, or has been long present in organs, the particular cells in the central nervous system which receive stimuli from that particular organ, take upon themselves a condition of increased irritability, and discharge on being irritated by stimuli of a lesser degree than that required under normal conditions. They would be discharged by a stimulus less than

AC, for example, AC'; consequently, when factors appear which produce a marked general nerve stimulation, such as toxemia, disease,
tiring, worry, overwork, malnutrition, anemia and weather changes,
the line CD representing general stimulation approaches AB, which
is the normal point of general nerve discharge. Such nerve cells as
have taken upon themselves a condition of increased irritability as a
result of preceding harmful stimulation will discharge somewhere
before the line AB is reached as, for example, at C'D'.

For example: Patients who have had pleurisy often suffer pain
in the chest on tiring, or because of weather changes, or when depressed by worry and other harmful influences, although they are
comfortable at other times and have no other pain during the action of these depressive conditions, except that expressed in the

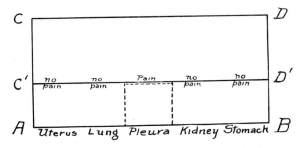

Fig. 30.—Graphic illustration of cause of recurrent pain in sensory neurons,
the cell bodies of which have been rendered hyperirritable by disease.
Line AB represents the point at which the sensory neurons connecting with the
uterus, lungs, pleura, kidney, and stomach, normally discharge when stimulated.
Line CD represents the stimulus and AC the strength of stimulus which the nerve
cells will normally withstand. If the degree of irritability of the nerve cells of all
the organs mentioned is normal, no pain would occur until CD has reached AB.
The dotted lines in the figure are drawn so as to illustrate that the neurons connected with the pleura have attained a state of hyperirritability, so that they discharge with a lesser stimulus than the neurons connected with other organs, and
when CD has reached the point C'D', pain is felt in the neurons connected with the
pleura, although it does not occur in the neurons connected with the other organs.

somatic sensory zones which are connected with afferent pleural
nerves. Tiring, worry, changes in weather, etc., cause the line CD
to approach AB, and if AB should be reached there would be a
general discharge of nerve energy shown from many of the organs
of the body. But long before CD reaches AB, for example, at
C'D', the pleural pain is felt, because the pleural sensory neurons
are in a state of hyperirritability and the line AC, which represents the strength of stimulus which the nerve cells of a given
organ, the pleura in this example, should normally withstand is

reduced to AC'. Other organs show no pain, as is indicated in the figure, because the excitability of the cell bodies of the neurons which receive stimuli from them is not increased.

References

1. Ross, J.: On the Segmental Distribution of Sensory Disorders, Brain 10: 333, 1887.
2. Mackenzie, J.: Some Points Bearing on the Association of Sensory Disorders and Visceral Disease, Brain 16: 321, 1893.
3. Mackenzie, J.: Symptoms and Their Interpretation, London, 1909, Shaw and Son.
4. Lennander, K. G.: Über die Sensibilität der Bauchhöle und über lokale und algemein Anästhesie ber Bruck- und Bauchoperationen, Zentralbl. f. Chir. 28: 209, 1901.
5. Head, Henry: Studies in Neurology, London, 1920, Oxford University Press, Vol. I, p. 63.
6. Davis, L., Pollock, L. J., and Stone, T. T.: Visceral Pain, Surg. Gynec. & Obst. 55: 418, 1932.
7. Davis, D., and Weiss, S.: The Significance of the Afferent Impulses From the Skin in the Mechanism of Visceral Pain. Skin Infiltration as a Useful Therapeutic Measure, Am. J. M. Sc. 176: 517-536, 1928.
8. Heinbecker, Bishop, and O'Leary: Pain and Touch Fibers in Peripheral Nerves, Arch. Neurol. & Psychiat. 29: 771-789, 1933.
9. Luciani, Luigi: Human Physiology, London, 1917, Macmillan Co., Vol. IV, p. 62.
10. Head, Henry: Loc. cit. Vol. I, p. 328.
11. Mackenzie, J.: Symptoms and Their Interpretation, London, 1909, Shaw and Son, p. 22.
12. Head, Henry: Brain 16: 127, 1893.
13. Luciani, Luigi: Loc. cit. Vol. IV, p. 68.

CHAPTER XIII

REFLEXES WHOSE AFFERENT IMPULSES COURSE IN THE SYMPATHETIC SYSTEM

DISTRIBUTION OF SYMPATHETIC NERVES

Every organ and tissue of the body is supplied by sympathetic nerves. (See Chapter III.) These course (1) in the blood vessels, and, by their action as vasoconstrictors and vasodilators, influence the most minute body structures; (2) they supply many structures, to which there are no known parasympathetic fibers, such as most of the blood vessels, the sweat glands, the pilomotor muscles, and most of the urogenital structures; (3) they activate certain structures in which the parasympathetics furnish the inhibiting fibers, such as the heart, sphincters of the gut and body and trigone of the bladder; and (4) they supply inhibitory fibers, which antagonize the activating parasympathetics to other tissues, such as the pupil, the lacrimal and salivary glands, the structures of the head, and the enteral system, consisting of the gastrointestinal canal and all of the organs derived embryologically from it, such as the lungs, liver, pancreas, and body of the bladder.

Sensory, more properly afferent, fibers are found, along with the motor sympathetic fibers, in all structures; and, when irritated, carry impulses centralward where they are transferred to other neurons through which, if the stimuli are sufficiently strong, or if they are repeated sufficiently often, they disturb normal physiologic equilibrium in other structures producing symptoms and signs of disease. These disturbances may be produced in either the skeletal structures, skin, subcutaneous tissue and muscles or in other viscera. Every organ and tissue may generate stimuli which, if sufficiently strong, result in reflex action in the skeletal structures which stand in reflex relationship to them through the spinal nerves which supply them and vice versa.

DISTRIBUTION OF SYMPATHETIC REFLEXES

Sympathetic reflexes are of three kinds—motor, sensory, and trophic—and each of them plays an extremely important rôle in clinical symptomatology; a rôle which, though as yet not fully appreciated, will, as it becomes better understood, more and more assume clinical value.

While the connector fibers which terminate in the ganglia of the sympathetic system arise only from the thoracic and upper lumbar segments of the cord, sympathetic nerves are distributed through their control of the blood vessels and in many cases by direct innervation of the tissues, to every part of the body; and sensory stimuli coming from the tissues through afferent neurons of the sympathetic system mediate in the cord with other neurons in the cervical, lower lumbar and upper sacral segments, as well as in the thoracic and upper lumbar; so that *all of the structures which are supplied by somatic spinal nerves, likewise many supplied by visceral nerves, are subject to reflex effects produced through sympathetic stimulation.* This stimulation follows the segmentation of the body in an orderly manner as described in Chapter X, according to the following law:

Every viscus receives its sympathetic connector fibers from certain segments of the cord and sends back its afferent stimuli to the same segments of the cord; and these stimuli complete the preponderating number of reflexes which arise from a given organ in the neurons arising from those segments, in such a manner that a given organ, when inflamed, expresses its reflexes regularly in the same structures. A notable exception to this rule is found in case of the lung, in which the impulses are transferred upward in the cord from the upper thoracic to the midcervical segments, before mediation with spinal nerves takes place.

Although variations from this law will be found now and then, the principle here laid down will hold for most of the spinal reflexes met in clinical practice. The variations which occur also follow a law laid down by Sherrington which is quoted on page 168, viz.: "Excitation of the central side of a severed thoracic root, e.g., seventh, evokes with special ease contraction of muscles or parts of muscles innervated by the corresponding motor roots, and *next easily muscles innervated by the next adjacent motor roots.*" This is well illustrated

by the heart and lung reflexes. While the heart as a rule expresses
its reflexes in the Ist to Vth thoracic segments on the left side, the
reflex may be met on the right side of the chest, or it may travel
upward into the adjoining cervical segments of the cord or downward into lower adjoining thoracic segments. The lung reflex offers
an exception to one of Sherrington's laws in that mediation of the
reflex does not occur in the same segments of the cord that receive
the impulses, but instead the impulse is transferred by intercalated
neurons from the upper dorsal segments which receive them from
the periphery, upward into the cervical portion of the cord; but it
does follow the other portion of the law in that the reflex action always takes place most readily through the same efferent fibers. It
reflects strongest, as a rule, in the IIIrd, IVth, and Vth cervical segments but may reflect in the adjoining segments either above or
below. Not infrequently reflex effects from the lung are mediated
through the brachial plexus simulating a brachial neuritis.

The fact that reflexes are at times more widely spread in the tissues than at other times is explained according to the principle that
the stimuli being stronger, the efferent impulses are transferred to
more neurons, making the area of reflex response greater.

From physiologic facts we enunciate a second law: *Every important internal viscus is so connected in the central nervous system
that it is able to produce reflexes through afferent fibers which course
with the sympathetics and efferent spinal nerves, in definite skeletal
structures; and, if acutely inflamed, should show motor reflexes and
altered sensation (pain); and, if chronically inflamed, trophic changes.
Therefore, spasm of muscles, altered cutaneous sensation and degeneration of muscles, subcutaneous tissue and skin, in areas having
definite limited segmental innervation become important diagnostic
phenomena.*

In the discussion of physiologic principles, I entered into the question of whether or not the sympathetic ganglia have the power of
producing reflexes and showed that there is a difference of opinion
among physiologists on this point (see page 96), so we are not in a
position to say whether a reflex may be carried from one viscus to
another without the afferent impulse going to the cord. It is important that this point be definitely settled, but the weight of physiologic evidence is against it. Clinical observation may produce data

which will help to solve this question. This I suggested in a discus-sion of the question of exophthalmic goiter,[1] where the cervical sympathetic ganglia have shown pathologic change. A determination of the priority of the relationship between the disease in the thyroid gland, the diseased sympathetic ganglia and the symptoms which develop in the structures supplied by the cervical ganglion cells, might aid in the solution of this most important question.

Not only must we conceive of afferent impulses traveling to the cord to connect with spinal nerves to express reflexes in the skeletal structures; but the reverse is equally true. *There is a continuous stream of impulses received by the sensory somatic nerves which are transferred to the connector neurons of the sympathetic system and expressed as reflexes in the internal viscera.* It is a common obser-vation that blood pressure may vary according to the temperature of the surrounding atmosphere or other medium surrounding the in-dividual; and also according to other forces which are applied to the sensory cutaneous nerves. The vegetative nervous system is the medium through which outward stimuli affect the organism. Man is spoken of as being a receptor organism influenced by all the forces in his environment, such as heat and cold, barometric pressure, wind movement, humidity, light, and darkness. The vegetative nervous system is the effector mechanism through which all of these forces are mediated and by which physiologic adjustment is made.

Another group of sympathetic reflexes which is not generally de-scribed is that in which both afferent and efferent impulses course over the sympathetic system. It must be made plain in this connec-tion that the afferent arm of this reflex is not a true sympathetic nerve but the somatic nerve which is distributed to sympathetically innervated structures. This opens up a large field for study because it suggests a sympathetic as well as a parasympathetic pathway over which one viscus may affect another. A well-recognized sympathetic reflex of this type is the dilatation of the pupil which occurs in pulmonary tuberculosis. Carlson[2] also cites reflex cardiospasm pro-duced by stimuli arising in the gall bladder, intestinal tract, and urinary bladder, and says: "the splanchnic nerves are the main afferent paths and, in part, the efferent paths for the reflex." Sym-pathetic-parasympathetic reflexes and the reverse also occur. See tables, pages 306 and 307.

RECIPROCAL REFLEXES IN DERMAL STRUCTURES AND SPLANCHNIC VISCERA WHICH COURSE OVER SYMPATHETIC NEURONS

The reciprocal relationship which exists between the dermal and visceral structures is probably closer than is generally realized. From time immemorial, physicians have attempted to treat visceral disease by applications to the surface of the body. During the past few decades, however, the development of medicine has been predominantly along the line of structural pathology, and as a result, such therapeutic measures as consist of applying substances to the surface of the body to influence internal viscera have been generally ridiculed. But now that we have begun to study pathologic physiology more intently, we begin to see that there is a definite basis for such therapeutic measures. Any such measure which is able to survive through centuries of use must have some basis, even though it is not evident from the knowledge existing at the time. It can readily be seen that there is a close relationship between the dermal structures and the viscera and no doubt as our knowledge in this field extends, we shall be able to see these relationships more clearly.

Petersen, Müller, and their coworkers have pointed out a most interesting reciprocal relationship between the dermal structures and the splanchnic viscera.[3, 4] They have shown that intradermal injection of protein is followed by immediate changes in the peripheral tissues; viz., vasoconstriction, lessened vascular permeability, goose flesh, decrease in water elimination, lessened heat elimination, and leucopenia. At the same time,[5] there occurs a different and opposite condition in the splanchnic organs of which the liver and stomach particularly have been studied. The vessels become more permeable, they dilate, the function of the organs increases, a leucocytosis occurs, and an increase of lymph flows from the organ as has been determined experimentally.

They further have shown that a leucopenia accompanies vasoconstriction, and a leucocytosis accompanies vasodilatation; and, that the state of the leucocytes in the peripheral blood may be taken as an index of the condition of the peripheral organs, and that the opposite condition may be assumed to be present in the splanchnic viscera.[3, 6] They consider that it has been proved that the responsible connecting pathway between the peripheral and splanchnic viscera is the vegetative nerves. As evidence of this, they point out that the reflex has been caused by applying an intradermal injection of protein to the sound leg of a man when it failed to be called out in the same patient by applying the same stimulus to the leg on which a periarterial asympathectomy, removing the afferent pathway for the stimulus, had been previously done.[7]

These workers designated these reciprocal conditions in the peripheral and splanchnic viscera as sympathicotonia and parasympathicotonia, but not with the usually accepted meaning of the terms as defined by Eppinger and Hess. According to Petersen and Müller[4, 5, 6] and Emden[7] the term peripheral sympathicotonia means peripheral vasoconstriction, lessened permeability of the vessels, leucopenia and so forth, while peripheral parasympathicotonia means the opposite: vasodilatation, increased vascular permeability, increased heat elimination, increased perspiration, and a leucocytosis. The relationship between the peripheral and visceral organs being reciprocal, peripheral sympathicotonia is always accompanied by a visceral parasympathicotonia and vice versa. Since these terms, sympathicotonia and parasympathicotonia, have become established in vegetative neurology as meaning an increased activity in their respective components of the vegetative system, it seems better, in order to avoid confusion in an already complicated nomenclature, that these newer phenomena noted by Petersen and Müller be designated in some other manner.

I suggest that these conditions be called hypervegetonia and hypovegetonia, since they are not intended to imply any definite relationship to either the sympathetic or parasympathetic nerves, but only increased or decreased activity in vegetative structures. The condition of lessened activity which accompanies vasoconstriction, since that means a lessened metabolic activity, could be designated as "hypovegetonia" and that of increased activity which accompanies vasodilation as "hypervegetonia."

NATURE OF SYMPATHETIC REFLEXES

We shall now discuss separately the three reflexes of visceral origin which manifest themselves in the skeletal structures through impulses which reach the cord by way of the sympathetic system—(1) the "visceromotor reflex," (2) the "viscerosensory reflex," and (3) the "viscerotrophic reflex," remembering the "sensory" is only a clinical conception.

The medical profession owes a great debt of gratitude to Ross, Head, Mackenzie and Sherrington for their pioneer work in the study of visceral reflexes. Their labors have had much to do with the establishment of these clinical manifestations as signs of visceral disease. At this time I wish to express my deep personal obligation to these observers for the aid and inspiration that I have received from their works in explaining the motor and trophic reflexes from the lung,[8, 9] kidney,[10] and intestines,[11] which have been described by me. Study of these reflexes and the underlying visceral nerve control leads to a wealth of observations which are not confined to the sympathetic and spinal nerves, but which apply also to the parasympathetics and cranial. This will appear as we proceed in our clinical discussion.

1. **Visceromotor Reflex.**—The visceromotor reflex is the only true sympathetic reflex in skeletal tissues. (The viscerosensory and viscerotrophic, produced through sensory nerves, are not real physiologic reflexes as will appear from the discussion.) It manifests itself in a contraction of skeletal muscles as a motor response to a sensory impulse coming from a viscus through the afferent fibers of the sympathetic system. These muscular contractions have long been recognized in the abdominal muscles, the contractures in cases of appendicitis, gall bladder inflammation, peritonitis, and gastric ulcer being particularly well known.

Aside from these there are others which are equally valuable as diagnostic signs. The spasm of the muscles over the right side of the abdomen when the ileum, cecum, and ascending colon are inflamed, and that of the muscles of the shoulder girdle and diaphragm when the pulmonary tissue is inflamed, and the spasm of the lumbar muscles when the kidney is inflamed, while not so generally known are equally important in diagnosis. The visceromotor reflex for each important organ will be discussed in Part III. The motor centers of the cord are shown diagrammatically in Fig. 31.

It is characteristic of the contraction of the broad skeletal muscle in the visceromotor reflexes, that the muscle as a whole does not necessarily contract. This is due to the peculiarity of the segmental relationship in the cord between the visceral afferent neuron and the efferent, motor neuron to the muscle. While a nerve which supplies a muscle may be made up of many fibers arising from many cells scattered through one or several segments of the cord, only part of those cells may be in reflex connection with the sensory cells which receive the impulse from the viscus and take part in the motor reflex. On this point Mackenzie[12] says:

"Some years ago I pointed out that these muscles could be demonstrated to possess the power of contracting in small sections in

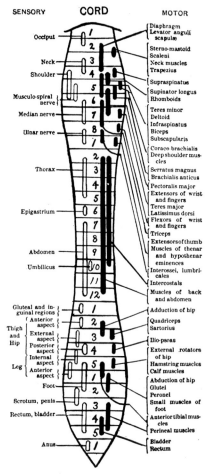

Fig. 31.—Diagrammatic representation of the spinal cord showing the important centers from which sensory and motor fibers take their origin. [(Jakob, Star, Sachs, Vana, Millis and Butler.) Abrams.]

From this figure one can observe the close relationship which exists between certain sensory and motor centers and gain information which will aid in correlating sensory and motor reflexes.

response to visceral stimulation. Later I found that Sherrington had described the difference in the reaction to nerve stimulation between these flat muscles and the muscles of the limbs. The fibers that constitute the nerve supply of any given muscle leave the spinal cord in separate bundles. If one of these bundles be stimulated, the whole length of a limb muscle like the sartorius will contract. On the other hand, if one of the bundles that constitutes the nerve supply of one of the abdominal muscles be stimulated, only a portion of the fibers of the muscle will contract.''

It can be seen then, that, physiologically, a portion of a flat muscle may respond by contracting, while the remaining portion remains relaxed. This is what we find clinically. In a visceromotor reflex affecting flat muscles only those fibers contract which are innervated by filaments whose nerve cells mediate in the cord with the cells of the afferent neuron which transmits the stimulus from the inflamed viscus. This may manifest itself in either a contraction of a given portion of several muscle bundles, as shown in the rectus in gastric ulcer, or in the contraction of entire bundles of muscles, as we see it in the sternocleidomastoideus and trapezius in pulmonary tuberculosis. As far as the muscles showing the motor reflex are concerned, we must remember that each afferent neuron coming from a viscus has certain spinal motor neurons with which it enters into reflex action most easily, according to Sherrington's law cited on pages 168 and 169.

A visceromotor reflex may be of short duration, passing away after a few days, or it may remain for months as we see it in the muscles of the shoulder girdle in pulmonary tuberculosis, and in the lumbar muscles in tuberculosis of the kidney; but when it persists for a long time, the tissues which are involved degenerate. Thus the muscles which show spasm in early tuberculosis, show degeneration (viscerotrophic reflex) when the disease has become chronic. The long-continued bombardment of nerve cells by harmful stimuli permanently impairs their function.

2. **Viscerosensory Reflex.**—The viscerosensory reflex is a convenient clinical conception but not a physiologic entity. It is rather a sensory stimulus transferred in the central nervous system to somatic sensory nerves whose cell bodies lie adjacent to the cell bodies of the afferent nerves which transmit the stimuli centralward from the viscus, according to the ideas of Ross, Mackenzie, and Head, as discussed in Chapter XII.

When a viscus is inflamed, its afferent impulses may produce both reflexes and pain in the corresponding somatic segmental zones. The strength of the afferent stimulus varies with the character of the organ involved. A hollow organ, with constricting muscles, such as the sphincters, or with circular muscles which respond with constriction to stimuli offer opportunity for strongest stimulation; hence for greatest pain. This we see in the various colics as compared to the inflammation in such solid organs as the lung. A misunderstanding regarding visceral sensations is undoubtedly due to the general thought that all sensory stimuli which are referred to somatic structures are painful. Such is not the case. They may be acutely painful, a dull aching, a discomfort, sensitiveness to heat and cold, or any other form of sensory disturbance. In pulmonary inflammation acute pain is rarely found unless the pleura is involved. Nevertheless, soreness and discomfort are common; so in other solid organs.

The viscerosensory reflex is closely bound to the subject of pain, although it includes other forms of sensation. That portion of the organism which comes into direct contact with the outside world is well supplied with sensory nerves, the skin having the most, and the subcutaneous tissue and muscles each having comparatively less. These nerves aid the organism in distinguishing different sensory stimuli, some of which are harmless, others pregnant with danger. They serve the purpose of informing the individual, through the higher centers, of the nature or nearness of objects, also as to whether or not they are harmful. They are the outposts of defense. In the internal viscera the danger is lessened because of their protected situation; consequently the viscera are supplied with nerves of much lower sensibility which do not have the power to react to all forms of sensory stimuli, heat for example. Crile[13] has discussed this very fully in his studies. Furthermore, the number of sensory fibers going to the viscera as compared with the number of motor fibers, is much smaller. According to Langley and Anderson, the hypogastric nerve contains 1 sensory, afferent fiber to 10 motor, efferent fibers; and the *nervus erigens* contains 1 sensory, afferent to 2 motor, efferent.

3. **Viscerotrophic Reflex.**—While the visceromotor and viscerosensory reflexes have been considered by others, I have failed to find a satisfactory discussion of the *viscerotrophic reflexes* in the

writings of other observers. This is probably because most study along the lines of clinical visceral neurology has heretofore been directed toward acute visceral inflammation. While acute inflammation of the viscera provokes the *visceromotor* and *viscerosensory* reflexes, the trophic changes[14, 15, 16] which depend upon reflex visceral stimulation are dependent upon a chronicity of the inflammation to bring them about. This is well illustrated by pulmonary tuberculosis, as will be described in Chapter XXIII.

CAUSE OF TROPHIC REFLEX.—So far as physiologists are able to determine, there are no special trophic nerves, but nutrition of tissue depends upon the nerves and blood supply to it. The skin, subcutaneous tissue, and muscles depend for their nutrition upon the spinal, cranial, and sympathetic nerves, particularly those controlling their vascular supply; consequently, we look to these nerves as being responsible for the *viscerotrophic* reflex in these structures. The function of body cells and their nutrition are inseparable. Therefore, trophic change must be looked upon as a disturbance in the blood supply and in the innervation of the part affected, and degeneration as a condition in which the mechanism which supplies nutrition to the part is not able to care fully for the nutritional requirements of the cells.

There has been considerable discussion as to the effect of the sympathetic fibers which have been found in striated muscle. Dusser de Barenne[17] has traced sympathetic fibers to the muscle fibers by the degeneration method, and De Boer[18] claims to have found a loss of tone when the sympathetics were sectioned. Observers favoring these theories claim that the sympathetics are a large factor in the control of the metabolism of muscles. Langley[19] rather favors the idea that the sympathetics join the muscle cells but calls attention to the fact that their action cannot be separated from that of the sympathetics supplying the blood vessels.

Clinically the areas of degeneration in skin, subcutaneous tissue, and muscles, which we can study so well in chronic inflammation of the pulmonary and pleural tissues follow both the skin and muscle segmentation. This rather indicates that the trophic reflex cannot be accounted for wholly as being caused through the sympathetic nerves supplying the blood vessels, although this theory has much in its favor. Rather does it seem that injury to those spinal nerves which mediate with the afferent neurons from the lung must be a factor. This, however, should not be taken to exclude the sympathetics of the vessels which supply nutrition to the tissues, for they undoubtedly have an important part.

Hunter[20] has recently suggested a much more important sympathetic innervation of the skeletal muscles than that carried through the blood vessels. He suggests that striated muscle consists of large and small muscle fibers; that the larger fibers are innervated by the spinal nerves which preside over muscle contraction, and that the smaller ones are innervated by sympathetic nerves and have control over the plastic tone of the muscle. They hold the muscle in position. If this work is corroborated, it suggests another manner in which the sympathetics may cause increased tension in muscles in the presence of reflex spasm caused by acute visceral inflammation, and degeneration in the presence of chronic inflammation. It also affords a practical method of surgical procedure in case of muscle dystrophies as suggested by Hunter. The validity of Hunter's theory, however, is seriously questioned.

Neurons may be injured in many ways. Certain poisons may alter their stability; they may be injured by chemical or mechanical action; by severe or persistent stimuli which act peripherally upon their corresponding segmental afferent neurons as is shown so plainly in pulmonary tuberculosis; or by malnutrition. While neurons may be able to endure excessive stimulation for a short period of time without harm resulting, yet, if long continued, they will be injured, and the tissues supplied will suffer nutritional change. Injury to a neuron as is effected by fatigue, toxins or excessive stimulation is exerted upon the synapse and results in easier transmission of impulses.

Injured neurons show in an increased irritability and a reduction of their functional capacity. Since the nerves that supply motor activity and sensation to the skeletal structures have at least a certain control over the nutrition of these tissues, might not therefore a prolonged injury to the synapses be followed by a reduction in motor power, or alteration in sensation and in a failure to maintain the nutrition of the structures—degeneration?

Whenever an organ is the seat of a chronic inflammatory process, the nerve endings in that organ receive stimuli greater than normal or more frequently than normal. Impulses are transmitted centralwards which continue as long as the inflammation lasts. If the cell bodies which give origin to afferent fibers are bombarded by such impulses over a long period of time, is it not probable that they and the cells which mediate with them become injured, and manifest an inability to functionate properly? Such injury would affect the stability of the reflex, and might result in trophic change in the tissues. In case of the sympathetic and vagal (parasympathetic) afferent nerves and the efferent spinal and the Vth cranial nerves in reflex connection with them, a degeneration of skeletal soft tissues—muscles, subcutaneous tissue, and skin—would result.

EXAMPLES OF TROPHIC REFLEX.—This reflex degeneration, for which I would suggest the term *viscerotrophic reflex* in harmony with the terms *visceromotor* and *viscerosensory* is well illustrated in the trophic changes in the soft somatic structures which are so commonly found in chronic pulmonary tuberculosis and pleuritis.[21] In pulmonary tuberculosis the skeletal tissues which are supplied by the cervical spinal nerves, particularly the IIIrd and IVth, are affected by this trophic reflex. The musculi, sternocleidomastoideus, scaleni, pectoralis, trapezius, levator anguli scapulae and crus and central tendon of the diaphragm, the skin and subcutaneous tissue supplied by the same segments, areas included in the neck and shoulders down to the IInd rib anteriorly, and the spine of the scapulae posteriorly show trophic changes, as shown in Fig. 53A and B, page 316. In chronic pleuritis, the trophic disturbance is expressed through the thoracic spinal nerves, so the musculi intercostales, the broad muscles of the back, and the skin and subcutaneous tissue over the thorax below the second rib, degenerate. Sometimes the degeneration is general; at other times, it is localized. Only such areas of soft structures are affected as are supplied by neurons whose cell bodies receive stimuli from the afferent neurons from the pleura.

Other examples of the trophic reflex are seen in the degeneration of the lumbar tissue in such chronic inflammations of the kidney as tuberculosis and multiple abscess; in the soft tissues of the abdomen when the gut is the seat of chronic inflammation; or when a chronic peritonitis is present. I, personally, have experienced chronic recurrent pain in two areas of degeneration over the left half of the abdomen which resulted from two attacks of diverticulitis, one in 1927, the other in 1941.

It is in chronic diseases of the lungs and pleura, however, where the trophic reflex is best observed, and where it is of greatest diagnostic worth. Chronic inflammation of the lungs and pleura is suggested at once when localized degeneration of the neck and chest muscles and the skin and subcutaneous tissue over them is observed. Inasmuch as these two viscera cause reflexes in different segments of the cord, the location of the degeneration is of differential value. This is discussed in Chapters XXIII and XXIV.

The sensory neurons in these degenerated areas frequently become hypersensitive and show pain long after all evidence of active disease has disappeared—even years after—so degeneration of the soft somatic structures often becomes of important diagnostic value.

References

1. Pottenger: A Study of the Symptoms of Exophthalmic Goiter, Endocrinology 2: 16, 1918.
2. Carlson, A. J., Boyd, T. E., and Pearcy, J. F.: Studies on the Visceral Sensory Nervous System. XIV. The Reflex Control of the Cardia and Lower Esophagus in Mammals, Arch. Int. Med. 30: 409, 1922.
3. Müller, E. F., and Petersen, W. F.: Klin. Wchnschr. 5: 53.
4. Müller, E. F., Myers, C. N., and Petersen, W. F.: The Nature of Shock Symptoms Occasionally Following Drugs or Vaccines, J. A. M. A. 88: 1128, 1927.
5. Petersen, W. F., and Müller, E. F.: Ztschr. f. d. ges. exper. Med. 54: 415, 1927.
6. Müller, E. F.: Evidence of Nervous Control of Leucocytic Activity by the Involuntary Nervous System, Arch. Int. Med. 38: 268, 1926.
7. Emden, H., and Freundlich, H.: Viol. Verein Hamburg, Feb. 3 and 17, 1925.
8. Pottenger: A New Physical Sign Found in the Presence of Inflammatory Conditions of the Lungs and Pleura, J. A. M. A., March, 1909.
9. Pottenger: Muscle Spasm and Degeneration, St. Louis, 1912, The C. V. Mosby Co.
10. Pottenger: Spasm of the Lumbar Muscles, A Diagnostic Sign in Inflammation of the Kidney, J. A. M. A., March, 1913.
11. Pottenger: Clinical Tuberculosis, St. Louis, 1917, The C. V. Mosby Co., Vol. ii, p. 43.
12. Mackenzie: Symptoms and Their Interpretation, London, 1909, Shaw & Son, p. 68.
13. Crile: Man, An Adaptive Mechanism, New York, 1916, Macmillan Co.
14. Pottenger: Further Observations Upon Rigidity of the Chest Muscles as a Sign of Pulmonary Involvement, Med. Rec., Oct. 23, 1909.
15. Pottenger: Muscle Spasm and Degeneration, St. Louis, 1912, The C. V. Mosby Co.
16. Pottenger: Clinical Tuberculosis, 1917, St. Louis, The C. V. Mosby Co., Vol. i, pp. 399, 412.
17. Dusser de Barenne: Arch. gesammit. Physiol. 166: 145, 1916.
18. De Boer: Centralb. Biochem. u. Phys. 18: 578, 1916.
19. Langley, J. N.: The Autonomic Nervous System, Part I. Cambridge, 1921, W. Heffer and Son, Ltd., pp. 68-80.
20. Hunter, John Irvine: Lectures on the Sympathetic Innervation of Striated Muscle, Brit. M. J. 1: 197, 251, 1925.
21. Pottenger: The Significance of Limited Respiratory Movement and the Visceromotor, Viscerosensory and Viscerotrophic Reflexes, in the Diagnosis of Pulmonary and Pleural Inflammations, J. Tuberc., February, 1919.

CHAPTER XIV

REFLEXES WHOSE AFFERENT IMPULSES COURSE IN THE PARASYMPATHETIC NERVES

DISTRIBUTION OF PARASYMPATHETIC REFLEXES

In order to comprehend parasympathetic reflexes, it is necessary to understand the relationship between various afferent and efferent cranial and bulbar nerves, on the one hand, and afferent and efferent sacral nerves, on the other. As is discussed on page 58 and emphasized in the preceding chapter, there is a very close relationship between the visceral afferent nerves which course with the sympathetic system and the spinal nerves which supply somatic structures. There is also a close reflex relationship between the spinal sensory nerves and the sympathetic motor nerves.

It is necessary to bear in mind that the medulla oblongata is but an expanded section of the spinal cord, and while the relationships are distorted because of the ventricles and other structures which are here formed, nevertheless much the same relationship exists between somatic and visceral neurons which arise in this part of the nervous system as exists between the sympathetic and spinal nerves lower in the cord. The vagus nerve contains both sensory and motor nerves which supply viscera. Afferent stimuli coursing centralward over one division of this nerve are capable of producing reflexes in other divisions of the same nerve; in other cranial motor nerves, those having both vegetative and voluntary functions; and in the sensory portion of the Vth cranial nerve. A great many of the common so-called "functional visceral disturbances," will be recognized as reflexes connected with the parasympathetic system, particularly the vagus. The relationship of the sensory and motor roots in the medulla are shown in Fig. 32.

The relationship between afferent sacral parasympathetics and efferent sacral somatic nerves, on the one hand, and afferent sacral somatic and efferent parasympathetic sacral nerves. on the other

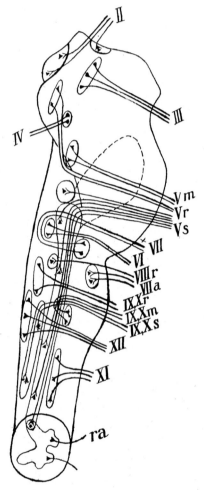

Fig. 32.—The sensory and motor nuclei of the medulla. *m*, motor ; *s*, sensory ; *r*, reflex roots. *VIIa*, nervus cochlearis ; *VIIIr*, nervus vestibularis. The remaining Roman numerals represent corresponding cranial nerves. (Bechterew.)

hand, in the production of reflexes, follows the same laws of segmentation as those followed by the sympathetic and spinal nerves
in the thoracic and upper lumbar segments of the cord.

RELATIONSHIP OF TRIGEMINUS NERVE TO PARASYMPATHETIC REFLEXES

To further explain parasympathetic reflexes which take place in
the internal viscera as a result of afferent impulses which arise in
tissues and organs supplied by the sensory fibers of the Vth cranial
nerve, such as the structures of the eye and the mucous membranes
of the nose and accessory sinuses, it is necessary to bear in mind that
the sensory fibers of the Vth cranial nerve (trigeminus) bear the
same reflex relationship to the motor neurons of the VIIth, IXth,
and Xth cranial nerves as the sensory spinal nerves do to the motor
neurons of the sympathetic system. The sensory somatic neurons
of the Vth cranial nerve also have the property of expressing sensation in response to stimuli which are carried centralward by parasympathetic fibers, particularly the Xth nerve. Many of the headaches which accompany diseases of internal viscera are probably
parasympathetic-sensory reflexes through the Vth cranial nerve. On
this point I desire to quote from Gaskell:[1]

"Similarly, in the mesosomatic region (Fig. 1 [Plate VI in this
text]) the groups of motor cells, known as the facial nucleus and the
nucleus ambiguus, represent the motor neurons of the splanchnic
segmentation, and represent therefore the motor neurons of the muscles of the mesosomatic appendages; they are quite separate from the
nucleus of the abducens, which supplies motor fibers to the only
remaining dorso-ventral muscles, a pair of which originally existed
in each segment, and from the hypoglossal nucleus containing the
motor cells of the longitudinal somatic muscles. These mesosomatic
groups also extend down the cord; the splanchnic group being
represented by the nucleus accessorius or the lateral horn of the
cervical region, which is formed from the lateral cell groups of the
anterior horn; the somatic group by the cells of the anterior horn,
supplying motor fibers to the longitudinal trunk muscles.

"Thus the cells of the motor neurons of the voluntary system, form
two well-defined groups in accordance with the double segmentation
of the striated musculature in the cranial region.

PLATE VI

THE REFLEX PATHS OF THE VOLUNTARY SYSTEM IN THE CRANIAL REGION

The afferent receptor neurons are shown in blue, the connector neurons in black, the efferent excitor neurons in red.

The splanchnic excitor neurons are shown in the lower part of the diagram; the somatic excitor neurons in the upper part. The receptor neurons for both systems all run in the fifth and tenth nerves which are shown in the lower part of the diagram.

The neurons in a vertical line all belong to the same segment, the first six lie in the prosomatic segments, and the remainder in the mesosomatic.

The receptor fibers of the somatic system all run in the fifth nerve, their nuclei lying in the Gasserian ganglion, *G. G.*

The ascending sensory root, *A.S.V.*, supplies the connector neurons of the prosomatic segments of the somatic system. These connector neurons, which lie close against the ascending root, communicate with the excitor neurons of the four segments comprising the nucleus of the third nerve, with the nucleus of the fourth nerve, and with the anterior portion of the nucleus of the sixth nerve in the respective segments. The descending sensory root, *D.S.V.*, communicates with the connector neurons of the mesosomatic segments of the somatic system. The connector neurons connect in the first mesosomatic segment with the more posterior portion of the excitor nucleus of the sixth nerve and the others with the series of nuclei which form the excitor nucleus of the twelfth nerve.

The receptor fibers of the splanchnic system in the prosomatic region all run in the fifth nerve. They form part of the ascending sensory root and connect in each segment with connector neurons which in their turn connect with the nuclei of the descending motor root of the nerve, *D.M.V.* The nuclei of the two posterior segments form the nucleus masticatorius, *N.M.* Some afferent fibers of the fifth nerve probably connect also with the connector neurons of the seventh nerve as shown in the diagram.

The afferent fibers of the mesosomatic segments of the splanchnic system all run in the sensory portion of the tenth nerve, their cells lying in the vagus ganglion, *V. G.*

A small ascending root connects with the connector neurons of the first three segments; the connector neurons in their turn connect with the motor nuclei, the first two of which give origin to the seventh nerve and the third to the ninth nerve.

The descending root, the fasciculus solitarius, *F. S.*, connects with the connector neurons of the remaining segments which lie in the dorsal nucleus of the vagus, *D.N.X.* The motor neurons of these segments form the motor portion of the tenth nerve, the segmental nuclei lying in the nucleus ambiguus, *N.A.* (Gaskell.)

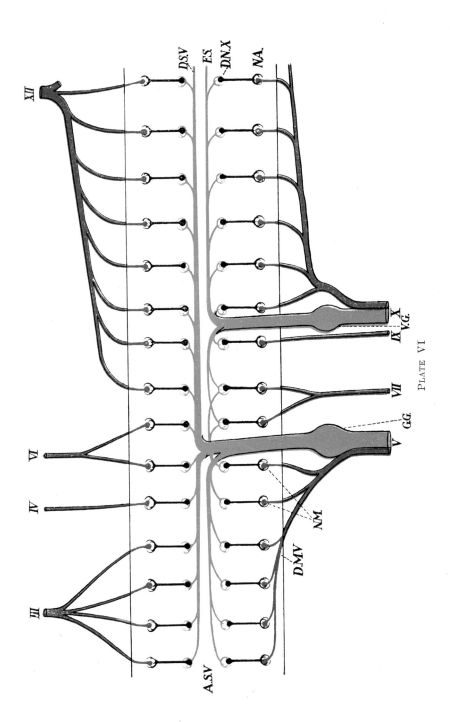

PLATE VI

"On the sensory side (Fig. 1 [Plate VI this text]) there are also two distinct sets of sensory fibers represented in the double segmentation, belonging respectively to the somatic and splanchnic segments. In the prosomatic region the sensory neurons for both segmentations are found in the Gasserian ganglion; but in the mesosomatic region the somatic sensory neurons belong mainly to the trigeminal and were also found in the Gasserian ganglion, while the splanchnic sensory neurons are found in the sensory ganglia on the facial, glosso-pharyngeal, and vagus nerves. So also there must be corresponding connector neurons for these two sets of segments, in order to carry out the primary or segmental reflexes, similar to those in the trunk region. These primary connector neurons are situated in the spinal region in the posterior horns (Fig. 2, A [Plate VII in this text]). We must look for the corresponding cells in the cranial region in two situations corresponding respectively to the posterior horns belonging to the somatic and splanchnic segmentations. The posterior horn cells of the cord are characterized by the presence of the substantia gelatinosa Rolandi close to them, and the characteristic of the descending sensory root of the trigeminal (Fig. 3, A [Plate VIII in this text]) is the presence of the substantia gelatinosa Rolandi along its whole length. In this substance are found cells with which the fibers of this root continuously make connexion, called by Edinger the end nucleus of the 'ascending' root. Such cells clearly correspond to a series of connector nuclei of the same kind as those belonging to the voluntary nervous system in the segments of the spinal cord, and form in my opinion the primary connector neurons of the somatic segmentation. I imagine therefore that, as far as the somatic segmentation is concerned, the primary or segmental reflexes, which must take place in each cranial segment as well as in each spinal one, are effected through these connector neurons, as represented diagrammatically in Fig. 3, A [Plate VIII in this text]. With respect to the splanchnic segmentation (Fig. 3, B [Plate VIII in this text]) in which the motor neurons are found in the nucleus of the facial, nucleus ambiguus and the accessory nucleus, and the sensory neurons in the ganglia on the roots of the corresponding nerves, we must look for the connector neurons in that part of the gray matter of the medulla oblongata which continues into the spinal cord as the posterior horn.

"The posterior horn cells belonging to the vagus segments in the medulla oblongata have become part of the mass of cells in the floor of the fourth ventricle, known as the dorsal nucleus of the vagus, and according to Edinger the sensory roots of the vagus terminate in many of these cells and in their continuation as a cell column close along the 'descending' root of the vagus (the fasciculus solitarius). In fact this group of cells forms the connector neurons belonging to the splanchnic segmentation in exactly the same manner as the corresponding group of cells in connection with the sensory trigeminal fibers form the connector neurons belonging to the somatic segmentation.

"I imagine therefore that, so far as the splanchnic segmentation is concerned, the primary or segmental reflexes, which must take place in each cranial segment as well as in each spinal one, are effected through these connector neurons, as represented diagrammatically in Fig. 3, B [Plate VIII in this text]."

EXAMPLES OF PARASYMPATHETIC REFLEXES

In our clinical experience for a long time we have had our attention called to some of the motor and sensory reflexes whose afferent impulses course through the sympathetic nerves. Particularly have we known the visceromotor reflex in appendicitis, cholelithiasis, peritonitis, and ulcer of the stomach; and the viscerosensory reflex in appendicitis, cholelithiasis, cholecystitis, gastric ulcer, diaphragmatic pleurisy, and angina pectoris. Later we were able to describe both motor and sensory reflexes for the lungs, kidney, and portions of the intestinal canal other than those above named, as well as many others.

With our increased knowledge we are warranted in assuming that every internal viscus having sympathetic fibers is connected with spinal nerves through afferent neurons of the sympathetic system; and that, if these afferent fibers in the viscus are sufficiently irritated by conditions which arise during disease of the viscus, they will produce their own "visceromotor" and "viscerosensory" reflexes; and if the disease becomes chronic, their "viscerotrophic" reflexes.

There is another group of reflexes which, aside from a few very definite instances, such as the slowing of the heart in certain abdominal lesions, are recognized even less, although they are met in every disease of consequence affecting important viscera.[2] I refer to the

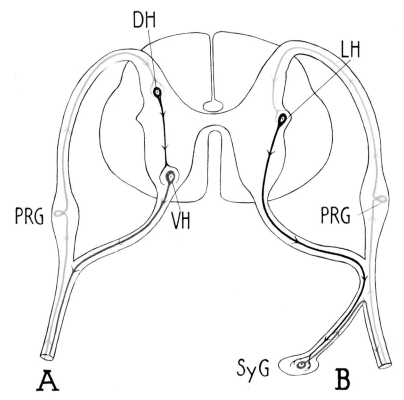

PLATE VII

THE REFLEX PATHS IN THE CORD

(*Green*—Sensory nerve; receptor neuron. *Black*—Connector neuron.
Red—Motor nerve; excitor neuron.)

A. Of the Voluntary System.

    The receptor neurons run in the posterior root, their cells lying in the
posterior root ganglion, *PRG.* The connector neurons lie in the dorsal horn,
DH, and connect with the excitor neurons lying in the ventral horn, *VH,*
whose processes run in the anterior root.

B. Of the Involuntary System.

    The receptor neurons run in the posterior root, their cells lying in the pos-
terior root ganglion, *PRG.* The connector neurons lie in the lateral horn,
LH, their processes running out in the anterior with the excitor neurons
lying in the sympathetic ganglia, *SyG.* The processes of the excitor neurons form the gray ramus communicans and run out in the spinal nerve.

(Gaskell.)

reflexes which take place from one viscus to another through various divisions of the parasympathetic system. This is well illustrated by disturbed motility, as it is frequently observed when some part of the gastrointestinal canal is inflamed. It is often met in appendicitis and cholecystitis. I have frequently observed the same reflexes in clinical pulmonary tuberculosis, also in tuberculous enteritis.

FUNCTIONAL DISTURBANCES AND THE PARASYMPATHETIC REFLEX

Physiologic study of parasympathetic reflexes gives us a basis for explaining innumerable so-called "functional disturbances" in organs other than the one inflamed. This I shall attempt to illustrate fully in the clinical section of this monograph. *As each organ is connected reflexly with superficial structures in the body wall through afferent neurons coursing in the sympathetic system and efferent neurons belonging to the spinal system; also through afferent neurons of the parasympathetic system arising in the midbrain and bulb and in the sacral portion of the cord and mediating respectively with structures supplied by efferent somatic neurons whose cell bodies lie in the midbrain and bulb, on the one hand, and in the sacral segments of the cord, on the other hand; so are organs connected reflexly which are supplied by afferent parasympathetic neurons which mediate with efferent parasympathetic neurons which supply other organs. So each organ when inflamed influences other organs reflexly; and, if the reflex action is sufficiently strong, function is perverted and symptoms on the part of that organ are produced.* Organs and tissues innervated by the Vth, VIIth, IXth, Xth, XIth, and XIIth cranial nerves show many parasympathetic reflexes.

NATURE OF PARASYMPATHETIC REFLEXES

We expect two groups of important reflex symptoms whenever an important thoracic or abdominal organ is involved in a severe inflammatory process: (1) *a group through the sympathetics which express themselves largely as motor, sensory, and trophic reflexes in the skin, subcutaneous tissues, and muscles,* (2), *a group through the parasympathetics which express themselves for the most part as motor, sensory, secretory, and probably later as trophic reflexes in other viscera.* This does not include the reciprocal reflexes which take place in the sacral segments of the cord between afferent parasympathetic neurons and efferent somatic neurons, on the one hand, and the afferent somatic neurons and efferent parasympathetic neurons, on the other hand, nor the many vasomotor changes that result from sympathetic stimulation: nor the many reflexes in the tissues of the head and face which result from parasympathetic stimulation: nor the many reflexes in which both afferent and efferent stimuli course in the sympathetic system; nor those in which the afferent stimuli arise in one component of the vegetative system and the effect is produced in tissues supplied by the other.

There are probably innumerable vasomotor phenomena of a reflex nature which are caused by both afferent and efferent impulses coursing over neurons belonging to the sympathetic system, could we but recognize them. From a theoretical basis we suspect these and cannot help feeling that they account for some of the obscure symptoms which are met with in visceral disease.

In the preceding chapters I referred to the reflexes which take place between the sympathetic and spinal nerves as "visceromotor," "viscerosensory" and "viscerotrophic," following the nomenclature as suggested by Mackenzie for motor and sensory visceral reflexes. It would clarify the discussion if we prefixed the term "sympathetic" to all such reflexes occurring in the soft tissues of the neck, chest, and abdomen, because they all originate from stimuli which course over afferent neurons of the sympathetic system. Likewise we should prefix the word "parasympathetic" to all such reflexes as express themselves in the skin, subcutaneous tissue, and muscles of the face and head, because they all originate from afferent impulses which course over the parasympathetic nerves (vagus); also, to reflexes which arise in the sacral region as a result of mediation with afferent sacral neurons.

The importance of bearing the distinction between sympathetic and parasympathetic reflexes in mind is self-evident, for we also have visceral reflexes arising in the parasympathetic sensory nerves which are of a motor, sensory, and trophic, and still others of a secretory, nature. These are for the most part reflexes which arise in one organ and are expressed in another, and might with greater propriety than those arising in the sympathetics, be called visceromotor, vis-

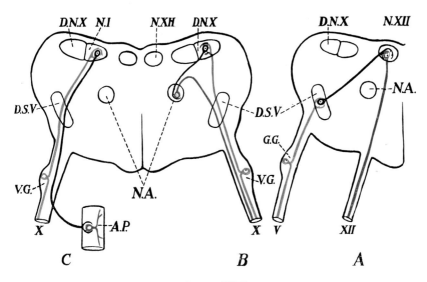

PLATE VIII

THE REFLEX PATHS IN THE BULBAR REGION

(*Green*—Sensory nerve; receptor neuron. *Black*—Connector neuron.
Red—Motor nerve; excitor neuron.)

A. Of the Somatic System.

The afferent neurons run in the fifth nerve, *V*, their cells lying in the
Gasserian ganglion, *GG*. These connect with the connector neurons lying
close against the descending root of the fifth nerve, *DSV*. The connector
neurons in their turn connect with the excitor cells which lie in the nucleus
of the twelfth nerve, *NXII*.

B. Of the Splanchnic System.

The receptor neurons run in the tenth nerve, *X*, with their cells lying in the
ganglion of this nerve, *VG*, and connect with connector neurons which lie
in the dorsal nucleus of the vagus, *DNX*. Processes of the connector cells
connect with the excitor neurons which lie in the nucleus ambiguus, *NA*,
their processes form the motor part of the tenth nerve.

C. Of the Involuntary System.

The receptor neurons run on the tenth nerve, *X*, with their cells in the
ganglion of this nerve, *VG*, and connect with connector neurons which lie in
the nucleus intercalatus of Staderini, *NI*, which forms a part of the dorsal
nucleus of the vagus, *DNX*. The processes of these connector neurons
run out in the vagus nerve, *X*, and finally connect with the excitor neuron
which lies on some peripheral organ; e.g., in the case of the intestine
lying in Auerbach's plexus, *AP*. (Gaskell.)

cerosensory, and viscerotrophic. In order to avoid confusion, however, I shall suggest that they be called: "parasympathetic motor," "parasympathetic sensory," "parasympathetic trophic," and "parasympathetic secretory." It will thus be seen that we have one common reflex arising from parasympathetic afferent stimuli which occurs less often as a result of sympathetic stimuli—a "secretory reflex."

IMPORTANCE OF THE PARASYMPATHETIC TROPHIC REFLEX

The trophic reflex of parasympathetic origin is not as readily recognizable as the trophic reflex of sympathetic origin. Yet its importance must be evident to any one who studies the effect of continuous harmful stimuli upon nerve cells. The parasympathetic trophic reflex probably becomes an important factor in reducing the resistance of the tissues so as to make them receptive for the implantation of causative microorganisms in such diseases as chronic pulmonary tuberculosis. I have suggested[3] as the probable explanation of the fact that a tuberculous infection in the larynx is nearly always secondary to a longtime existing infection of the lung, that it is favored by a continuous reflex stimulation of the laryngeal nerves which supply this organ with trophic as well as motor and secretory impulses. This results in trophic changes in the tissues, causing them to become less resistant. In support of this suggestion, I would cite the commonly recognized fact that the laryngeal lesion is most apt to appear on the side which corresponds to the more chronic and greater inflammatory process in the lungs. I would further call attention to the importance of this parasympathetic trophic reflex in preparing the soil for implantation of bacilli in the intestinal tract. Infection in both the intestine and larynx manifests itself, as a rule, after the disease has existed in the pulmonary tissue for a prolonged period of time. Its existence and peculiarities indicate that it may be a surface infection. Such a surface infection might be facilitated by lowered resistance due to such trophic changes as result from the reflex parasympathetic stimulation. Reflex trophic change probably injures many organs in the course of chronic visceral disease, especially those of the gastrointestinal tract.

COMMON PARASYMPATHETIC SYMPTOMS AND SYNDROMES

Many of the common symptoms which have been looked upon as being of a nervous type, the so-called "functional disorders," will be readily recognized as belonging to this group. Many of the cases of hyperchlorhydria, nausea, hypermotility, spastic colon, bradycardia, asthma, hay fever, epiphora, cough, hoarseness, so-called nasal and nasopharyngeal catarrh, may be due to reflex irritation of the parasympathetic fibers which activate the organ or structures involved, the afferent stimulus coming through the parasympathetics from the same or some other organ or organs. Other types are due to general parasympathetic irritability and are precipitated by either physical or psychic stimuli. In this class are included many phobias of the neuropath, so well described by Dejerine.[4]

The importance of these reflex symptoms may be inferred from the nerves which make up the parasympathetic group of the vegetative system. The system comprises all vegetative fibers in the IIIrd, VIIth, IXth, and Xth cranial nerves, and the pelvic nerve. All smooth muscle structures and all secreting glands supplied by these nerves as well as all structures supplied by the Vth, VIIth, XIth, and XIIth cranial nerves may be affected by parasympathetic reflexes. The closeness with which various organs are bound in reflex relationship seems to vary greatly; so does the direction, in which the reflex travels, vary. There is a close relationship, for example, between the various portions of the gastrointestinal canal; and it would seem from our clinical observation that the reflexes travel almost with equal facility in either direction. Next, there seems to be a close association between the gastrointestinal canal and those organs which belong to it embryologically, the respiratory tract, liver, and pancreas. The heart is also closely bound to all of the above organs. In other words, all organs innervated by the vagus (Xth cranial nerve), are intimately bound together and are capable of readily transmitting reflexes to, and of receiving reflexes from, each other. In case of the eye, the reflex influence on other organs is well established in case of eye strain. Many years ago Gould wrote voluminously on this point; but unfortunately the truths which he uttered were not understood. The eye is also unquestionably influenced by visceral disease, but here the data at hand do not make the point certain. The larynx seems to be influenced more than it influences other organs. These relationships will be made more definite in the clinical portion of this study.

References

1. Gaskell: The Involuntary Nervous System, London, 1916, Longmans, Green & Co., p. 5.
2. Pottenger: Diagnostic Value of the Lung Reflexes in Pulmonary Tuberculosis, California State J. Med. 16: 502, 1918.
3. Pottenger: Clinical Tuberculosis, St. Louis, 1917, The C. V. Mosby Co., Vol. ii, p. 17.
4. Dejerine and Gauckler: The Psychoneuroses and Their Treatment by Psychotherapy, Translated from the French by Smith Ely Jelliffe, Philadelphia, 1915, J. B. Lippincott Co.

CHAPTER XV

SYMPATHETIC AND PARASYMPATHETIC SYNDROMES

As is shown in the chapter dealing with the physiologic activity of the sympathetics and parasympathetics, and again in the discussion of the innervation of each particular organ and system of smooth musculature, the syndromes indicative of sympathetic and parasympathetic stimulation are wholly different.

In studying vegetative syndromes one must not think too narrowly. He must not stop with nerves, but must think in terms of the entire neurocellular mechanism as described in Chapter VII, for the state of the cellular colloids and their content in ions modify nerve action, and secretions from the various endocrine glands influence it. He must also always bear in mind that disturbances in these syndromes may be of psychic origin, and even if of physical origin are subject to modification by psychic states.

SYNDROME OF SYMPATHETIC STIMULATION

If we consider the more important structures of the body, we find that stimulation of the sympathetics, either general or local, is followed by some of the following common symptoms found in disease:

Dilatation of the pupil; protrusion of the eyeball; lessened lacrimal secretion; lessened salivary secretion; lessened mucous secretion in the nose and throat; lessened secretion in the gastrointestinal tract, showing particularly as a hypochlorhydria and retarded digestion; lessened motility in the gastrointestinal tract, showing as a slowness in the peristaltic wave, contraction of sphincters of the gut, and a general relaxation of the intestinal musculature leading to limited dilatation and to the common type of constipation found in the acute infectious diseases; rapid pulse and at times rise of blood pressure, although vasoconstriction in one area is accompanied by compensatory vasodilatation in others; increase in glycogen content of the blood, its being forced from the liver; increase in body temperature due to (1) an increased production of heat resulting from increased chemical action,[1] and (2) decreased elimination due to vasoconstriction in superficial vessels; diminution in the amount

216

of urine; contraction of the ureter; contraction of the uterus; pale skin, goose flesh, and increased sweating. Increased adrenal and thyroid secretion also follow sympathetic stimulation; and this in turn produces symptoms varying in degree according to the amount of extra secretion formed.

SYNDROME OF PARASYMPATHETIC STIMULATION

A preponderance in activity on the part of the parasympathetics produces some or many of the following common symptoms: contraction of the pupil; widening of the eye slits; increased lacrimation; increased secretion of the nasal, oral, and pharyngeal mucous glands, conditions commonly known as catarrh; increased salivary secretion; contraction of the laryngeal muscles such as is found in laryngospasm; increased bronchial secretion such as is found in bronchitis; spasm of the bronchial musculature as found in asthma; hypermotility and hypersecretion of the gastric glands including that of hydrochloric acid; hypersecretion and hypermotility of the intestine, leading to colicky pains and states of either spastic constipation and stasis or diarrhea, depending much on the degree of stimulation and whether the circular or more longitudinal fibers are the recipients of the increased stimulation; irritable bladder; and incontinence of urine and feces. Sweating is also found in conditions which are accompanied by the above group of symptoms, as well as those belonging to the sympathetic syndrome.

SPECIAL SERVICE RENDERED TO THE ORGANISM BY THE SYMPATHETIC AND PARASYMPATHETIC SYSTEMS

The sympathetic and parasympathetic nervous systems have separate and distinct functions to perform for the organism. Various phases of this question have been discussed by Cannon,[2] Crile,[3, 4] Brown,[5] the writer,[6] and others. In this discussion I shall partially follow one of my recent papers.[6] The sympathetic system governs man's defense. It includes, aside from the sympathetic division of the vegetative nervous system, those endocrine glands which are particularly strongly sympathicotropic, the adrenals and thyroid. This is the system which reacts in such conditions as pain, shock, fear, anger, rage, cold, injury, and infections. It protects the individual against outward enemies; prepares him for resistance or flight, and sustains him during the effort. It provides the non-specific defense in case of infection. It is the protective and energy-expending system of the body. It also presides largely over the genital system, although erection of the penis is due to parasympathetic stimulation.

The parasympathetic system, on the other hand, provides sustenance for the individual. It presides over the ingestion and digestion of food; the ejection of the waste from the alimentary canal, and partially regulates respiration. The hypersensitiveness of tissues which follows infection and accompanies antibody formation seems to be associated with the parasympathetic system. Its function is to maintain the organism as an individual. It controls the food preparatory to storing it in the form of potential energy or incorporating it in the tissues, the actual building up process, while the sympathetics control the tearing-down process.

There are also certain products of glands of internal secretion which are parasympathicotropic; among them may be mentioned the internal secretions of the pancreas, and *secretin*, which is produced by the duodenal glands near the pylorus. The intestinal effect of pituitrin is also parasympathicotropic.

Of the two divisions of the vegetative system the sympathetic is the more widely distributed, consequently sympathetic action is more general than parasympathetic. If we conceive of the body as a tube of which the skin and structures allied to it embryologically, make up the outer surface; the gastrointestinal tract and the structures embryologically related to it, the inner surface; and the walls as being filled with vessels; then we are in a position to understand the relative extent of sympathetic and parasympathetic activity. The smooth musculature of the skin, the pilomotors and sweat glands, most of the urogenital structures, and blood vessels of the body are innervated by the sympathetics. The sphincter muscles of the bladder and gastrointestinal canal are activated by the sympathetics and inhibited by the parasympathetics, while action of the muscles and glands of the enteral system is inhibited by the sympathetics. On the other hand, the parasympathetics furnish the appetite and carry on digestion. They augment all of the necessary juices—salivary, gastric, intestinal, pancreatic and biliary—for the digestion of food, and the motor power of the intestine for mixing it with the secretions and propelling and ejecting it from the body.

They also send inhibiting fibers to the sphincters and some fibers to the urogenital system. In conjunction with the voluntary system they control the oxygen supply of the body through respiration, although the amount of oxygen required depends upon the double need for both anabolic and catabolic processes. It might be said that the parasympathetics control the intake, digestion, and assimilation of food, help provide the oxygen for its oxidation, and then hand it over to the sympathetic control for utilization.

The sympathetic system presides largely over the reproductive organs of the animal, and protects him from harm; the parasympathetic system provides nourishment and energy which is stored to be utilized in his behalf in case of need.

This conception of the vegetative nerves and endocrine glands, points to four purposes which they are intended to fulfill; procreation, growth, nourishment, and defense. These are factors of the greatest importance to the organism, when considered in its animal status.

The functions performed by the sympathetic and parasympathetic systems necessarily dovetail somewhat into each other; for both food and oxygen must be carried to the tissues where oxidation takes place, and various waste products resulting from tissue action must be carried to their respective points of elimination by the blood vessels which are sympathetically activated structures.

It might at first thought seem strange that a protective mechanism which provides the individual with the means for escape from, or combat with, an enemy, or for resisting an infection, or for overcoming an injury, should have an inhibitory action upon the functions of the gastrointestinal canal which provides the nourishment which is the basis of the energy used for protection. But if we go way back in the stage of evolution, we find that the life of the individual was short and that a suspension of its digestive activity was of little importance in comparison with its preservation from its enemies. A heroic effort was often immediately necessary, and it was all important that the entire energy of the body be directed toward the supreme task of defense, otherwise the animal would perish.

The parasympathetics have little opportunity to interfere with sympathetic action in the defense program, because their action is so limited in the sympathetically activated structures. They have no connection with the sweat glands and pilomotor muscles, little with the genitourinary system, and act on the circulatory system by inhibiting and slowing the heart and causing vasodilatation. They seem further to play no part in the innervation of the adrenals, pituitary or thyroid, and probably have no control over glycogen when it has once been stored in the tissues for use. So, while the organism is provided with food and oxygen by the parasympathetics, they seem to have no veto upon its use when once provided.

There are stages in the development of animal life in which activities of the organism are correlated only by means of internal secretions, and others in which they are correlated by both internal secretions and nerves of simple and comparatively rudimentary action; as the organism becomes still more complex, however, a complicated central nervous system is developed which is presided over by the will, whose particular function it is to correlate and integrate the function of all parts of the body.

When this stage of development has been reached, vegetative control through the glands of internal secretion and the sympathetic and parasympathetic nerves, is no longer an independent affair. While organisms are still able to carry on body functions, for a time and after a fashion, even though separated from the central nervous system, yet as long as they are connected with it, they are subject to stimuli which are transmitted to it through the central nervous system, and to ideas and emotions which arise in the psychic centers.

It is a long way, developmentally speaking, from the opening and closing of the oscula of the sponge in response to the movements of sea water, or the response of the earthworm, with its simple nervous system, to outward stimuli, to the fine adjustments and responses of man with his well-developed and finely adjusted central nervous system, and his psychic centers. Yet, throughout all this gap the same vegetative functions have been cared for in the same general way. The vegetative nervous system and the glands of internal secretion of man serve him in the same manner, only more elaborately, than they served organisms way down in the scale of evolution.

General Sympathetic Responses

We shall now discuss briefly some of the functions which are performed by these systems.

Defense Against an Enemy. It is now evident that stimuli which affect the human body may be either of physical or psychic origin.

A man sees a source of danger, he is imbued with fear, and decides either to defend himself or make his escape. Whichever course he decides upon he wills to bring the necessary muscles into action. But this decision would be entirely useless if it were not for the vegetative nerves and endocrine glands. Muscles cannot perform work unless they are provided with glycogen and oxygen for its oxidation. Six or eight times as much blood must pass through muscles which are in action as must pass through them when at rest, in order to supply the needed energy. A certain amount of glycogen is stored up in the tissues, particularly the muscles and the liver, ready to be used at any time, but more may be needed so through sympathetic stimulation and increased action on the part of the adrenal medulla, glycogen is forced from the liver ready to be utilized. When the struggle comes, if it is of short duration this stored supply may be sufficient for the purpose; if not, more must be provided not by ingestion and digestion of food but by transforming the body tissues into glycogen. All of this requires oxygen, and the tissues at a given time have only about enough oxygen for their actual needs; so pulmonary ventilation increases from a normal of 5 to 8 liters to 30 or 50 liters per minute; or if the struggle is exceedingly severe, to 100 liters or more per minute. Much of this preparation is accomplished by the vegetative systems.

It may be necessary that this defense be called into action at once. This is accomplished through the centers in the hypothalmus. The emotion of fear and the desire for self-preservation cause psychic impulses to be transmitted to the proper centers in the brain and cord, and, even before the individual moves a muscle in the struggle, impulses are sent by way of the sympathetic centers in the brain through his sympathetic system (nerves, adrenals, and thyroid). As a result of these impulses his heart beats rapidly, carrying more blood to the muscles and brain, the glycogen is forced from the liver so that it can be delivered to the muscles, the blood pressure rises to insure a more rapidly flowing stream, the coagulation power of the blood increases, ready to check the flow of blood in case of injury, his pupils dilate, his hair stands on end, his sweat glands become active in order to eliminate the excess of heat produced in the struggle; at the same time there is an inhibition of action in the gastrointestinal tract so that all energy may be directed for the time being to the brain, heart, and muscles which require all possible energy for the conflict. When the struggle begins, these conditions are maintained as long as is necessary or until the mechanism of defense is exhausted and the individual is overcome. As energy is used up and acids are formed in the blood, they stimulate the respiratory center and cause pulmonary ventilation to keep pace with the demand for oxygen. This last function is the only one of all the important phenomena connected with the struggle against outward foes in which the parasympathetics seem to take any considerable part.

Infections.—So is it in infections; the struggle for the destruction of toxins as it affects vegetative structures is manifested through the sympathetic system—a dry skin, lessened elimination with increased production of heat resulting in a rise of temperature, rapid pulse, increased thyroid and adrenal action, and an inhibitory effect on the gastrointestinal tract as shown in a loss of appetite, and a decrease in secretory and motor power of the stomach and intestines, producing slow digestion and constipation. It is thus seen that those phenomena which are most evident in the normal defense of the organism against infections prior to the production of specific cellular reaction belong to the syndrome of sympathetic action. The phenomena attendant upon the condition of antigen-tissue reaction, however, are recognized as belonging to parasympathetic syndromes.

The combat of infections is also accompanied by psychic stimuli, but what effect these have in starting action in the defensive mechanism we do not know.

It will be appreciated that there is a marked difference between the body's reaction to the severe acute infections and the more chronic and milder ones. In both of these the defense may eventually break down, but in the acute cases we can sometimes study it more readily, where the patient goes into collapse with rapid, inefficient heart muscle, low blood pressure, sweating, and falling temperature. In some severe infections recovery is followed by marked asthenia. This was seen often following influenza during the pandemic of 1918-1920. It is evidence of general nerve injury but particularly of the sympathico-adrenal system. There is a hypo-adrenia, the glands failing to recover quickly from the injury. This same condition of exhaustion of the mechanism of defense is a part of the picture in chronic infections, such as tuberculosis.

Shock.—Shock is another condition which shows marked disturbance of the sympathetics. Shock is favored when the person receiving an injury has his defensive mechanism already depressed by such conditions as fatigue, excitement, exposure, and infection. The condition of the control of the vessels in shock is such that it seems like a sympathetic paralysis. The Rouget cells which contract the capillaries and which are supplied by sympathetic fibers are so injured that the capillaries dilate, their walls become permeable to the plasma, their lumen becomes engorged with corpuscles, blood pressure falls, and the patient dies because he cannot get blood to the heart.

Injury and Asphyxia.—In conditions of injury and asphyxia it is the sympathetic system that bears the brunt of the struggle.

High Blood Pressure.—There is a high blood pressure which is commonly found, particularly in women, which is due to sympathetic stimulation; and it is quite possible that prolonged stimulation of the sympathetics might produce deleterious effects and result in arterial degeneration.

GENERAL PARASYMPATHETIC RESPONSES

Anaphylaxis affords an example of a general stimulation which affects the parasympathetics.[7] Mild anaphylaxis shows the following symptoms: bronchial spasm and increased bronchial secretion, nausea, vomiting, diarrhea, and itching of the skin. Severe anaphylaxis shows increased motility of the intestinal tract with relaxation of the anal sphincter resulting in involuntary discharge of feces; increased activity of the bladder musculature with relaxation of the sphincter, causing incontinence of urine; perspiration; low blood pressure; fall in temperature and collapse. From this we conclude that the symptoms of anaphylaxis, except those of severe anaphylaxis in which the higher centers are predominantly affected, belong to the parasympathetic syndrome.

LOCAL PARASYMPATHETIC SYNDROMES

Local syndromes of parasympathetic stimulation are common such as hay fever, which shows hyperirritability of the Vth and VIIth cranial nerves; asthma, which shows hyperirritability of the pulmonary branches of the vagus; hypermotility and hyperchlorhydria which may be due to hyperirritability of the gastric vagus, and increased motility and secretion in the intestine, and spastic constipation, due to hyperirritability of the sacral innervation of the colon.

It must also be remembered, however, that hyperchlorhydria may be due to a marked stimulation of the sympathetics controlling the pylorus which causes a contraction of the sphincter muscles, thus interfering with the emptying of the acid contents.

ANTAGONISM OF SYMPATHETICS AND PARASYMPATHETICS

In order to make the antagonistic action of the sympathetics and parasympathetics in the important structures of the body more apparent, I append Table III on page 225.

Some antagonistic action of the sympathetics and parasympathetics is evident in all structures where these two components of the vegetative system meet. Their normal action maintains physiologic equilibrium in these structures the same as antagonistic nerves maintain balance in the voluntary system. This has been described by Meltzer,[8] as the *law of contrary innervation*.

We find disturbances in the working of this law in many common clinical syndromes, such as pylorospasm, cholecystitis, inflammation of the biliary passages, patulous ileocecal valve, and other sphincter disturbances. We also see it in hay fever, asthma, and the various changes in motility and secretory activity of the gastrointestinal tract. This contrary innervation is taken into consideration in the treatment of constipation by enemas of magnesium sulfate; in transduodenal lavage in cholecystitis and diseases of the biliary passages in which the same salt is used, and in the employment of adrenalin in the treatment of asthma.

DEGENERATIONS

From our study of reflexes, it can be seen that a reflex action continuing for a prolonged period of time, has deleterious influences upon the nerve cells which are active in producing the reflex. In the skeletal tissues this is shown in such trophic reflexes as I have described in connection with inflammation of the lung and kidney. We may also infer that the same trophic change occurs in the internal viscera when nerve cells or the nerve components of a reflex are kept in continuous action over a long time. This I have mentioned on page 379 in connection with the reflexes in the larynx and in the intestinal tract causing degenerative changes and preparing the soil for

TABLE III

EFFECT OF STIMULATION OF SYMPATHETICS AND PARASYMPATHETICS ON IMPORTANT VISCERA

	SYMPATHETICS	PARASYMPATHETICS
Pilomotor muscles	Stimulate	No effect
Musculature of sweat glands	Contract muscle, and force out sweat from glands	No effect
Sweat glands	Stimulate	Possibly stimulate
Vasomotor system	Contract or dilate according to strength of stimulus	No general effect, dilate in few structures
Heart	Increase rapidity	Slow
Eye	Dilate pupil Contract Müllerian muscle	Contract pupil
Lacrimal glands	Decrease secretion	Increase secretion
Mucous membrane of nose and throat	Decrease secretion	Increase secretion
Respiratory tract	Relax musculature and decrease secretion	Stimulate musculature Increase secretion
Salivary glands	Decrease watery component of secretion	Stimulate watery components of secretion
Stomach	Decrease motility and secretion, including hydrochloric acid. Controls blood vessels	Increase motility and secretions, including hydrochloric acid
Intestinal tract	Relax musculature and decrease secretion and control blood vessels	Stimulate musculature and increase secretion
Sphincters	Contract	Relax
Ureter	Contract	No effect
Uterus	Contract	No effect
Bladder	Contract muscles of trigone and sphincters. Relax musculature of body	Relax musculature of trigone and sphincters, stimulate musculature of body

the implantation of the tubercle bacillus. It seems to me perfectly rational to consider that degenerative processes result from interference with the normal trophic stimuli to a part or organ.

With this in mind I would suggest the possibility of the thickening of the arterial walls, such as we see in amyloid degeneration in the presence of chronic suppuration, and in general arterial degeneration, being at least partly due to toxins acting through sympathetic neurons on body cells. It is not at all improbable that continuous action of toxins upon sympathetic nerve cells would result in injury to them and in trophic changes in the tissues which they supply; and inasmuch as the entire vascular system is innervated by the sympathetics, it is probable that such changes should result partly by direct injury to the cells, causing disturbance in their ionic content, and partly from toxins acting upon the vasomotor neurons. This suggestion would include amyloid and atheromatous degeneration as a part of the sympathetic syndrome. I do not make these assertions as facts, but only for the purpose of stimulating thought along this line.

References

1. Pottenger, F. M.: Fever, a Part of the Syndrome of Toxemia, New York M. J., August, 1916.
2. Cannon, W. B.: Bodily Changes in Fear, Anger, Pain and Rage, New York, 1915, D. Appleton Co.
3. Crile, Geo. W.: The Origin and Nature of the Emotions, Philadelphia, 1915, W. B. Saunders Co.
4. Crile, Geo. W.: Man an Adaptive Mechanism, New York, 1916, Macmillan Co.
5. Brown, Langdon W.: The Sympathetic Nervous System in Disease, London, 1920, Frowde and Hodder & Stoughton, Ltd.
6. Pottenger, F. M.: The Special Services Rendered to the Human Organism by the Sympathetic and Parasympathetic Systems, Including Both Nerves and Glands of Internal Secretion, Endocrinology 5: 205, 1921.
7. Pottenger, F. M.: Relationship of the Syndrome of Anaphylaxis to the Vegetative Nervous System, New York M. J., August, 1917.
8. Meltzer, J.: Disturbances of the Law of Contrary Innervation as a Pathogenetic Factor in the Diseases of the Bile Ducts and Gall Bladder, Am. J. M. Sc. 153: 469, 1917.

PART III

INNERVATION OF IMPORTANT VISCERA WITH A CLINICAL STUDY OF THE MORE IMPORTANT VISCEROGENIC REFLEXES

CHAPTER XVI

INTRODUCTORY

In Parts I and II of this monograph, I have endeavored to lay a foundation for the application of known physiologic facts pertaining to vegetative or visceral neurology, to the everyday practice of clinical medicine. While I realize fully that all clinical phenomena expressed in tissues supplied by visceral nerves cannot be satisfactorily explained alone by the study of their relationship to the nerves which supply these tissues, yet such a study will greatly simplify many of our clinical pictures, facilitating diagnosis and aiding in the application of therapeutic measures. One should bear in mind that action of the visceral nerves is secondary to the normal rhythmical action of body cells; that nerve action both influences and is influenced by the colloids of the cells and the ions which they hold in chemical and physical union; and further that the visceral nerves are supplemented in action by various chemical substances, such as the normal products of the endocrine glands, and disturbed by pathologic substances resulting from normal and abnormal metabolic activity. One should also remember that the action of visceral nerves is markedly influenced by the physical and psychic states of the individual; that the relative irritability of the sympathetic and parasympathetic systems differs in different individuals, and that this irritability may even vary in different organs of the same individual. These are some of the chief variants which account for the variability of symptoms in diseases of internal viscera. One must not expect visceral neurology to explain every visceral action, since it is only one factor in physiologic control. If only it is accepted for what it will explain, it will well repay

most careful study. When vitamins are understood we will have
forged another link in the chain responsible for variability in physiologic activity.

GROUPING OF STRUCTURES SUPPLIED BY THE
VEGETATIVE NERVES

Before proceeding to the clinical discussion, it is well to call to mind
the classification of the tissues supplied by the vegetative nerves
according to their embryologic formation; for this makes clear their
innervation. This has been discussed in Part I, page 46, but I shall
repeat the salient facts here. A study of Plate I, page 46, will
acquaint one with the innervation of the principal structures supplied by the vegetative nerves.

1. **The Subdermal Musculature.**—A group known as the subdermal musculature, because it is situated immediately under the skin,
consists of the pilomotor muscles and the muscles of the sweat glands.
It is innervated by the sympathetic nerves alone.

2. **The Vasodermal Musculature.**—The smooth muscle in the walls
of the blood vessels and the muscle of the heart, which Gaskell believes is related to the skin muscles, hence calls the vasodermal musculature is activated throughout by the sympathetics. In the heart
there are also parasympathetic fibers which inhibit action. Some
parasympathetic dilator fibers exist in the vessels in certain structures, as noted on page 361.

3. **The Sphincter System.**—The sphincter system of the genitourinary and gastrointestinal tracts is supposed by Gaskell to have
originally been a part of the dermal musculature which has slipped
into the gut in the same way that the parasympathetically controlled
musculature has gained access to the heart. The sphincters are
activated by the sympathetics and receive inhibitory fibers from the
parasympathetics, the opposite from the other structures in the
gastrointestinal canal.

4. **The Urogenitodermal System.**—This system consists of most
of the structures belonging to the genitourinary system. It is formed
from the segmental duct. Its name, as suggested by Gaskell, shows
its relationship to the dermal tissues. This system is activated by
sympathetic nerves; and many of the structures belonging to it are
void of parasympathetic fibers, as described in Chapter XXXIII.

5. **The Enteral System.**—While those tissues in Groups 1 to 4 belong to the dermal system, are formed from the ectoderm, and are activated by the sympathetics, the enteral system is derived from the endoderm and activated by the parasympathetics. The former consist of musculature which lies immediately under or originated immediately under the skin; the latter, of a musculature lying or originating immediately under the surface of the gut. The enteral system is activated by the parasympathetics and receives inhibitory fibers from the sympathetics. This system consists of the entire gastrointestinal canal, with the exception of the sphincters, the respiratory system, liver, pancreas, and bladder, except the trigone.

6. **Smooth Musculature of the Head.**—There is a group of muscles belonging to the structures of the *eye* which receives its innervation from the vegetative system, and which is important because of its reflex relationship with other nerves; likewise the lacrimal gland and certain structures in the nose, accessory sinuses, pharynx and larynx, which are vegetative in character.

Since the enteral system is of great interest from the standpoint of the study of reflexes, and can be used to advantage in illustrating the physiologic antagonism which exists between the two systems when supplying the same structures, I shall discuss it first.

THE ENTERAL SYSTEM

It will be noticed that structures belonging to the enteral system are innervated by both parasympathetics and sympathetics. I mention parasympathetics first because all of these structures except the sphincters are activated by the parasympathetics. Muscular contractions are produced by stimulation of the parasympathetics, and the activity of the secretory glands is increased by stimulating them. Stimulation of the sympathetics, on the other hand, produces an inhibitory effect upon all muscles except the sphincters, and upon the secreting glands. When the active force in the parasympathetic system balances the inhibitory force of the opposing sympathetic system, normal physiologic action is maintained; but when either system overcomes the antagonizing force of the other, then the physiologic balance is disturbed and symptoms result.

PLATE IX

THE DISTRIBUTION OF THE CONNECTOR FIBERS (BLACK) AND EXCITOR NEURONS (RED) OF THE BULBOSACRAL OR ENTERAL SYSTEM

The vagus nerve, *V.*, contains the connector nerves of the excitor neurons of the main viscera as far as the ileocolic sphincter, *I.C.S.* The motor neurons all lie on the organs themselves.

The pelvic nerve, *P.*, contains the connector fibers of the sacral outflow and connects with peripheral excitor neurons on the large intestine and bladder.

The vagus nerve thus contains the connector neurons to the motor cells of the heart, *H.*, which have to do with the slow wavelike contraction which is only found in certain tortoises, such as *Emys Europea*, and does not appear to exist in higher forms. The vagus nerve also contains the connector fibers to the excitor neurons on the bronchi in the lung, *Lu.*, and also the connector fibers to the excitor neurons on the gall bladder and bile duct lying on the liver, *Li.;* it also contains the connector fibers to the excitor neurons of the esophagus, *OE.;* the stomach, *St.;* and the small intestine, *S.I.;* which here lie between the muscle layers in Auerbach's plexus.

The pelvic nerve, *P.*, which arises from the three sacral roots, *S.* 1, 2, and 3, contains the connector fibers to the excitor neurons of the large intestine, *L.I.*, and also the connector fibers of the excitor neurons of the body of the bladder, *B.*

(Gaskell.)

Many physiologists describe the vagus as supplying the colon as far as the descending portion as mentioned in the text.

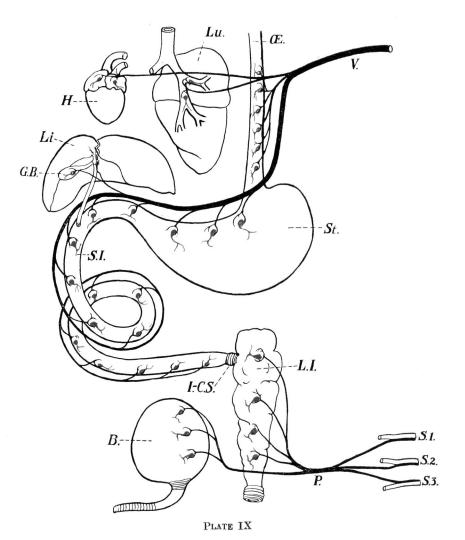

PLATE IX

It will be further noticed that nearly all structures belonging to this system, the esophagus, stomach, small intestine (ascending and transverse colon, according to some authors), liver, pancreas, pharynx, larynx, and lungs, are activated by the vagus nerve. It will be noticed further that the enteral system is the system which is *particularly* activated by the vagus nerve. The only other real important structure which is cared for by it is the heart. Because of this close relationship in innervation, there is a very close reciprocal relationship between the various organs making up the enteral system; also between them and the heart, and a disturbance in one of these organs causes reflex disturbance in other organs supplied by the vagus nerve more readily than it does in organs supplied by the parasympathetic fibers coursing in other nerves. This relationship is shown in Plate IX from Gaskell.

The interrelationship of the various portions of the enteral system, also the interrelationship of the organs of the enteral system and the heart, may be inferred from Fig. 34, page 242. This shows the vagus extending from the esophagus to the descending colon, although Gaskell teaches that the vagus supplies the small intestine only and the sacral nerve the entire colon. In all organs of the enteral system supplied by the vagus, it furnishes the activating fibers. In each organ, however, with possibly the exception of the esophagus and the cardiac end of the stomach (Carlson shows sympathetic fibers here also), it is opposed in its action by inhibiting fibers which belong to the sympathetic system, shown in the figure as arising from the semilunar, aorticorenal, and superior mesenteric ganglia. It will also be noted that the descending colon, rectum, and bladder are cared for by the lumbar and sacral portions of the cord. The parasympathetic fibers arising in the sacral portion of the cord, and coursing in the pelvic nerve, activate these structures, except the trigone of the bladder. The sympathetic fibers whose cells lie in the superior mesenteric ganglion and which are connected with the central nervous system by connector neurons arising in the lumbar portion of the cord, furnish the inhibiting fibers to the descending colon, rectum, and body of the bladder.

The preganglionic fibers from the thoracic and upper lumbar segments of the cord representing the sympathetic system are indicated by solid lines, which end in ganglia. These are the "con-

PLATE X

THE CONNECTOR FIBERS AND EXCITOR NEURONS OF THE SPHINCTER SYSTEM OF
INVOLUNTARY MUSCLES

The upper figure shows their arrangement in the mammal and the lower figure their arrangement in the reptile (young crocodile).

The connector neurons form two groups: an upper group rising from the last dorsal and first three lumbar roots and all running to the superior mesenteric ganglion, *S.M.G.*, which lies at the point of origin of the celiac axis, *C.A.*, from the aorta, *Ao.*, and a lower group rising from the second to fifth lumbar roots, L.2 to L.5, and running to the inferior mesenteric ganglion, *I.M.G.*, which is situated just above the bifurcation of the aorta.

The excitor neurons from the superior mesenteric ganglion innervate the ileocolic sphincter muscle, *I.C.S.*, which lies at the junction of the small intestine, *S.I.* and the large intestine, *L.I.*

The excitor neurons in the inferior mesenteric ganglion supply in the mammal the internal sphincter muscle, *I. Sp.*, the sphincter of the bladder, *S.B.*, and the muscle of the urethra, *M.U.*

The cavities of the bladder and large intestine are here entirely separate, but have been evolved from the arrangement shown in the lower figure. In the reptile the cloaca is composed of a continuous tube divided into three portions. 1. The coprodeum, *C.D.*, which corresponds to the large intestine of the mammal. 2. The urodeum, *U.D.*, which corresponds to the bladder cavity of the mammal and into which the ureters, *Ur.*, open, and 3, the proctodeum, *P.D.*, which is the hindmost chamber. A muscle corresponding to the internal sphincter of the mammal separates the coprodeum from the urodeum, and is innervated by excitor neurons in the inferior mesenteric ganglion. A similar muscle also separates the urodeum from the proctodeum; this corresponds with the sphincter muscle of the bladder and the muscles of the urethra, and is innervated by excitor neurons in the inferior mesenteric ganglion.　　　　　　　　　　　　　　　　　　　　　　　(Gaskell.)

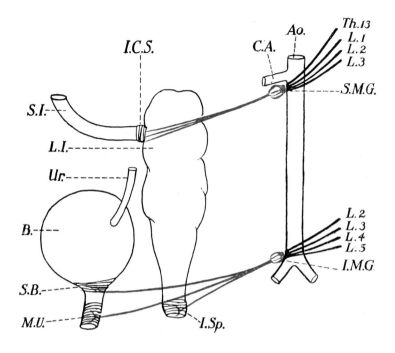

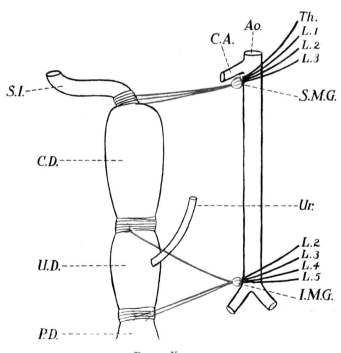

PLATE X

nector neurons'' of Gaskell. They are medullated. They end in motor cells in the ganglia; and the fibers emerging, represented in the figure by broken lines, are nonmedullated. These latter are the true sympathetic motor fibers.

The fibers of the pelvic and vagus nerves, representing the parasympathetic system, are indicated by solid black lines ending in cells which lie within the organ innervated. No ganglia interrupt the parasympathetic fibers until they enter the organ supplied.

The genuine parasympathetic system of nerves for the enteral system lies within the walls of the organ. In the intestine it is represented by the plexuses of Auerbach and Meissner. The motor cells to the bronchi, liver, pancreas, colon, and body of the bladder also lie within their walls. The vagus and pelvic nerves which connect visceral motor cells with the medulla and sacral portion of the cord are not in reality motor nerves but only ''connectors.''

The innervation of the sphincters is not illustrated in this figure. The ileocecal, rectal, vesical and probably pyloric sphincters are activated by the sympathetic fibers and receive their inhibiting fibers from the vagus and the pelvic nerve, as shown in Plate X.

The symptoms which arise on the part of the organs belonging to this system may be grouped either around the sympathetic nerves or the parasympathetic nerves. This holds for both organic and so-called ''functional diseases.'' An alteration in either muscular action or secretory function may result from disturbance in nerve equilibrium. This may result either from a disease in the organ itself, disturbance of nerve equilibrium through central stimulation, or a reflex from some other organ which is connected with it through its nerve supply. It is important for the clinician to learn to think in terms of visceral neurology.

As a matter of differential diagnosis between organic and functional disturbances, it may be stated broadly that a motor or secretory disturbance in any important organ belonging to the enteral system, unless accompanied by sensory, motor, or trophic reflexes in the skeletal structures, is not due to inflammatory organic change in the tissues of that organ. The only exception to this statement which occurs to me would be found in conditions where the amount of tissue involved in the organic change would be so small in extent or the irritation so mild in degree that the reflex action would involve so few efferent neurons as not to be detected; or it might be the stimulation would be so mild as not to be able to overcome the resistance in the nerve path and make itself evident in reflex action. It cannot be assumed, however, that all disturbances accompanied by pain are due to organic changes in the viscera, as, for example, pylorospasm is sometimes accompanied by pain and yet not due to organic change; so are colicky pains often present which are not dependent upon organic lesions in the gut.

We can now approach the various reflexes which manifest themselves upon the part of the stomach, intestines, liver, pancreas, respiratory tract, and bladder in a manner to make them intelligible. In these reflexes we often have a definite help in differentiating organic from inorganic lesions. One must not forget, however, that there are many complex conditions which arise, and many complex causes of symptoms which must be considered. One is safe in assuming, in discussing diseases of the viscera belonging to the enteral system, that a parasympathetic stimulation tends to produce reflexes in both the organ in question and in other organs, and that they are prone to show most markedly in other organs belonging to the same (enteral) system. Stimulation, arising in sympathetically innervated tissues, may cause reflex action in other viscera, but action less easy of recognition than that in tissues supplied by spinal nerves; for this produces visceromotor, viscerosensory, and viscerotrophic reflexes, which are expressed in the skeletal tissues, as described in Chapter XIII.

Parasympathetic reflexes will be recognized as an increased muscular and secretory activity throughout the enteral system with the exception of the sphincters which will be relaxed.

Sympathetic reflexes will show as spasm of the skeletal muscles, as in appendicitis, gall bladder diseases, and pulmonary inflammation; as pain in the skin areas and muscles which are reflexly bound to the organ inflamed through the spinal sensory nerves; and in atrophy of the soft tissues when the inflammation of the viscus becomes chronic.

Familiarity with these reflexes must not cause the observer to think that the study of symptoms is so simple a matter as tracing the paths of reflexes. Sometimes a reflex action which should be expected will not be present; at other times action will be due to causes which are not reflex in character. When an important organ is inflamed, *there is a tendency* for the afferent impulses to cause reflex action although such action may not materialize in symptoms which are recognizable, because of compensation or inhibition; and, under certain circumstances, action, the reverse of that which is expected, may occur.

TISSUES ACTIVATED BY THE SYMPATHETICS

It is evident that the tissues belonging to Groups 1, 2, 3 and 4, will not present the number of reflexes that are found in the *enteral system*. The fact that some of the structures, such as the blood vessels, pilomotor muscles, and muscles of the sweat glands, consist of small amounts of muscle widely scattered, makes it impossible to recognize reflexes arising in them. The nerves supplying these tissues arise from segments widely scattered, hence there is not sufficient concentration of afferent stimuli to produce recognizable reflexes. In other structures, notably those of the urogenitodermal system, the organs again become more important, have an innervation which comes from a more limited area of the cord, hence show reflexes on the part of the sympathetic and spinal nerves in much the same manner as the organs of the enteral system.

THE EYE

The eye is in relationship with both sympathetics and parasympathetics, and shows symptoms dependent upon both sets of nerves.

THE LACRIMAL GLANDS AND VEGETATIVE FIBERS IN THE NOSE, ACCESSORY SINUSES, PHARYNX, AND LARYNX

These structures are important from both the standpoint of originating impulses which cause reflexes in the viscera, such as asthma resulting from nasal and sinus affections; and as being tissues which are influenced reflexly by stimuli arising in other viscera, such as cough and hoarseness produced by stimuli originating in the pulmonary and pleural tissue and the increase in nasal and pharyngeal secretion (catarrh) caused by stimuli arising in the lung and gastrointestinal tract.

In my description of the various organs and systems, I shall make no attempt to exhaust the number of reflexes that may occur, but only to describe those which are most evident, and try to make plain the paths through which they travel.   Those dealing with the respiratory system will be found more complete than the other systems, because my opportunities for observation have been greater in this field.

The clinical discussion of each organ will be preceded by a brief description of its innervation, for I believe that this will increase the interest in the anatomic and physiologic aspects of the subject, as well as add to the clearness of the discussion.

CHAPTER XVII

THE ESOPHAGUS

I. INNERVATION OF THE ESOPHAGUS

The upper third of the esophagus is composed of striated muscles. The lower two-thirds is composed of unstriated and is innervated by the vegetative system.

Swallowing is a reflex act. It is partly voluntary and partly involuntary. The esophagus is composed of both circular and longitudinal fibers. The sensory fibers in the soft palate (trigeminal) are the starting point for the swallowing reflex. Stimulation of the glossopharyngeal inhibits swallowing; central stimulation of either the superior or recurrent laryngeal promotes it. The most important part in the act of swallowing as carried on in the esophagus, is performed by the recurrent laryngeal nerve which sends four branches to the esophagus. The esophagus, like the other parts of the gastrointestinal canal, possesses ganglia of its own, which form plexuses on the surface of the smooth muscle, instead of between the layers as in other parts of the intestinal tract. Fig. 33 shows the innervation of the muscles of deglutition.

It is generally taught that no sympathetic fibers go to the esophagus, but that nerve tonus is maintained by both activating and inhibiting fibers belonging to the vagus. Carlson and Luckhardt[1, 2] have shown, however, that the lower portion of the esophagus is provided with sympathetic fibers. This agrees with clinical experience. The sympathetic innervation seems to arise from the Vth to Xth thoracic segments, the same as that for the stomach.

The movement of the bolus in the esophagus is performed by a reflex excited either from the pharynx or from the pharyngeal wall. The latter causes a relaxation of the muscular fibers below and a contraction of those above. This we know as the law of the intestines.

II. THE ESOPHAGUS: CLINICAL CONSIDERATION

When passing through the esophagus, food excites a reflex which causes the muscular tone of the stomach to relax. Hurst[3] describes the relationship of this reflex to the sensation of fullness, either in normal or in dilated stomachs.

The tonus of the stomach remains fairly constant no matter whether it contains little or much food. This tonus is probably influenced only through the vagus in the cardiac end of the stomach, while in the pyloric portions it is affected through the activity of both the vagus and sympathetic nerves. Pressure in the stomach calls forth a sensation of fullness.

The esophageal reflex performs a very important function. Each time that a bolus of food goes through the esophagus, an impulse is sent to the stomach musculature through the vagus, which, while maintaining an adequate degree of tonus, enlarges the stomach cavity to the extent necessary to receive the additional food. A sensation of fullness indicates that the muscles are taut and gives the individual the feeling of satiety. The esophageal reflex then is one the purpose of which is to prepare the stomach for the incoming food. This action is exerted upon the cardiac end of the stomach where the vagus alone or at least largely controls the muscle tonus.

The esophagus furnishes one common sensory reflex, that of head or brow ache which accompanies the rapid eating of very cold substances, such as ice, ice cream, and water ices. Hurst[4] accounts for this as being a referred pain in which the afferent sensory impulse courses from the lower end of the esophagus through the vagus and the efferent impulse passes out over the sensory fibers of the Vth nerve. This relationship is evidence of the fact that the vagus and the sensory portion of the Vth cranial nerve have the same relationship to each other as the sympathetics and the spinal sensory nerves.

Stricture of the esophagus may be dilated with little pain; and cancer of this organ is often comparatively painless. These clinical facts may be taken as proof of the paucity of afferent sympathetic fibers in the esophageal wall. The fact that some pain is present which is reflected to the lower third of the sternum, however, indicates that there is not a total absence of afferent nerves, but that a few stray fibers are distributed to this organ. From the location of the pain over the lower third of the sternum, we infer that such fibers probably arise from the same areas in the cord as those which supply the stomach; viz., segments Vth to Xth. In harmony with sensory reflexes in other portions of the intestinal canal, afferent sympathetic fibers arising from these segments would carry impulses back to the cord and transmit them to sensory spinal nerves from the Vth to the Xth, but particularly the upper ones, which would transfer the pain to the periphery, in this case to the area over the lower portion of the sternum. In the case of cancer of the esophagus, the details of which were recently given me by a friend, the patient suffered from pain in the upper left chest and down the inner aspect of the arm. This is further evidence of the probability

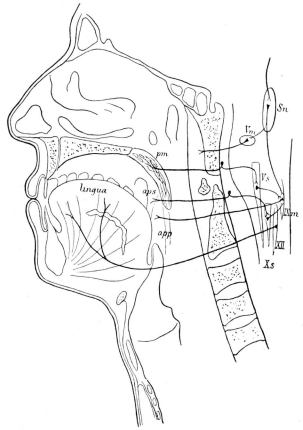

Fig. 33.—Showing the innervation of the muscles of deglutition. *Sn*, substantia nigra; *Vm*, motor center of trigeminus; *Vs*, sensory root of trigeminus; *IXm*, motor center of glossopharyngeus; *XII*, center of hypoglossus; *Xs*, sensory center of the vagus; *pm*, soft palate; *aps*, arcus palatoglossus; *app*, arcus palatopharyngeus. (Bechterew.)

of the esophagus having afferent sympathetic fibers, and further indicates that they are able to form sensory reflexes with nerves arising from the upper thoracic segments of the cord since this pain occurred in the same area as that from cardiac affections. To account for this pain being expressed in the sensory nerves arising from the upper thoracic segments, we must think of the possibility of the reflex spreading on account of the strength of the stimulus, according to the law found on page 53.

References

1. Carlson, A. J., and Luckhardt, A. B.:   Studies on the Visceral Sensory Nervous System.   X. The Vagus Control of the Esophagus, Am. J. Physiol. 57: 299-335, 1921.
2. Carlson, A. J.:   Studies on the Visceral Sensory Nervous System.   XIII. The Innervation of the Cardia and the Lower End of the Esophagus in Mammals, Am. J. Physiol. 61: 14, 1922.
3. Hurst, Arthur F.:   The Sensibility of the Alimentary Canal, Oxford Medical Publications, 1911, pp. 20-31.
4. Hurst: Loc. cit., p. 52.

CHAPTER XVIII

THE STOMACH

I. INNERVATION OF THE STOMACH

The stomach is a part of the great enteral system of the body, which comprises the entire gastrointestinal tract and all structures which are embryologically derived from it, such as the lower respiratory system, the liver, pancreas, and part of the genitourinary system. Its innervation is shown in Fig. 34, also in Plate IX from Gaskell, page 230.

The gastrointestinal tract offers a splendid opportunity for studying the antagonistic action of the sympathetics and parasympathetics. That definite reaction will not always follow stimulation of tissues by either component of the vegetative system is evident from the fact that the content of the cells in electrolytes differs and the electric conductivity and the pH of the tissues differ under conditions of activity and rest, and also under conditions of health and disease. This is especially evident if we consider the fact that sympathetic reaction is closely bound up with calcium and with a low pH of the tissues and the parasympathetics with potassium and sodium and a high pH of the tissues.

The innervation of all of these tissues is alike in that stimulation of the parasympathetics under ordinary conditions of physiologic stability will cause activation of the musculature with the exception of the sphincters; while stimulation of the sympathetics under similar conditions produces inhibition of muscular action, with the exception of the sphincters which they activate, and the possible exception of the cardiac end of the stomach and esophagus. It has been generally taught that there is no sympathetic innervation to the cardiac end of the stomach and esophagus, but clinical observation and Carlson's work both indicate its presence. An equilibrium of action is maintained when the excitability of the parasympathetics and that of the sympathetics equal each other, or when the excessive excitability in the one is still short of overcoming the excitability of the other.

241

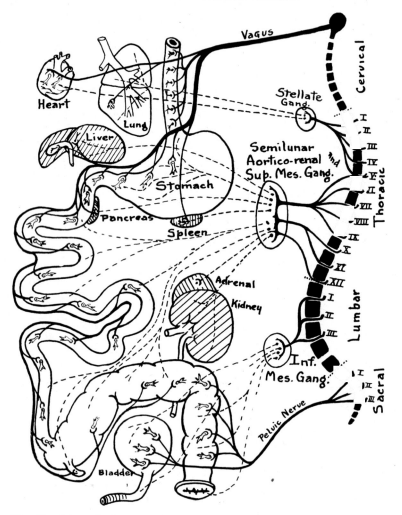

Fig. 34.—Schematic illustration of the double innervation of the heart and enteral system.

The vagus and pelvic nerves are represented by solid black lines with the ganglia in the walls of the organs themselves. These furnish parasympathetic fibers to all of the organs of the enteral system.

The black lines running from the thoracic and upper lumbar segments of the cord to the ganglia represent connector neurons of the sympathetic system; the broken lines running from the ganglia to the organs illustrate the nonmedullated fibers which furnish the sympathetic nerve supply to the various organs. All organs here represented, with the exception of the adrenal gland and the ileocecal, vesical, and anal sphincters, are activated by the parasympathetics and receive inhibitory fibers from the sympathetics. These latter are activated by the sympathetics, and with the exception of the adrenal gland, receive inhibitory fibers from the parasympathetics.

The vagus is shown in the drawing to innervate the ascending and transverse colon, although Gaskell teaches that these are innervated by the pelvic nerve.

Parasympathetics.—The stomach receives its motor fibers from the vagus, the principal nerve of the parasympathetic system. Stimulation of the vagus has a tendency to produce two distinct actions: 1, an increased tone in or a contraction of the musculature of the stomach; 2, increased activity of the acid glands of the stomach. Abnormally increased vagus stimulation results in hypermotility, and an increase of hydrochloric acid and water.

The motor cells which supply the stomach lie in the walls of the organ itself, while the connector neurons run as medullated fibers from the visceral nucleus of the vagus to connect with them after entering the organ.

The fibers of the vagus supply the entire stomach, pylorus to cardia, and the lower two-thirds of the esophagus.

Sympathetics.—The sympathetic nonmedullated fibers going to the stomach have their motor cells in the celiac ganglion the same as those to the liver and spleen. They pass to the stomach through the celiac plexus. The medullated connector fibers which run from the spinal cord arise from the Vth to the IXth (or even XIIth according to some authors) thoracic segments. While these are the same segments which supply the small intestine, we assume that the upper segments, particularly, supply the stomach; and the lower ones the intestine; because the afferent fibers and the connector neurons for given viscera emerge in the same white rami and the reflex pains from the two are reflected in this order. See Fig. 27, page 179.

Sympathetic fibers are distributed freely to the pyloric end of the stomach. It has usually been taught that there are no sympathetic fibers in the cardia, but Carlson[1] and Bickel[2] maintain that both activating and inhibitory fibers for the cardia course in both the sympathetics and vagus.

The sympathetics have the property of inhibiting motility and secretion of water and hydrochloric acid, and stimulating the secretion of enzymes according to Bickel. These effects are well shown in cases of severe toxemia and also in states of extreme emotion. A sympathetic inhibiting reflex, causing relaxation of the stomach musculature, also may be produced by stimuli arising in any other portion of the alimentary canal from the esophagus to the colon; also in other organs which mediate with the gastric sympathetics.

Digestive Control Both Nervous and Chemical.—The control of digestion is partly chemical and partly nervous. Hunger is due to a particular contraction of the stomach brought about through stimulation of the vagus (parasympathetic). Hunger calls for food which may, either psychically, or mechanically, through its presence, start the secretion of gastric juice. When once acid appears in the stomach, it passes the pylorus and stimulates the secretion of *secretin* which is the chemical substance which stimulates further production of gastric secretion and the production of pancreatic secretion.

When digestion once starts, it can continue to its finish probably without further stimulation of the vagus nerve. Secretin and the plexus of nerves (Auerbach's and Meissner's) lying in the walls of the gut are sufficient. But it must be understood that the digestive process at no time is independent of stimuli which travel over the parasympathetics and sympathetics; on the other hand, these systems, when stimulated, carry activating and inhibiting impulses which greatly affect the normal tonus of the stomach, and the digestive process.

II. THE STOMACH: CLINICAL CONSIDERATION

The stomach is an organ which has been very much misunderstood in clinical medicine. It is influenced by many pathologic conditions within the body. While it is not subject to many diseases of a truly organic nature, there is scarcely a disease or an emotion that does not produce effects in the stomach. This is especially evident because of its position at the beginning of the gastrointestinal tract and its function. It is not only a reservoir for food, but it is an organ in which a very important step in digestion takes place. Many symptoms on the part of the stomach are explainable as stimulation of either the sympathetics or the vagus (parasympathetics), and may be profitably studied from this viewpoint. The cause may lie within the organ itself, or in organs or structures far removed. It is closely bound in innervation and in function with other portions of the digestive system.

The musculature of the intestinal tract may be reflexly activated through the parasympathetics and inhibited through the sympathetics by impulses arising in many organs, but particularly in other portions of the alimentary tract and in the lung, liver, pancreas, and body of the bladder, which are related to it embryologically. This accounts for the absence of hunger in many people who are constipated, the impulses arising from the stimulation of the sigmoid and rectum by the fecal mass.

If clinicians would familiarize themselves with those conditions within the body which produce general sympathetic stimulation, such as toxemia, fear, anger, and pain; and parasympathetic stimulation, such as is caused by anaphylaxis and other tissue-antigen reactions; and the psychic states and endocrine disturbances as they affect different individuals; and recognize the organs which particularly bring the stomach into reflex relationship with them through the vegetative nerves, they would have the foundation for explaining functional disorders which constitute a great percentage of gastric disturbances. If they would study the visceromotor and viscerosensory reflexes which result from afferent impulses coming from the stomach through the sympathetic system and which are transferred to the skeletal structures through the spinal nerves, they would have at their command localizing symptoms which are fairly definite.

If we study gastric symptoms from the standpoint of visceral neurology, we can approach such conditions as nausea, vomiting, hypochlorhydria, hyperchlorhydria, hypomotility, hypermotility, pylorospasm, and dilatation of the stomach, in a manner which makes many of them intelligible which would otherwise be inexplicable; and also in a manner which will often point the way for their relief.

Psychic Influence on Digestion.—All functional disturbances in digestive organs cannot be looked upon as being of reflex origin. There are conditions, such as psychic states, toxemia, anaphylaxis, and endocrine imbalance which by acting, either through the sympathetics or parasympathetics, or upon the cells themselves, also disturb physiologic activity. The effect of psychic states upon the secretion of saliva and the gastric juice and the inhibitory action of toxins upon these secretions as met in acute infectious diseases, will illustrate this point.

The digestive tube is susceptible to influences of many kinds. Scarcely can an impulse arise in any part or organ of the body, whether it be in the nature of pleasing or harmful emotions, normal or deleterious products resulting from metabolism, impulses arising from normal or pathologic processes in organs, or stimuli acting upon the sensory nerves of the body, without affecting the enteral system.

The improvement of digestion which accompanies joy and happiness has long been known; therefore, the habit of having the company of friends at meals, and making them occasions of joy is rational. The reverse of this is equally true. The person who goes to the table in an unhappy and discontented state of mind, or when in a fit of anger, rarely has perfect digestion. Such individuals by their gloom and their often self-inflicted psychic load may do more to depress their appetites and prevent digestion than any diseases from which they may be suffering. Such harmful psychic states, too, counteract the effects of remedial measures, no matter how accurately they may be suited to the patient's needs.

Digestion also depends upon habit. We become accustomed to eating our meals at certain hours and unconsciously time our appetites and digestion accordingly. Either advancing or delaying the mealtime often makes its impress not only on the sharpness of the appetite and the enjoyment of the food, but also upon the efficiency of digestion.

Under many conditions people lose their appetites. In chronic disease this often becomes quite serious. One of the most serious factors to be overcome under such conditions is the feeling on the part of the patient that "he cannot eat"; that "he has no desire for food." This often becomes a serious barrier to appetite and may continue to exist long after the condition which was responsible for it has passed away. It is to be explained on the basis of the inhibition of a conditioned reflex, which previously had been established, the nature of which has been described by Pavlov.[3]

At stated intervals food is set before one and he eats. The eating of the food is natural. It is an unconditioned reflex. The time of eating, however, is a conditioned reflex, and after being repeated sufficiently often, it becomes established as a habit; and, as the set time approaches, impulses are set going in the cortex which are transmitted to the alimentary tract, causing hunger.

Those factors which are associated with the taking of food, such as the time of the meal, the setting up of the table, the announcing of the meal, and the appearance of food on the table, all make definite and individual impressions, which are associated in the cortex of the brain with eating. So all or any one of them may act as a stimulus to the cortex which responds by sending impulses to the nerve centers which preside over the mechanism responsible for hunger and digestion, and immediately appetite appears and gastric juice is secreted. If anything interferes with the eating of the meal and the interference is repeated sufficiently often, then the factors associated with the taking of food no longer arouse appetite and gastric secretions.

Since harmful and depressing emotions express themselves primarily through the sympathetic component of the vegetative system, they relax the musculature of the entire gastrointestinal canal and depress the secretion of its glands, and so inhibit appetite and digestion.

Emotional or physical stimuli may disturb the equilibrium of the gastrointestinal tract by disturbing the balance in any of the normal controls; the ion balance in the cells, particularly the K and Ca balance, the hormone balance, and finally the vegetative nerve balance.

One can readily see how a physiologic equilibrium might exist and yet be at its best so delicate, so near toppling over, that it would be disturbed on the slightest provocation. This is the condition that we meet often in the clinic in the nervously and psychically unstable. This is well illustrated in constitutional vagotonia where a slight stimulus to the parasympathetic neurons—one that would not affect a stable equilibrium—is followed by symptoms of parasympathetic overbalance in the tissues, producing such syndromes as hay fever, asthma, spastic colon, nasopharyngeal catarrh, and bronchitis.

Gastric Visceromotor Reflex.—The visceromotor reflex (Fig. 35) from the stomach is well known to clinicians. The stomach receives its sympathetic nerve supply from the semilunar ganglion which is connected with the spinal cord by connector fibers arising from the Vth to the IXth thoracic segments. Afferent impulses, going back to the cord as a result of diseased conditions in the stomach, are transferred most readily to the spinal nerves arising in the same segments (Vth to IXth), but particularly to those of the VIth and VIIth.

The gastric visceromotor reflex manifests itself in the upper portion of the rectus abdominis muscle. This muscle takes its innervation from the intercostal nerves arising from the thoracic segments, Vth to XIIth. That portion of the muscle which is particularly affected in the reflex is the upper portion of the left rectus, which is supplied by the VIth and VIIth spinal thoracic nerves. It will thus be seen that while the stomach is supplied by sensory neurons whose cell

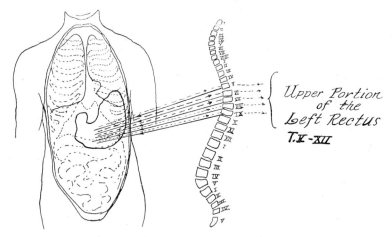

Fig. 35.—Showing the gastric visceromotor reflex.
Lines connecting the stomach with the thoracic segments of the cord from Vth to IXth represent sympathetic nerves. Solid lines represent the sympathetic nerves supplying the stomach. Broken lines represent afferents of the sympathetic system which carry impulses to the cord. Broken lines in the other side of the cord represent corresponding spinal nerves which receive the impulses from the sensory sympathetic nerves and transmit them to the muscles shown, producing the gastric visceromotor reflex. The broken lines running from the stomach to the VIth and VIIth segments of the cord are heavier, indicating that these are the principal paths of the impulse.

bodies lie in the ganglia on the posterior roots of all thoracic segments from the Vth to the IXth, the path of least resistance is in the neurons of the VIth and VIIth segments; consequently, structures innervated by the VIth and VIIth thoracic nerves are most likely to show the gastric reflex. When the impulse is exceedingly strong, however, as it may be when the organ is severely inflamed, the reflex may affect any of the segments, in the wider area.

Gastric Viscerosensory Reflex.—A viscerosensory reflex from the stomach usually shows itself on the left side in the epigastric region and often in the back as shown in Fig. 36A and B in those skin areas which are supplied by the VIth and VIIth thoracic nerves. Sometimes the pain is also felt in other segments, either higher or lower than these, depending considerably upon the severity of the stimula-

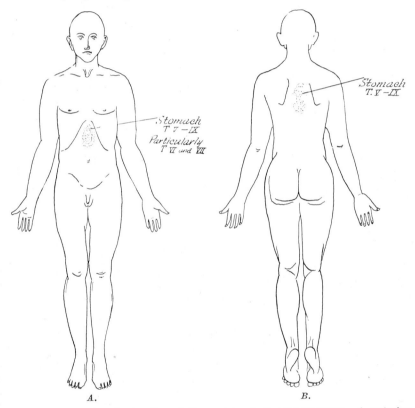

A.   B.

Fig. 36.—Showing the location of the gastric viscerosensory reflex. *A*, anterior view ; *B*, posterior view.

While the stomach is connected by afferents of the sympathetic system with the Vth to IXth segments of the cord, pain is expressed particularly in the VIth and VIIth sensory zones anteriorly. Posteriorly, pain is felt at times over the entire group of segment from Vth to IXth in the median line or to the left of it.

tion. Widespread pain is particularly felt in the lower intercostals when the stomach is markedly distended with gas. The natural stimulus of the sensory nerves of hollow viscera is distention of the muscular coat.

Hurst[4] opposes the theory as suggested by Mackenzie that visceral pain does not exist in the organ involved, and believes that the viscera show both a distinctly visceral and a referred or somatic pain expressed reflexly through the spinal nerves.

It will be noticed that both the viscerosensory and visceromotor reflexes from the stomach show in the same structures as those from the pancreas as described in Chapter XXI.

Gastric Parasympathetic Reflexes.—As gastric parasympathetic reflexes we understand disturbances in the stomach the stimuli for which arise in other tissues; or reflexes in other tissues the stimuli for which arise in the stomach. The impulses causing these reflexes course at least one way, usually both, over parasympathetic fibers, producing increased tone or contraction of the muscles and increased secretory activity in the glands. The gastric parasympathetic reflexes are particularly marked in other organs belonging to the enteral system and less marked in other tissues supplied by the parasympathetics. When the stomach wall is inflamed, as by ulcer, we should expect increased tonus in the muscle coat of the stomach itself, and hypermotility in the intestines beyond. We should also expect a reflexly increased secretion in the stomach, intestines, and probably in the liver and pancreas, which are also closely connected with it. Hurst considers that peristalsis results from the stimulation of the hydrochloric acid. While it may be so, the vagus nerve when stimulated also causes increased secretion, and increased muscular activity. It does not seem probable that the motility should depend wholly on the acid content and be independent of nerve (vagus) influences. The evidence is sufficient to show that vagus stimulation produces peristalsis both under normal and pathologic conditions.

As a parasympathetic motor reflex, we now and then find a bradycardia, the efferent impulses traveling through the cardiac branches of the vagus nerve.

The increased flow of saliva and rhinopharyngeal secretion which now and then are observed in gastric diseases may be of reflex origin, the afferent impulse being carried by the vagus and the efferent coursing in the VIIth and IXth cranial nerves. These effects may also be of central origin.

The Manner in Which the Stomach Is Reflexly Influenced by Other Organs.—The stomach shows parasympathetic motor and parasympathetic secretory reflexes as a result of irritation in many other organs. Hyperchlorhydria is associated with hypersecretion of the watery elements of the gastric juice, and with a heightened activity of the gastric muscle or with a spastic pylorus which delays emptying. Carlson[5] finds an increased secretion only.

HYPERMOTILITY.—Hypermotility is not uncommonly noticed in cases of severe eye strain. The afferent impulses are probably transferred centralward through the sensory fibers of the Vth (trigeminus) nerve while the efferent impulses are carried through the motor fibers of the gastric vagus.

The writer has had ample opportunity to test this reflex, having always suffered from eye strain. Overuse of the eyes has always been followed by nausea, motor and secretory changes in the gastrointestinal tract and headache.

Hypermotility is commonly found in gall bladder diseases, pancreatitis, and appendicitis, particularly in the chronic forms, and in chronic inflammations of the intestines, such as tuberculous infiltration and ulceration and diverticulitis. In such cases the afferent impulses are carried centralward through the respective sensory fibers of the vagus and are transmitted to the stomach through the motor neurons of the gastric vagus.

Hypermotility is frequently found associated with asthma and hay fever. Whether it is due to a reflex stimulation, the efferent impulse traveling centralward in the sensory fibers of the pulmonary branches of the vagus in case of asthma, and in the sensory fibers of the nasal branch of the Vth cranial nerve in hay fever, and being transferred to the gastric motor neurons; or whether it is part of a general condition in which the excitability of the nerve cells in the parasympathetics seems to predominate (vagotonia) is not quite clear from its clinical manifestations. The latter, however, seems the more probable.

Pulmonary tuberculosis, prior to the stage of wasting, is commonly accompanied by hypermotility and hyperchlorhydria, the path of the reflex being the one just mentioned in connection with asthma. This condition, together with other evidences of parasympathetic stimulation in the gastrointestinal tract, as described in Chapter XXIII, is often so accentuated in early tuberculosis that the patient has his attention centered on the gastrointestinal tract instead of on the lungs.

Common causes of reflex hypermotility are chronic appendicitis, gall bladder inflammation, pulmonary tuberculosis, and eye strain.

HYPERCHLORHYDRIA.—The parasympathetic secretory reflex, as shown in hypersecretion of hydrochloric acid and water is often present and manifests itself under much the same conditions as increased muscular tonus and hypermotility.

HYPOMOTILITY.—Hypomotility is frequently found accompanying both acute and chronic toxemia. Under such circumstances the sympathetic nervous system is stimulated centrally, and the functions of not only the stomach, but also of the entire gastrointestinal tract are inhibited because of a preponderance of sympathetic over vagus action. This is frequently prevented, however, by there being at the same time a marked reflex parasympathetic stimulation resulting from inflammation of some important viscus which is capable of maintaining the normal nerve equilibrium or even of overbalancing the action of the sympathetics, such as was mentioned in connection with pulmonary tuberculosis above. Hypochlorhydria might result from a destruction of the gastric glands as a result of certain degenerative changes in the stomach wall. Hypomotility also may result from degeneration of the muscle coat of the stomach. Both are present during such states of chronic toxemia as accompany active tuberculosis, as mentioned above.

DILATATION OF THE STOMACH.—Under normal conditions the stomach is prepared for the reception of a bolus of food by a reflex originating in the esophagus as described in the preceding chapter. A feeling of fullness, such as that which marks the satisfaction of hunger, results from a distention of the gastric muscle. In cases of dilatation of the stomach, the appetite as a rule is poor, partly because the esophageal reflex, in preparing the stomach for the reception of a bolus of food attempts to relax muscles of the stomach which are already more or less relaxed. This is an explanation for the common symptom of fullness and inability to take food noted by patients suffering from a dilatation of this organ.

NAUSEA AND VOMITING.—Nausea and vomiting are indicative of a reversal of normal peristalsis. In many instances they seem to be due to vagus (parasympathetic) reflexes. They may be precipitated through the centers of sight or smell, and often result from disease within the stomach and intestines. They are common accompaniments of gall bladder disease, other diseases of the liver, pancreatitis, appendicitis, and such diseases of the intestines as tuberculosis, all of which have a tendency to block motility above the seat of inflammation. They also occur in inflammatory conditions of the kidney and ureter, testicle, ovary and uterus. Both may result from eye strain. They are commonly found in pulmonary tuberculosis, particularly at the time when necrosis and caseation are taking place. When lung tissue is breaking down with the absorption of toxins, the patient is at times markedly nauseated. Nausea is also found in affections of the heart muscle accompanied by dilatation. Nausea is commonly accompanied by a parasympathetic secretory reflex manifested through the efferent motor fibers of the VIIth and IXth cranial nerves. This shows itself in increased salivation, and at times in increased secretion of the nasal mucous membrane; and, if the nausea is severe and accompanied by vomiting, lacrimation may also be present.

CARDIOSPASM.—Carlson[1] has shown that the cardia is innervated by both sympathetics and the vagus of the parasympathetic system, and that cardiospasm may be caused through efferent fibers belonging to both of these systems. Cardiospasm may be present accompanying diseases of the gall bladder, appendix, lungs, and urinary bladder, or, in fact, any of the more important internal viscera. If both sympathetic and parasympathetic stimulation may cause cardiospasm, this represents a departure from the ordinary rule that one component of the vegetative system activates and the other inhibits action in structures which are supplied by both systems, but the fact may be dependent on the electrolytic content of pyloric cells, which varies with different states of activity. The other alternative is that the action is transposed from one system to the other. This does occur at times when the cells of the system stimulated become markedly hypersensitive (Sollmann[6]).

The presence of purely sympathetic reflexes, those which both arise and are expressed in the gastrointestinal canal, and, in the production of which, both afferent and efferent impulses course over the sympathetic system must always be looked for in clinical practice.

No doubt this type of reflex is responsible for many of the inhibitions of motility in the stomach; for, as Pearcy and van Liere[7] have shown, stimuli arising in any portion of the canal from the esophagus to the rectum may cause inhibition in any other segment. This probably is a frequent cause of the lack of appetite which is commonly noted in those habitually constipated.

References

1. Carlson, A. J., Boyd, T. E., and Pearcy, J. F.: Studies on Visceral Sensory Nervous System. XIV. The Reflex Control of the Cardia and Lower Esophagus, Arch. Int. Med. 30: 409, 1922.
2. Bickel, A.: Der experimentelle Beweis für das Vorkommen inneren Hungers, Klin. Wchnschr. 4: 538. Quoted by Kuntz, Albert, The Autonomic Nervous System, Philadelphia, 1929, Lea & Febiger, p. 216.
3. Pavlov, I. P.: Conditioned Reflexes, London, 1927, Oxford University Press.
4. Hurst, Arthur F.: The Sensibility of the Alimentary Canal, London, 1911, Oxford University Press, Chapter 6.
5. Carlson, A. J.: The Secretion of Gastric Juice in Health and Disease, Physiol. Rev. 3: 1, 1923.
6. Sollmann, Torald: The Pharmacology of the Autonomic System, Physiol. Rev. 2: 479, 1922.
7. Pearcy, J. Frank, and van Liere, E. J.: Studies in the Visceral Nervous System. Reflexes from the Colon. Reflexes to the Stomach, Am. J. Physiol. 78: 64, 1926.

CHAPTER XIX

THE INTESTINAL TRACT

I. INNERVATION OF THE INTESTINAL TRACT

1. **Innervation of the Small Intestine.**—The small intestine is the place where alimentary digestion is completed and absorption begins. It is a very important organ, and the health of the individual is either conserved or impaired according to what occurs to the ingesta while passing through it and the colon. This in turn depends largely upon secretion and motility.

Like the stomach, it is supplied by both parasympathetic and sympathetic nerves: the former, activating; the latter, inhibiting action, except in case of the sphincters which are activated by the sympathetics and inhibited by the parasympathetics. The innervation of the intestinal tract is shown in Plate IX, page 230, and in Fig. 27, page 179.

PARASYMPATHETICS.—The parasympathetic neurons which innervate the small intestine have their motor cells in the plexuses of Auerbach and Meissner, which lie in the intestinal walls. The motor cells in these plexuses are connected with the central nervous system through connector neurons from the vagus.

When the vagus is stimulated, these neurons are activated and tend to increase peristaltic action and the secretion of the intestinal glands.

The gastrointestinal tract, in fact, all vegetative structures, possesses a degree of independence of the central nervous system, the power to function residing in the cells of the structure, as emphasized by Alvarez.[1] These cells, however, are not independent of nervous influence, but are intimately influenced by the plexuses of Auerbach and Meissner as shown by Parker[2] and are stimulated to action from without by the parasympathetics. Possibly effects are produced through these plexuses which spread far from the point of stimulation.

SYMPATHETICS.—The sympathetic fibers to the small intestine arise from motor cells in the superior mesenteric ganglion which receive their connector fibers through the greater splanchnic nerve, which is formed by fibers arising in the Vth to IXth thoracic segments. The same ganglion also supplies vasoconstrictor nerves to the vessels of the small intestine. The fact that the reflex pain from the intestine manifests itself in the umbilical region, while that from the stomach is in the epigastrium, warrants the conclusion that the intestine receives its principal afferent fibers from segments of the cord lower than those of the stomach.

When the greater splanchnic is stimulated, the muscular coat of the intestine is relaxed, the activity of the secreting glands is depressed, and the blood vessels are either constricted or dilated according to the degree and character of the stimulation.

The intestinal mucosa also produces chemical substances (hormones) which influence both secretion and peristalsis, as *secretin* produced in the pyloric end of the duodenum. So does the chemical and physical state of the cell determine what reaction will take place. Then, too, action will depend upon the state of nutrition.

The action of the splanchnics, according to Bechterew,[3] varies according to the condition of the blood. If the circulation stagnates and the splanchnic vessels become filled with a markedly venous blood, then stimulation of the splanchnic nerves causes increased peristalsis, the reverse of that which normally follows. The explanation is that CO_2 in the blood in some manner reverses or transfers what would ordinarily be a sympathetic action and causes a parasympathetic action instead. This reversibility has been studied by many investigators and deserves to be borne in mind when interpreting unusual and unexpected clinical reactions. (See Chapter VII.)

2. **The Innervation of the Colon and Rectum.**—Like other portions of the alimentary canal, the colon receives its nerve supply from both the parasympathetics and sympathetics, as shown in Plate I, page 46, and Plate IX, page 230, and also in Fig. 34, page 242.

PARASYMPATHETICS.—The parasympathetic fibers to the colon and rectum, as above mentioned, may be from two sources: the ascending portion, and probably as far as the descending colon are supplied by connector fibers from the vagus through the plexus solaris, and the remaining portion of the colon proper, the sigmoid and rectum, receive their connector fibers from the sacral portion of the cord through the pelvic nerve (*nervus erigens*) and plexus hemorrhoidalis.

Schmidt[4] has recently shown that cutting the vagi causes degeneration of the large intestine as far as the descending colon. Cutting the sacral nerves shows degeneration of the entire colon but less pronounced in the ascending and transverse portions. This seems to correct some of the confusion which has heretofore existed and indicates that the ascending and transverse colon only, are innervated by the vagus, while the entire colon is innervated by the sacral nerve.

The motor cells for these structures, like those higher up in the gastrointestinal canal, lie on or in the walls of the gut. The rectal reflexes occur largely through the sacral nerves and manifest them-

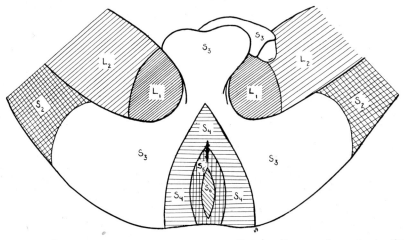

Fig. 37.—Showing the cutaneous areas supplied by the sacral nerves in the perineal region. (After Dejerine.)
Reflexes in these areas are very common from those organs supplied by the pelvic nerve.

selves in the areas shown in Fig. 37, but may appear in any structures innervated by segments higher in the cord.

Stimulation of the pelvic nerve causes both a contraction of the muscles of the colon and also an increase in its glandular activity.

SYMPATHETICS.—Sympathetic connector fibers for the colon come through the lower thoracic and upper lumbar segments of the cord. Those which supply the cecum, appendix, ascending and transverse colon, find their motor cells in the superior mesenteric ganglion, while those which supply the descending colon, sigmoid, and rectum are in the inferior mesenteric ganglion. The nerves for the descending colon probably arise from the left half of the cord, for reflexes caused by inflammation involving this portion of the colon and the sigmoid are expressed on the left side of the body.

As in other portions of the canal, sympathetic stimulation relaxes the musculature (except the internal anal sphincter which it activates) ; lessens the secretory activity of the glands and produces vasoconstriction or vasodilatation according to the character of the stimulus or the condition of activity in the cells.

3. **The Innervation of the Sphincters.**—In the innervation of the gastrointestinal tract, the parasympathetics are the activating nerves for both the smooth musculature and secretory glands, while the sympathetics are the inhibitory nerves. This holds true, with the exception of the sphincter muscles, for all parts of the digestive tract, and those structures formed from it, such as the respiratory tract, the liver and pancreas, and part of the genitourinary tract.

The sphincter system is not an intimate part of the general muscular system of the gut. Gaskell[5] considers that it probably represents a part of the dermal musculature ; and indicates that probably muscles innervated by both sympathetics and parasympathetics originally extended from the stomach to the anus, but with the elongation of the gut the sympathetically innervated muscles have been left in certain areas to act as sphincters. While, throughout the intestinal musculature, exclusive of the sphincters, the parasympathetics activate and the sympathetics inhibit; in case of the sphincters the sympathetics activate and the parasympathetics inhibit.

SYMPATHETICS.—The sympathetic nonmedullated fibers which supply the sphincters arise from two ganglia. Those for the pylorus and ileocecal sphincters arise from the superior mesenteric ganglion, the connector fibers originating in the Vth to IXth thoracic and the XIth thoracic to the IIIrd lumbar, respectively, and those for the internal anal sphincter arise from the inferior mesenteric ganglion, their connector fibers coming from the IInd and IIIrd lumbar segments. The sphincter system is shown in Plate X from Gaskell, page 232.

The sphincter of the bladder and the musculature of the urethra are also activated by nonmedullated fibers whose motor cells lie in the inferior mesenteric ganglion and which are connected with the spinal cord by connector fibers from the IInd to IVth lumbar segments. The urethra belongs, embryologically, to the sphincter system.

There is some doubt about the innervation of the pylorus. It is most reasonable, however, that it should follow the rule of the other sphincters. The law of "contrary innervation" alone will satisfy the conditions which are met in the clinic. It is rational that its innervation should be the opposite of the stomach and duodenum, organs which it serves. The cardia, according to Carlson[6] is activated by both sympathetics and vagus and both can be responsible for cardiospasm as previously mentioned.

PARASYMPATHETICS.—Parasympathetic innervation of the cardia, pylorus, and ileocecal sphincters is through the vagus (Xth cranial nerve). For the ileocecal sphincter (and probably for the pylorus)

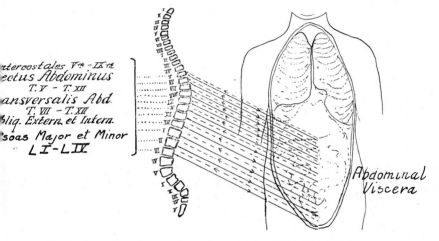

Fig. 38.—Paths of the visceromotor reflexes of the abdominal viscera.

Lines connecting the abdominal viscera with thoracic segments from Vth to XIIth, and lumbar segments from Ist to IIIrd, represent sympathetic nerves. Solid lines represent the sympathetic nerves supplying the viscera. Broken lines represent afferent nerves of the sympathetic system which carry impulses to the cord. Dotted lines on other side of cord represent corresponding spinal nerves which receive the impulses from the afferent sympathetic system and transmit them to the muscles shown, producing the visceromotor reflexes of the various abdominal organs.

This gives opportunity for many reflexes, as may be inferred from Fig. 22, p. 155. First, the stomach, liver, and pancreas, supplied by the Vth to IXth thoracic segments, the principal reflex in VIth and VIIth segments; second, small intestine, innervation thoracic segments Vth to IXth, principal reflex in VIIIth and IXth; third, colon, innervated from IXth thoracic to IIIrd lumbar, principal reflex in Xth, XIth, and XIIth thoracic segments; fourth, kidney, innervated by Xth thoracic to Ist lumbar, principal reflex in XIth and XIIth thoracic, and Ist lumbar.

the motor cells which give origin to the inhibitory fibers lie in Auerbach's plexus within the gut. Stimulation of the parasympathetics as a rule inhibits the sympathetic activity and relaxes the sphincter. In case of the cardia, however, this seems different as quoted above.

Parasympathetic innervation of the internal anal sphincter arises through connector fibers from the sacral portion of the cord and passes peripheralward through the pelvic nerve to meet motor cells lying upon the rectal wall in the rectal plexus. Stimulation of these antagonizes the sympathetics in their activation of the sphincter muscle and relaxes it.

The sphincters of the bladder and the urethra belong to this same group but will be considered in connection with the genitourinary structures in Chapter XXXIII.

II. THE INTESTINAL TRACT: CLINICAL CONSIDERATION

Sympathetic Reflexes

Intestinal Visceromotor Reflex.—The intestinal tract, from the stomach to the rectum receives sympathetic fibers from the lower seven thoracic and upper three lumbar segments of the cord. Apparently, judging from the clinical manifestations of pain and the motor reflexes, there is from above downward a progressive innervation in the gut from the stomach to the anus, as mentioned on pages 156 and 178 and illustrated by Figs. 22 and 27.

While the visceromotor reflex from the stomach manifests itself in a spasm of the upper portion of the left rectus, that of the small intestines and ascending colon, so far as we have been able to determine in such cases as tuberculous ulceration, expresses itself on the right side of the body in spasm of the external and internal oblique and the transverse abdominal muscles innervated by the intercostals VIIth to XIIth. The appendix shows a motor reflex in the transverse abdominal, the oblique and psoas. (See Fig. 39, page 262.)

In this connection we must also mention the diaphragm reflex described by Sale,[7] in the presence of inflammation of abdominal organs, particularly the appendix and gall bladder. The efferent components of these reflexes are the lower intercostal nerves which supply the lower intercostal muscles, the abdominal muscles and the costal portion of the diaphragm. In case of the gall bladder there is also a reflex to be reckoned with which takes place through the phrenics and affects the crus and central tendon of the diaphragm. The abdominal diaphragm reflex differs from the pulmonary diaphragm reflex in that the latter as it is best known is produced through the phrenics, while the former is produced through both the intercostals and phrenics. The stomach, small intestines, upper portion of the colon, liver and pancreas receive their sympathetic innervation from the Vth to XIIth thoracic segments. Afferent stimuli from these organs are transmitted to these same segments for producing reflex action. The nerves arising from the lower thoracic segments of the cord, innervate: first, the lower intercostal muscles; second, *the costal portion of the diaphragm;* and, third, a portion of the muscles of the abdominal wall. The liver, pancreas, stomach, adrenals, and upper pole of the kidney also are in reflex relationship with the crus and central tendon of the diaphragm through the afferent fibers of the phrenic which supply them. Therefore, inflammation of abdominal viscera which are connected reflexly with the lower intercostal nerves or with the phrenics, may produce a diaphragmatic motor reflex which causes a lessening of the respiratory movements of this muscle. For a further description of the diaphragm reflex, see also Figs. 48 and 50, pages 298 and 309.

Intestinal Viscerosensory Reflex.—The viscerosensory reflex from the gastrointestinal tract shows itself in pain as a rule in or near the midline of the body, extending from the ensiform to the pubis. Most commonly when the stomach is involved, the area immediately below the ensiform on the left is the seat of pain; when the small intestine is involved, the point of painful sensation is centered around the umbilicus, and when the colon is inflamed, it is centered between the umbilicus and the pubis as shown in Fig. 27, page 179. A deep pain on pressure, or feeling of soreness may be felt over the abdominal muscles at the same time. Aside from this pain expressed in and near the median line, and the deep soreness, we quite often find a pain which is located over some inflamed part. Mackenzie does not recognize this pain over the organ as being in the organ. The pain of appendicitis is one of the best known of all the viscerosensory reflexes. It expresses itself in the right lower quadrant of the abdomen, and is usually accompanied by some degree of boardiness of the underlying muscles. However, the pain which comes from distention of the intestines seems to be centered more in the median line. The area of pain in appendicitis is shown in Fig. 39.

I had an opportunity to observe an attack of appendicitis and ulcerative colitis simultaneously in the same individual, which illustrates the difficulty of differential diagnosis. The patient was a male seventeen years of age. He was suffering at the time from early clinical tuberculosis, and had been undergoing sanatorium treatment for four months. He was in full weight and apparently in perfect physical condition. Suddenly he complained of nausea and vomited his supper. This was followed shortly by severe pain in the lower left quadrant of the abdomen where the skin became markedly

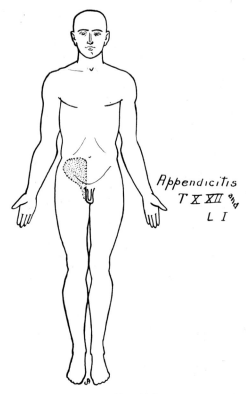

Fig. 39.—Showing area of pain in appendicitis. Pain may be found anywhere in the lower quadrant of the abdomen on the right side, sometimes extending down into the scrotum.

sensitive. A disease of the appendix was not suspected at first. He was put on a restricted diet, but when nausea continued, all food was withheld. He had no rise in temperature. Owing to the fact that he was accustomed to doing much walking and mountain climbing his abdominal muscles were hard. On this account it was difficult to determine pathologic rigidity of the muscles; yet those on the right side seemed to be slightly more rigid than those on the left. There was also slight tenderness on the right side. The patient complained of constipation, much gas in the bowels and colicky pains. A stool, passed the second day after the onset of symptoms, contained large quantities of mucus.

In a second attack, one month after the first, nausea and vomiting were again present. The gas pains were not as marked as in the previous attack. The muscle rigidity was quite marked on the right side. There was also pain on the left side. The temperature reached 99°.

It will be noticed that the patient showed both sympathetic and parasympathetic reflexes. The parasympathetic reflexes were particularly those due to increased motor and secretory action in the intestinal tract—nausea, vomiting, constriction of gut causing colicky pains, and increased mucus. This, with the sensitivity over the lower portion of the abdomen, particularly on the left side, made colitis the most prominent feature of the clinical picture; yet the rigidity of the muscles on the right side afforded localizing symptoms which pointed to an appendix as being also probably an offending organ.

The appendix was removed one month after the first attack, and, at operation, a small ulcer 1 cm. long and ⅕ cm. wide was found which had penetrated to the peritoneal coat. Other portions of the mucous membrane of the appendix were the seat of small hemorrhagic areas. The symptoms in this case were misleading. It was difficult to determine whether we were dealing with a colitis or an appendicitis, or both. All was cleared up, however, one month after the operation when the patient was seized with a further attack of pain in the lower left quadrant of the abdomen, similar to that which he had at his first attack. This made it evident that the patient had had two distinct pathologic lesions: one, in the appendix which was removed by operation and another in the colon, which produced trouble again later. At the time of the first attack it was difficult to determine whether the pain on the left side was not a transference of the sensory impulse in the cord over to the efferent sensory neurons arising from the left posterior horn and resulting from stimuli coming from the appendix; or whether the stimuli arose from those portions of the colon which naturally reflect in the left lower quadrant. We see this transference at times in angina when the pain is transferred to the right side of the chest.

Surgeons are prone to say when finding pain on the left side of the abdomen that the appendix is situated on the left side or that the tip hangs over. This is faulty reasoning. No matter where the appendix lies, this does not change the relationship of afferent and efferent neurons which produce the pain; consequently the pain is always transferred in the same way, and the neurons over which it spreads are limited. It matters not whether the appendix be on the left or on the right; whether it be high or low in the abdomen, the natural place for the pain is in the right lower quadrant of the abdomen. When the pain extends over on the left side, the cause is either a transference of efferent stimuli in the cord, a complicating disease on the part of other viscera which normally produce reflexes on the left, or peritoneal involvement.

Peritoneum.—The peritoneum is much like the pleura so far as its innervation and reflexes are concerned. The nerves which supply the abdominal cutaneous zones with sensation send fibers to the underlying parietal peritoneum. This explains the clinical observation that a localized peritonitis which involves the parietal peritoneum gives pain and causes spasm of the muscles in the overlying area. Thus anterior peritonitis is best expressed anteriorly, and posterior, posteriorly. This is of importance in the study of intestinal and other visceral adhesions.

Parasympathetic Reflexes

Parasympathetic Reflexes Shown in the Intestinal Tract Itself and in Other Organs, the Impulse Originating in the Intestinal Tract.— Numerous sympathetic and parasympathetic reflexes arise from sensory stimuli which originate in the intestinal tract. Many of these express themselves in other parts of the intestinal tract. These, however, account for only a small proportion of the disturbance in function met on the part of the intestine. Reflexes in the intestinal tract, which arise in other organs, on the other hand, are extremely common.

The parasympathetic reflexes affecting the gastrointestinal tract which are best known clinically are those which arise from inflammation of the appendix and gall bladder. The gall bladder embryologically belongs to the intestinal tract and this should be taken into consideration clinically. Afferent stimuli arising from any portion of the gastrointestinal tract may produce reflexes in other parts of the tract—increased secretion and increased muscle tone. This is well illustrated in diseases which produce inflammation of the intestinal walls, such as tuberculosis, typhoid fever, and dysentery. When an inflammation exists in any part of the gut it slows the contents above and hastens them below the point of irritation. Consequently inflammation in the intestine has a tendency to produce localized or general increased muscle tone and increased secretion, including hydrochloric acid, in the stomach, and increased secretion and increased tonus in the muscles of the intestine. This shows itself in several different ways. Sometimes the increased muscular tone produces no recognizable symptoms; again it results in an uneven contraction of the circular muscles of the intestine, producing colicky pains; sometimes, in a general contraction, particularly of the circular muscles of the colon, producing spastic constipation; and again, if the longitudinal fibers are more involved than the circular, in an increased peristalsis, causing loose stools or diarrhea. Stimuli applied to any part of the intestine act in much the same manner, according to what is known as the law of the intestine: they slow the action above, and hasten it below. The effect produced depends upon the severity of the stimulation. Sometimes an antiperistaltic action is produced. The nearer the point of irritation to the proximal portion of the intestinal tube, the more likely this is to occur. Thus gastric and duodenal ulcer and diseases of the gall bladder are more prone to be accompanied by vomiting than disease farther down the tube, such as appendicitis and diseases of the colon.

It must not be forgotten, however, that sympathetic afferents have a tendency to produce inhibition of gastrointestinal activity. This has been shown by Pearcy and his coworkers as quoted in Chapter XVIII.

As a result of reflex stimulation several different common syndromes arise as will be noted as the discussion proceeds. Hypermotility is common in chronic affections of the intestinal tract, particularly appendicitis and chronic irritative affections, such as those of an infectious or parasitic nature. Nausea is common under such conditions, and vomiting sometimes occurs.

Parasympathetic reflexes may fail to appear if the irritation is slight or if the inhibiting sympathetics are markedly stimulated at the same time by such conditions as toxemia and pain.

A determining factor of great importance, which is particularly well shown in the parasympathetic reflexes in the gastrointestinal tract, whether the stimuli arise in the tract itself or in other organs, is the normal degree of excitability of the neurocellular mechanism of the individual. Individuals who are normally vagotonic and some who are pathologically so, as in chronic allergic states, with hay fever, and asthma, are particularly prone to parasympathetic reflexes in the gastrointestinal tract. It is also marked in many psychic states and in certain conditions of endocrine imbalance, such as the vagotonic type of Graves' disease, and in those conditions in which the sympathicotropic secretion of the corpus luteum is temporarily withdrawn as in pregnancy, or permanently as in the menopause either artificial or natural.

COLICKY PAINS.—Colicky pains are recognized among the most common symptoms complained of by patients who suffer from increased excitability of the intestinal vagus. This subject has been investigated by Alvarez,[8, 9] whose papers are interesting and instructive. The stimulation affects the intestinal muscles irregularly, thus producing increased tonus or spasm with constriction of the lumen at irregular intervals. Above the constriction, the passage of the contents of the bowel is slowed. The gas which develops during digestion is not carried off. This results in a distention of the gut and colicky pains. They are due primarily to parasympathetic overstimulation causing constriction and secondarily, to dilatation. Above the points of constriction stimuli caused by the distention are carried to the cord over the sympathetic afferent neurons, and produce the intestinal viscerosensory reflex. If constriction persists, distention likewise persists and the musculature of the intestine becomes thinner than normal and its peristaltic power decreases. This condition is accompanied by disturbance in the secretory power of the gut. Dilatation, however, occurs most readily in the presence of mechanical obstruction.

SPASTIC CONSTIPATION.—Spastic constipation is a condition in which the musculature of the intestinal tract, particularly the colon, shows an increased tonus. This tonus may be of any degree, varying from a marked contraction in which the lumen is almost closed and the gut appears as a cord, to that of slight spasm of the muscles here and there throughout the length of the organ. Such a condition probably represents a hyperirritability of the entire neuromuscular mechanism. The calcium ions in the cells of the intestinal wall are probably decreased and the vagus system is thus predominant. This gives a hint for treating conditions of this kind. The intestinal tract should be relieved of all irritating material and such remedies as atropine, which opposes parasympathetic action, and calcium should be utilized; also measures which improve the general nerve tone of the patient.

Rectal injections of magnesium sulfate have been recommended to overcome this condition (Soper[10]). According to the action of magnesium on the biliary tract and on the heart muscle, we would expect it to relieve atonic instead of spastic constipation, because it reinforces parasympathetic irritability which is already increased in spastic conditions of the colon. Calcium, on the other hand, should be the remedy for spasticity because of its sympathico-tropic action and its relaxing effect upon the musculature of the gut. It is quite probable that we will be obliged to change our conception of the diagnostic points in spastic colon, now that we understand visceral neurology better. Ribbon-like movements which have long been attributed to a spastic condition of the colon may be due to the fecal mass passing through a tight sphincter caused by an increase in sympathetic activity. This is a condition which should be relieved by magnesium.

Spastic conditions which arise from diseases of the intestinal tract may be due to chronic appendicitis or to any irritative condition in the tract, such as tuberculous infiltration and the parasitic diseases of the intestine. Conditions in other organs which produce spasticity reflexly, such as affections of the lungs and gall bladder, and eye strain, will be considered later in this chapter.

In conditions accompanied by high fever the toxemia, expressing itself through the sympathetics, may prevent spasticity, though conditions favoring it may be present.

INTESTINAL STASIS.—Intestinal stasis may be due to many conditions, such as a general weakness of the musculature of the intestinal tract, conditions which produce marked sympathetic stimulation, such as toxemia as noted commonly in acute infectious diseases; irritation arising in some other portion of the gastrointestinal canal or in neighboring organs bound closely to it; pain; worry; and mechanical conditions which interfere with the onward movement of the ingesta. It is more commonly due, however, to an underlying hyperirritability of the intestinal neuromuscular mechanism, either changes in the chemical and physical states of the cells themselves or in the para-sympathetics. If of a reflex nature, the stimulus may come from some other portion of the gastrointestinal tract or from some other organ.

When the contents of the intestinal tract are delayed in their movement through the intestine, they undergo certain changes which are more or less irritating and injurious to the intestinal wall. Stasis from this cause is usually accompanied by the absorption of toxins. If the condition is a chronic one and the toxemia is not too severe, it may express itself in an irritability and a lowering of the efficiency of nerve cells, acting much the same as the chronic toxins of such diseases as tuberculosis, syphilis, and malaria, in lowering the efficiency of the patient. If, on the other hand, the toxemia be greater, then the syndrome of acute toxemia may present. In fact, a very common syndrome in intestinal stasis is that which is usually spoken of as "biliousness." Such attacks are recurrent; the patient will be free for a period and then will have some degree of toxemia. This is usually ushered in by feelings of malaise, headache, and possibly aching of the body, sometimes nausea and vomiting, and often a slight rise of temperature. The condition is usually acute, lasting only one or two days. It can often be relieved by a brisk cathartic. If nothing is done, the attack will usually end of its own accord; the irritation of the muscular coat increases peristalsis, and after a time the toxins, acting through the sympathetic nerves, might produce sufficient inhibitory effect to cause a relaxation of the spasm of the musculature and permit the passing on of the ingesta.

DIARRHEA.—The difference in stimulation which results in the spasticity of the bowel and a diarrhea, is not well understood. Some authors believe it is a difference in the strength of the stimulus, and others believe it depends upon whether the stimulus affects the circular or longitudinal fibers of the intestine; but, whatever it is, we know that diarrhea is a very common result of acute irritative conditions in the intestinal tract. Chronic diarrhea results at times from ulceration of the intestinal mucosa, such as occurs in tuberculosis, typhoid, and amebic infection. It seems quite probable that diarrhea may be due to a marked irritation of the nerve cells in the plexuses of Auerbach and Meissner, in which the stimulus arises within the lumen of the gut and is directly applied. Very severe irritation, however, may be present at times without producing diarrhea. I have seen the entire intestinal tract from the pylorus to the descending colon studded with tuberculous infiltration and ulcers without producing any disturbance in the daily evacuation of the bowel. At other times I have seen it produce a constipation, and still at other times result in diarrhea. There is no doubt but that many of the attacks of so-called "colitis," in which there are two or three mushy bowel movements a day, often accompanied by considerable gas and colicky pain, arise from sensory stimulation coming either from without or within the bowel itself, although the latter is probably the more common.

It will thus be seen that the more common conditions which we find in the gastrointestinal tract—nausea, vomiting, hyperchlorhydria, hypermotility, colicky pains, spastic constipation, intestinal stasis, and diarrhea, may all result from reflex irritation. It is also probable that they may be produced by direct irritation of the plexuses of Auerbach and Meissner, the stimulus arising within the bowel. They are expressions of increased parasympathetic neuromuscular irritability. The source of the irritation which causes the reflex may be either within or without the bowel. Successful therapy demands an understanding of their relation to the vegetative nerves and the ionic content of the cell.

Hirschsprung's Disease.—In the lower colon hyperirritability of the sympathetics may cause a chronic dilatation of the colon (Hirschsprung's disease). Stimulation of the parasympathetics will cause such colons to empty, but since the sympathetic system is the one at fault, surgeons have attempted to relieve the condition by resecting the left lumbar ganglia, or by doing a lumbar ramisectomy, or by resection of the inferior mesenteric and superior hypogastric plexuses.

Bradycardia.—Bradycardia may be produced as a result of stimuli arising in the intestinal tract. This is sometimes seen in typhoid fever. I have called attention to it as being a suggestive symptom of intestinal tuberculosis. There is a marked tendency to slow the heart by stimuli which come from the lung. Inflammation of the appendix will at times produce a slow pulse. I have observed it in diverticulum of the sigmoid; in fact, stimuli arising in any part of the intestinal tract may influence the vagus nerve and reflexly produce a slowing of the heartbeat.

Whether or not a bradycardia will occur cannot depend entirely upon a reflex vagus stimulation. Other conditions may be present which demand an increased circulatory effort and force an accelerated heart contraction in spite of the vagus stimulation. This is well illustrated in asthma, where the vagus stimulation is overcome by the demand for oxygen, resulting in an acceleration of the heartbeats.

A test for the diagnosis of typhoid fever was proposed by the medical department of the British Army, a description of which was given by Marris.[11] Friedlander and McCord[12] describe the rationale of the test thus:

"The patient lies horizontally and is instructed to remain completely at rest throughout this test, which is not employed until at least one hour has elapsed from the last meal. The pulse rate is counted minute by minute until it is found to be steady; ten minutes of such counting usually suffices. Atropine sulphate is then injected hypodermically in the dose of $\frac{1}{33}$ grain, preferably over the triceps region to insure rapid absorption. An interval of twenty-five minutes is allowed to elapse, and the pulse rate is again counted, minute by minute, until it is clear that any rise which may follow the injection has passed off; fifteen or twenty minutes may be necessary for this purpose when the pulse rate is raised at the first count.

"If, for example, a near constant pulse rate of 70 was exhibited at the preliminary counting, and a maximum of 96 was exhibited as the pulse rate subsequent to atropine injection, the inference after this acceleration of twenty-six beats per minute would, under the provisions of the test, be that the condition was not typhoid. If, however, the rate after atropine had attained only to 78 beats per minute as the maximum, the inference is tenable that the existing condition is one of the typhoid group. The test does not discriminate between typhoid and paratyphoids A and B. In Marris' report, the line of demarcation for the interpretation as existing typhoid or nontyphoid is placed at 15; that is, if the acceleration following atropine is less than fifteen per minute, typhoid is indicated. A 'positive' atropine reaction is one giving rise to little or no increased heart rate after atropine administration (fourteen or less per minute). A 'negative' reaction is one giving rise to an increase of fifteen or greater."

In explanation of this test it has been suggested that atropine shows a specific antagonism to the action of the typhotoxin. Such an explanation is not necessary. Knowing the action of atropine in antagonizing the action of the vagus nerve, the rationale of this test is easy to explain. When typhoid fever is present, the inflammation in the intestinal tract produces a marked stimulation of the vagus nerve endings in the intestine, which produces a reflex inhibitory action upon the heart, having a tendency to keep the pulse slow in spite of the accelerating action of the atropine. The reason the pulse does not show a marked bradycardia oftener, is because there are other factors present, which exert an accelerator effect on the heart. The pulse is often relatively slow in such intestinal conditions as typhoid fever, appendicitis, and tuberculous infiltration and ulceration.

The pulse rate is a resultant of the sympathetic accelerating and the vagus slowing impulses, and therefore varies in different people according to their nerve balance and in the same individual at different times according to the nerve stimulation and respiratory and circulatory demands upon the body.

If a dose of atropine sufficiently large to overcome the inhibitory action of the vagus is administered to a normal individual, the pulse rate increases very markedly. In case of the typhoid patient, the reflex stimulation of the cardiac vagus produced by the intestinal inflammation is difficult to overcome, therefore the atropine is not able to relieve the inhibitory action of the vagus so completely. The result is that the pulse is not accelerated to the same extent that it is in the normal individual.

It would seem that a test of this kind could be used advantageously if the rationale of its action were properly understood; but the source of error would undoubtedly be great if a given increase in pulse rate would be required for a positive reaction. The amount of increase in the pulse rate would depend upon the individual. There are many people who are markedly vagotonic. These, unless cardiac accelerating influences are present, show a slower pulse rate than those who are sympathicotonic. I would like further to suggest that typhoid fever is not the only disease that would show this reaction to atropine. Pulmonary tuberculosis is at times accompanied by a relatively slow pulse rate when the patient is at rest and observed

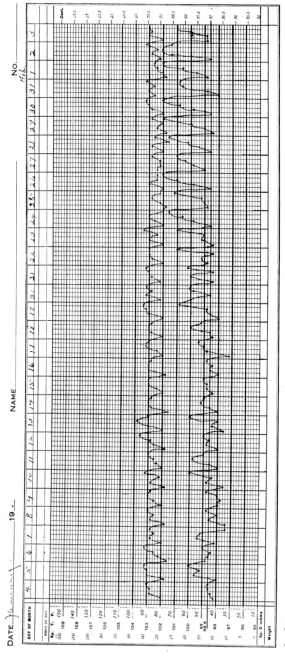

Sp.—Sputum.

Fig. 40.—Reflex bradycardia due to tuberculous involvement of the intestine.

It will be noted that on the seventeenth day of January a continuous elevation of temperature started which increased, reaching its maximum of 102° about a week later and continuing for a number of days. This was associated with definite symptoms of tuberculosis of the intestine. During the first half of the month the temperature was not far above normal, and the pulse reached a maximum of about 90 per day. With the increase in temperature to 102° during the last half of the month the maximum pulse rate shows a slight decrease instead of increase. This is a reflex bradycardia from the intestine. The afferent impulses course through the sensory fibers of the intestinal branches of the vagus; and, mediating in the medulla with the efferent cardiac motor fibers of the vagus, produce cardiac inhibition with slowing of the pulse.

under the conditions of this atropine test. Tuberculosis and other inflammatory infiltrations and ulcerations of the intestinal tract should give the same reaction. It might also occur in conditions of inflammation of the gall bladder.

While the test has a definite physiologic basis, it is a test for abnormal vagus stimulation rather than for typhoid fever.

Fig. 40 is a chart taken from a patient suffering from tuberculosis of the intestine. It will be seen that the pulse rate does not increase in proportion to the amount of toxemia present as indicated by the height of the temperature curve. One must not, however, always expect to find the pulse slow in intestinal tuberculosis, for the demands made upon the circulation and the condition of the circulatory apparatus itself differ so greatly that the rate of heart contraction must necessarily vary; but it occurs sufficiently often to show that there is a tendency for this vagus reflex to be present. The heart action must always be considered in connection with the neurovegetative status of the patient and the demands which are made by the energy output of the cells. When this is large, the heart contractions must increase in rapidity or more blood must be delivered at each contraction, or both conditions must obtain.

HECTIC FLUSH.—Hectic flush is now and then present as a viscerogenic reflex from the gastrointestinal tract. Hectic flush is better known as a symptom of inflammation of the lung (pulmonary tuberculosis), but patients who suffer from spastic constipation and intestinal stasis often complain of much the same syndrome, although, as a rule, it is not so marked in character. I have seen a dilatation of the blood vessels occur in the cheek in patients suffering from intestinal disturbances. This could be accounted for as a parasympathetic reflex, the afferent impulse traveling through the sensory fibers of the vagus, the efferent through the fibers of the Vth cranial nerve, which exert a dilator effect upon the blood vessels of the mouth and cheek.

INCREASED NASAL AND PHARYNGEAL MUCUS (CATARRH).—It has been long noticed that patients suffering from intestinal disturbances are prone to have catarrh. We have always thought there was some relationship but could not explain it. The study of the parasympathetic reflexes shows how this may occur. Sensory stimuli originating in the intestine may travel centralward over the vagus and be transmitted through the motor neurons of the VIIth cranial nerve and result in the increase in secretory activity of the mucous glands of the nose and nasopharynx, giving an increase in catarrhal symptoms. In other cases the symptoms on the part of the two structures are to be considered as part of a general parasympathetic hyperirritability.

HERPES.—Herpes labialis is sometimes found in infection of the intestinal tract, the afferent impulse coursing over the vagus, and stimulating centrally the Vth cranial nerve. While it is most common in colds and pneumonia, I have seen it in intestinal infections as well. This seems to be one of the axon reflexes.

Headaches.—The headache which accompanies intestinal disturbances is often of a reflex nature. The impulse arising in the gastrointestinal tract passes centralward over the sensory fibers of the vagus or pelvic nerve and is transferred to the trigeminus producing pain in different areas of its distribution.

Parasympathetic Reflexes Shown on the Part of the Intestinal Tract, the Impulse Originating in Other Organs.—Aside from the many reflex disturbances in the normal function of the intestinal tract above described, which originate from stimuli coming from the intestinal tract itself, there are many instances of reflexes on the part of the intestinal tract, which originate from stimuli arising in other organs. The splanchnics which control the blood vessels of the intestinal tract are stimulated by many impulses which come from the surface of the body, some of these producing vasoconstriction, others producing vasodilatation. The amount of blood in the splanchnic area is influenced by cutaneous stimulation. This fact explains the well-known clinical observation that chilling of the surface of the body is detrimental in cases of diarrhea. Chilling produces constriction of the surface vessels, driving the blood inward to the splanchnics which become congested. It also suggests that the benefit of hot applications to the abdomen in treatment of such conditions may be due to relieving the irritation of the plexuses of Auerbach and Meissner by withdrawing the blood from the splanchnics and directing it to the vessels of the skin. Any organ whose afferent stimuli mediate with the motor neurons of the intestinal parasympathetics, is able to produce reflex action in the intestinal tract.

Eye strain is frequently accompanied by nausea, hyperchlorhydria and spastic constipation, particularly in patients in whom the excitability of the nerve cells of the parasympathetics is naturally high. This is caused by afferent stimuli from the eye coursing in the sensory neurons of the Vth cranial nerve, mediating with the motor neurons of the intestinal branches of the vagus.

Inflammation of the lungs, stomach, liver, gall bladder, and pancreas is very prone to produce the same group of intestinal symptoms as is described above as originating from stimuli originating in the intestinal tract. These organs are particularly closely bound to the intestinal tract by reflexes—so much so, that increased parasympathetic excitability as represented by hyperchlorhydria, hypermotility throughout the gastrointestinal tract, spastic constipation, colicky pains, and intestinal stasis, has as its most common reflex cause, inflammatory conditions in the lungs, gall bladder, and appendix. All such reflex parasympathetic stimulation results in two different actions: 1, an increased motor stimulus tending to increase the normal contraction of the intestinal musculature; 2, increased secretory stimulation tending to alter the normal activities of the glands of the mucosa.

The common result of the parasympathetic-motor reflex as expressed in the intestinal tract is an unequal contraction of the muscles of the intestine, resulting in disturbed rhythm and in an interference with the normal movement of the ingesta within the intestinal canal. The result of this increased muscular tonus depends upon whether it is expressed mainly in the circular or in the more longitudinal muscles. If the former, the ingesta is delayed; if in the latter, peristalsis may be either slowed or increased. Whenever the muscle tonus of the intestinal tract is reflexly stimulated, the secretion from the glands may also be increased.

In the everyday clinical observation of disturbed function on the part of the intestinal tract, the cause of such disturbance may be found in other organs or in the intestine itself. While, as mentioned above, the reflex may come from the eye, or from any of the structures which belong to the enteral system, we must not forget that the heart, the kidney, and many of the other urogenital organs are reflexly connected with the intestinal tract. Nor must we forget the effect of major emotions.

A plausible explanation for one of the common syndromes on the part of the gastrointestinal canal is, that it is at least partly a reflex trophic disturbance caused by impulses arising in other organs. It appears, clinically, as an atonic condition in which the stomach musculature weakens and dilates. Digestion slows and the emptying time is prolonged. The patient usually eructates much gas and frequently suffers from an annoying acidity which may be due either to an actually increased percentage of hydrochloric acid or to a concentration due to slowing of its passage through the pyloris; or, it may be high in organic acids due to slow digestion and increased fermentation. The cardia usually being patulous, the contractions of the gastric musculature force the acid contents up into the esophagus and mouth, causing burning.

The lessened tonus usually extends to other portions of the digestive canal, as well, causing slow digestion and absorption with much discomfort, and frequently colicky pains. Constipation is often an accompaniment.

This is often found to some degree in patients suffering from chronic extensive pulmonary tuberculosis. It also accompanies chronic heart lesions and chronic diseases of the gall bladder. In some instances it has a nutritional as well as reflex cause. In those instances in which it is of reflex origin the stimulating impulses pass from the involved organ over the afferent fibers of the vagus and are transmitted to efferent vagal fibers supplying other portions of the gastrointestinal tract.

It is most stubborn; but if the primary disease improves, unless the trophic changes have been too long present, the syndrome also improves. Its relief, otherwise, consists in measures which will aid digestion and improve the tonus of the musculature of the gastrointestinal tract. A highly nutritious diet is indicated which often is difficult to institute because of lack of appetite. If HCl is deficient, it should be administered. Antispasmodics are frequently helpful. Frequent feedings are also of value.

Action of Toxins on Motility and Secretory Activity of the Intestinal Tract.—Toxins, no matter from what source, produce injury (fatigue) of nerve cells, and produce a general widespread sympathetic effect through the neurocellular mechanism. Consequently, in all cases of toxemia, and particularly those of acute toxemia, we find a tendency to sluggishness of action in the gastrointestinal tract. There is a tendency to deficiency of secretion and deficiency of motility in the gut proper, brought about through the inhibitory action of the sympathetics in overcoming the vagus mechanism. This manifests itself in activating the sphincters as well as inhibiting the activity of the gut proper.

Action of Such States as Anger, Fear, and Pain Upon the Motility and Secretory Activity of the Intestinal Tract.—The effect of such emotional states as anger, fear, and pain upon the process of digestion has long been known to physiologists and clinicians. The subject has been given careful study by Cannon and his coworkers. They have shown how these various emotional states, acting through the sympathetic centers in the diencephalon, spread their effects throughout the entire body, and in the intestinal tract inhibit both motility and secretory activity. All clinicians meet this action in their everyday practice.

ENDOCRINE GLANDS.—Whenever there is a marked disturbance in the equilibrium of the endocrine system, this reacts upon the vegetative nerves and may produce effects in the gastrointestinal system, now of one type, now another. Pituitrin exerts a special activating influence on the musculature of the intestine for which it may be used when an evacuation of the bowel is desired without the use of cathartics by the mouth. Thyroid substance is known to exert a favorable influence on constipation in hypothyroid states.

References

1. Alvarez, Walter C.: The Mechanism of the Digestive Tract, ed. 2, New York, 1928, Paul B. Hoeber.
2. Parker, G. H.: The Elementary Nervous System, Philadelphia, 1919, J. B. Lippincott Co.
3. Bechterew: Die Funktionen der Nervencentra, Jena, 1908, Gustav Fischer, p. 271.
4. Schmidt, C. A.: Distribution of Vagus and Sacral Nerves to Large Intestine, Proc. Soc. Exper. Biol. & Med. 30: 739, 1933.
5. Gaskell: Involuntary Nervous System, London, 1916, Longmans, Green & Co., pp. 45, 131.
6. Carlson, A. J., Boyd, E. T., and Pearcy, J. F.: Studies of the Visceral Sensory Nervous System. XIV. The Reflex Control of the Cardia and Lower Esophagus, Arch. Int. Med. 30: 409, 1922.
7. Sale: A Study of Diaphragmatic Movements in Acute Abdominal Inflammations, J. A. M. A. 71: 505, 1918.
8. Alvarez: The Prevention of Post Operative Gas Pains, California State J. M. 16: 338, 1918.
9. Alvarez: Differences in the Behavior of Segments From Different Parts of the Intestine, Am. J. Physiol. 45: 342, 1918.
10. Soper, H. W.: Magnesium Sulphate Solution in the Treatment of Spastic Contracture of the Rectum and Sigmoid Colon, Am. J. M. Sc. 156: 205, 1918.
11. Marris: Use of Atropin as Aid to Diagnosis of Typhoid Fever and Paratyphoid A and B Infections, Brit. M. J. 2: 717, 1916.
12. Friedlander and McCord: The Atropin Test in the Diagnosis of Typhoid Infections, J. A. M. A. 70: 1435, 1918.

CHAPTER XX

THE LIVER AND GALL BLADDER

I. THE INNERVATION OF THE LIVER AND GALL BLADDER

The liver, embryologically, is formed from the alimentary canal and consequently has the same innervation. The secretion of bile varies according to the character of the food ingested. It is greatest on a meat diet, somewhat less on carbohydrates, and least on an exclusive fat consumption.

The glycogenic function of the liver is of no less importance than the biliary function. The response of the liver to sympathetic stimulation and to that of certain hormones, such as adrenalin, thyroxin, and extract of the hypophysis, to which it gives up its glycogen to the blood, shows this function to be of great import to the body economy.

The secretion of bile is influenced by nerve activity, and seems to be further influenced by certain products of internal secretion. *Secretin* formed in the duodenum acts upon the liver as well as on the pancreas.

Ivy[1] has recently shown that purified extracts of the duodenal and jejunal mucosa, when injected intravenously, cause the gall bladder to contract and expel its contents. It has been proved that this substance is not *secretin.* Ivy has suggested the name of *cholecystokinin* for it.

The gall bladder and ducts are surrounded by unstriped musculature. The gall bladder is seen to contract and discharge its contents under the influence of a diet rich in fats.

This musculature is arranged about the papilla of Vater in the form of a sphincter. Like the urinary bladder, the activation of the sphincter and the bladder differs.

There is considerable confusion regarding the innervation of the gall bladder, common duct, and sphincter. Some observers have arrived at the conclusion that the sympathetics activate the musculature of the gall bladder and inhibit the sphincter at the papilla of Vater, while the vagus inhibits the musculature of the bladder but activates the sphincter. Others hold the reverse of this, and a third group believe that both systems activate and inhibit in the same manner as has been described for the cardia by Carlson. The innervation given below is based on the work of Bainbridge and Dale[2] and seems to be confirmed by the action of magnesium sulfate in the treatment of gall bladder affections. In this connection it must be stated that magnesium opposes the action of calcium in vegetative structures, and calcium is associated with stimulation of the sympathetics in the gastrointestinal canal.

The innervation of all those sphincters of the enteral and urogenital systems which have been worked out carefully, with possibly the exception of the cardia, shows sympathetic activation and parasympathetic inhibition, and it is most probable that this follows the same rule.

Parasympathetics.—The parasympathetic supply comes from the vagus. The vagus, according to the general law, supplies activating fibers to the bile ducts and the gall bladder, and inhibiting fibers to the sphincter of the papilla of Vater.

Sympathetics.—The sympathetics oppose the parasympathetics. They inhibit the action of the vagus in its control of the biliary ducts, gall bladder, and sphincter. When stimulated, they cause relaxation of the biliary ducts and gall bladder, and contraction of the sphincter of the papilla of Vater.

The sympathetic supply to the gall bladder comes from motor cells in the semilunar ganglion which receives connector fibers from the thoracic segments from the Vth to the IXth.

Not only are the sympathetics inhibitory to the action of the vagus in the liver and gall bladder, but they furnish vasomotor control for the liver. Stimulation of the sympathetics contracts or dilates the vessels according to the degree and character of the stimulation, thus altering the secreting power of the gland. It also mobilizes the glycogen found in the liver (Cannon[3]).

Spinal Nerves.—The liver and gall bladder receive nerve fibers from the phrenics. There is one branch of the phrenic, the phrenico-abdominalis, which courses with the sympathetics from the celiac plexus to the liver (Müller[4]). This becomes important at times in symptomatology, for the afferent impulses are carried back to the IIIrd and IVth cervical segments of the cord through the right phrenic and thus produce reflex pain in the right shoulder.

II. LIVER AND GALLBLADDER: CLINICAL CONSIDERATION

Hepatic Visceromotor and Viscerosensory Reflexes.—The liver and gall bladder receive their sympathetic innervation from the semilunar ganglion, the connector fibers arising from the Vth to IXth thoracic segments of the cord. These are the same segments that supply the stomach. The visceromotor reflex, however, which results from inflammation of the liver and gall bladder, shows itself in the right rectus instead of the left (Fig. 41). One viscerosensory reflex (Fig. 42, *A* and *B*) expresses itself in the epigastrium in much the same way as the sensory reflex from the stomach, but

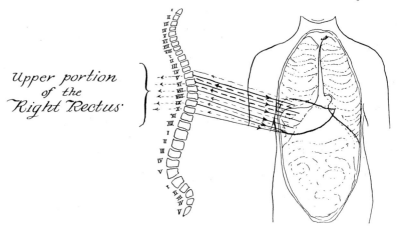

Upper portion of the Right Rectus

Fig. 41.—Showing the hepatic visceromotor reflex.

Lines connecting the liver and gall bladder with the thoracic segments of the cord from the Vth to the Xth represent sympathetic connectors. Solid lines represent sympathetic nerves supplying the liver and gall bladder. Broken lines represent the nerves of the sympathetic system which carry afferent impulses to the cord. Broken lines on the other side of the cord represent corresponding spinal nerves which receive the impulse from the afferent sympathetic system and transmit them to the upper portion of the left rectus, producing the hepatic visceromotor reflex. The broken lines running from the liver to the VIth and VIIth segments of the cord are heavier, indicating that these are the principal paths of the impulse.

more to the right of the median line. It may follow the costal margin and at times is found in the back in the zones of the Vth to IXth intercostal nerves. Another important viscerosensory reflex from the liver is that which takes place through the phrenic. The phrenic nerve sends filaments to the liver and gall bladder. Inflammation of these organs sends afferent stimuli centralward through the phrenics which may express pain through the sensory spinal nerves with which they mediate in the cervical segments of the cord. This reflex is shown strongest above the clavicle and spine of the scapula, in those surface areas over the neck and shoulders which are supplied by the IIIrd and IVth right cervical sensory nerves, the same as are involved in right diaphragmatic pleurisy and in tuberculosis of the right lung. This is shown in Fig. 42, *A* and *B*.

Hepatic Parasympathetic Reflexes.—The liver and gall bladder, aside from the visceromotor and viscerosensory reflexes in the

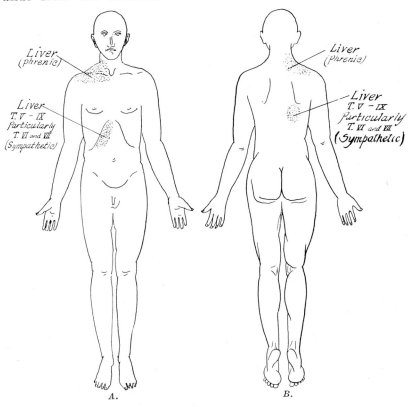

Fig. 42.—Hepatic viscerosensory reflexes.

Lower through the sympathetics, upper through the phrenics. *A*, anterior; *B*, posterior. The hepatic viscerosensory reflex shows itself on both the anterior and posterior surfaces of the body.

The shaded area in the lower portion of the figure represents pain due to afferent impulses which travel from the liver to the cord through the sympathetic system. The efferent impulses express themselves through the thoracic spinal nerves and show themselves particularly in the VIth and VIIth right thoracic cutaneous zones.

The upper area of pain is due to afferent impulses which travel from the liver to the cervical portion of the cord through the sensory fibers of the phrenics, where they connect with efferent neurons which express the pain in the IIIrd and IVth cervical sensory zones.

somatic structures, just described, show parasympathetic motor and secretory reflexes in other organs. These may be particularly well recognized in the stomach and intestinal tract, as cardiospasm, hyperchlorhydria, gastric and intestinal hypermotility, spastic constipation, colicky pains, and intestinal stasis; and later relaxation of musculature, decrease in secretion, and increase in gas from increased formation or lack of absorption. Sometimes they cause an intestinal block. The best known clinical conditions for producing these symptoms are gall bladder disease, chronic appendicitis, chronic heart disease, and chronic pulmonary tuberculosis.

Icterus may be followed by bradycardia caused by the abstraction of calcium from the heart muscle by the bile salts. When an inflammatory condition of the gall bladder is accompanied by bradycardia, however, the possibility of a motor reflex through the vagus must be considered among the probable causes.

The gall bladder and bile ducts are embryologically in close relationship with the stomach and intestines, and frequently produce reflex, increased motility, and secretory activity in them. They also at times are affected by reflexes from the stomach and intestines. A reflex spasm of the bile ducts is now and then described, resulting from inflammation in the stomach and intestines. Such conditions are sometimes relieved by an injection of atropine through its relaxing effect upon the vagus nerve. Adrenalin should also be employed in such cases.

Spasm of Sphincter of Common Duct.—Sometimes a spasm of the sphincter of the common duct occurs and simulates gallstone colic. The treatment of this condition is not well established because of the uncertainty of the innervation. The fact that certain cases have apparently yielded to atropine and adrenalin might indicate that the vagus supplies adrenergic fibers to the sphincter, or that the spasm is caused by structures, outside the sphincter, activated by the vagus. Spasm of the sphincter, if due to sympathetic activation, as suggested by Bainbridge and Dale, should yield to magnesium sulfate, for this antagonizes sympathetic action; or to pilocarpine or acetylcholine which increases parasympathetic action. In explaining such paradoxical observations as these, one must always bear in mind that under conditions of excessive hyperirritability, stimuli which would naturally be expressed in one system may be transferred to the other; that each system may have adrenergic fibers or that they may be due to changes in electrolytes in the cells.

Cholecystitis and Inflammation of the Bile Ducts.—A treatment for cholecystitis and inflammation of the biliary ducts based upon the theory of contrary innervation has been suggested by Meltzer[5] and made practicable by Lyon.[6, 7, 8, 9, 10] It consists of introducing a quantity (25 c.c.) of a 33⅓ per cent solution of magnesium sulfate into the duodenum through a duodenal tube. This process has been called transduodenal lavage. The action of the magnesium is to dilate the duodenum and the sphincter and thus favor an outflow of bile. The magnesium acts by inhibiting the action of the sympathetics and allowing the vagus to act with less opposition. This dilates the sphincter and contracts the gall bladder, thus causing a free flow of bile. It also causes a free flow of bile from the biliary passages in the liver. This application of the knowledge of the antagonistic action of the vagus and the sympathetics in the innervation of the gall bladder and biliary ducts is another illustration of the practical value of the study of visceral neurology. In accounting for paradoxical reactions met in the institution of gall tract drainage one must take into consideration the following conditions which are liable to alter reactions in vegetative structures:

1. Whether the individual possesses a stable equilibrium, is a vagotonic, or a sympathicotonic; and the possibility of both adrenergic and cholinergic fibers in both systems.

2. The manner in which the ionic content of the cells in the diseased structures may be altered by the pathologic process, such alterations being able to interfere with nerve response. Inflamed tissues always show increased activity.

3. The possibility of transference of effect from one system to the other when the system stimulated is excessively irritable.

Such paradoxical reactions are found repeatedly in all branches of clinical practice; but if one is conversant with these vagaries in the reaction of the neurocellular mechanism, he will not go far astray in his clinical interpretation.

References

1. Ivy, A. C., and Oldberg, Eric: Observations on the Cause of Gall-Bladder Contraction and Evacuation, Proc. Soc. Exper. Biol. & Med. 25: 113, 251, 1928.
2. Bainbridge and Dale: J. Physiol. 33: 1908.

3. Cannon, W. B.: Bodily Changes in Fear, Hunger, Pain and Rage, New York, 1915, D. Appleton and Co., p. 66.
4. Müller, L. R.: Das Vegetative Nervensystem, Berlin, 1920, Julius Springer, p. 157.
5. Meltzer, J.: Disturbances in the Law of Contrary Innervation as a Pathogenetic Factor in the Diseases of the Bile Ducts and Gall-Bladder, Am. J. M. Sc. 153: 469, 1917.
6. Lyon, B. B. Vincent: Diagnosis and Treatment of Diseases of the Gall Bladder and Biliary Ducts, Preliminary Report on a New Method, J. A. M. A. 73: 980, 1919.
7. Lyon, B. B. Vincent: The Treatment of Catarrhal Jaundice by a Rational, Direct and Effective Method, Am. J. M. Sc. 159: 303, 1920.
8. Lyon, B. B. Vincent: Choledochitis, Cholecystitis and Cholelithiasis, New York M. J. 112: 23, 56, 1920.
9. Lyon, B. B. Vincent: Can the Gall-Bladder, Biliary Ducts and Liver Be Medically Drained? A Further Consideration of Some Aspects of Diagnosis and Treatment of Cholecystitis and Choledochitis by a Method of Physiologic Drainage, Am. J. M. Sc. 160: 515, 1920.
10. Lyon, B. B. Vincent: Non-Surgical Drainage of the Gall Tract, Philadelphia, 1923, Lea & Febiger.

CHAPTER XXI

THE PANCREAS

I. THE INNERVATION OF THE PANCREAS

The pancreas has two very important functions which depend upon: 1, a secretion which is poured into the intestinal canal through the pancreatic duct; and, 2, one which is poured into the veins that leave the organ. The former has to do directly with intestinal digestion, the latter with carbohydrate metabolism.

In its relationship to the two divisions of the vegetative nervous system, the pancreas resembles the salivary glands. Stimulation of the vagus produces an increased flow of thin secretion, while stimulation of the sympathetics produces a secretion which is thick and tenacious. The vagus, however, is the chief secretory nerve of the pancreas. The chief stimulant of the external pancreatic secretion seems to be *secretin*, yet the amount and character of the secretion is influenced by the vegetative nerves.

The internal secretion of the pancreas isolated by Banting, Best and their coworkers,[1] at Toronto, has been given the name of insulin. This product is one of the great advances made in organotherapy. While not a cure for diabetes, it increases the tolerance of diabetics for carbohydrates, and is able to tide those who have a very much reduced tolerance over crises which might otherwise prove fatal. In certain instances, too, the function of the pancreatic cells seems to be restored after a period of insulin administration. It is one of the important advances in clinical therapeutics of modern times.

Parasympathetics.—The parasympathetic connector fibers arise from the visceral nucleus of the vagus and connect with motor cells within the pancreas. When stimulated, secretion is increased.

Sympathetics.—The sympathetics which supply the pancreas have their motor neurons in the semilunar ganglion along with those of the stomach and liver; and the medullated fibers which connect these cells with the spinal cord arise from the Vth to IXth thoracic segments of the cord.

Stimulation of these motor cells decreases pancreatic secretion and causes either contraction or dilatation of the blood vessels.

The internal secretion (insulin) which is produced by the pancreas is poured into the veins, and, circulating through the body, comes in contact with and acts upon other organs of internal secretion. This secretion seems in some particulars to be antagonistic to both thyroid and adrenal activity, and has much to do with maintaining the normal carbohydrate balance in the body.

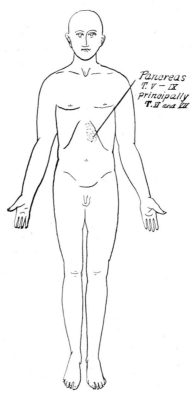

Fig. 43.—Pancreatic viscerosensory reflex. This reflex is shown in the same cutaneous sensory zones as the gastric viscerosensory reflex shown in Fig. 36,A.

Insulin stimulates the parasympathetic mechanism and furnishes a test for parasympathicotonia. If a marked hypoglycemia follows a small dose of insulin administered after the individual has ingested from 50 to 100 grams of glucose, this is taken as evidence that the individual is a parasympathicotonic. Insulin is antagonized in this respect by adrenalin and thyroxin.

A secretion of pancreatic juice is stimulated by the hormone, *secretin* (Bayliss and Starling) which is formed in the duodenal glands adjacent to the pylorus. The glands are stimulated to the production of *secretin* by the acid contents of the stomach, coming in contact with them on entering the intestine.

II. PANCREAS: CLINICAL CONSIDERATION

Pancreatic Viscercmotor and Viscerosensory Reflexes.—As far as reflex disturbances in the pancreas itself are concerned, taking place through the sympathetic and vagus nerves, our knowledge, as yet, is

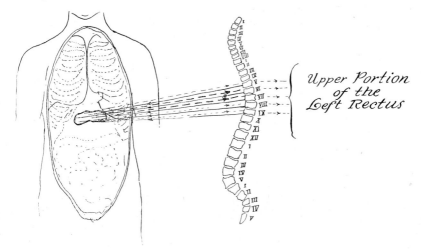

Fig. 44.—Showing the pancreatic visceromotor reflex.
Lines connecting the pancreas with the thoracic segments of the cord from the Vth to the IXth represent sympathetic connectors. Solid lines represent the sympathetic nerves which supply the pancreas. Broken lines represent afferents of the sympathetic system which carry sensory impulses to the cord. Broken lines on the other side of the cord represent corresponding spinal nerves which receive the impulse from the afferent sympathetic system and transmit them to the upper portion of the left rectus producing the pancreatic viseromotor reflex. The broken lines from the pancreas to the VIth and VIIth segments of the cord are heavier, indicating that these are the principal paths of impulse.

very meagre. We do know, however, that a stimulation of those sympathetic motor cells which are in connection with the thoracic segments from the Vth to IXth will inhibit the secretion of the pancreas. We further know that when the pancreas is inflamed, there is a sensory visceral reflex. The center for such reflex is in the epigastrium on the left side of the median line, as shown in Fig. 43. This is in the same area that shows the sensory visceral reflex when the stomach is inflamed. In most cases of acute pancreatitis, the inflammation is very severe and the pain excruciating. It will be recalled that under these conditions the reflex spreads to adjacent neurons, so it is not uncommon to find pancreatic pain on the right side of the median line, also in the neck and shoulder, and down over the abdomen on the left side. The fact that it is found in the neck and shoulder would indicate that there might be connection with the phrenic nerve, the same as there is in the liver and diaphragm.

A visceromotor reflex also appears in the upper portion of the left rectus the same as when the stomach is inflamed, as shown in Fig. 44.

Pancreatic Parasympathetic Reflexes.—The parasympathetic reflexes from the pancreas, as best observed, express themselves mainly in the stomach, producing nausea and vomiting, but also produce other motor and sensory disturbances in both stomach and intestines.

Reference

1. Banting, F. G., and Best, C. H.: The Internal Secretion of the Pancreas, J. Lab. & Clin. Med. 7: 251, 1922.

CHAPTER XXII

THE DIAPHRAGM

I. INNERVATION OF THE DIAPHRAGM

The diaphragm is a very important muscular organ. Since it belongs to the skeletal structures, it receives its main nerve supply from the spinal nerves. The upper surface of the diaphragm is covered by the pleura, the lower is covered by the peritoneum. It is impossible to separate these structures physiologically, so we must treat them together. The diaphragm is supplied by both vagus and sympathetic fibers belonging to the vegetative system, and by the intercostals and phrenics of the spinal system. This brings the diaphragm into reflex connection with both the thoracic and abdominal viscera; and also with the superficial tissues of the shoulder girdle, thorax, and abdomen. While one surface of the diaphragm is covered with pleura and the other with peritoneum, the main portion is made up of striated muscle. This organ consists of two distinct parts: the central tendon and the costal portion.

Sympathetics.—The sympathetic nerve supply for the diaphragmatic pleura is probably the same as that of the costal pleura, and, therefore, we must assume that it comes from two sources: first, from the same source that supplies the pulmonary tissue (the upper five or six thoracic segments); second, from the sympathetic fibers which course with the intercostal nerves (VIth to XIIth thoracic segments).

The peritoneal surface of the diaphragm receives its nerve supply from the same source as that which supplies the peritoneum in general. The sympathetic supply courses with the intercostal nerves, VIth to XIIth, and passes through the celiac plexus.

Parasympathetics.—The parasympathetic nerve supply of the diaphragm consists of fibers of the vagus belonging to the pulmonary plexuses and the fibers of the vagus which belong to the abdominal plexuses.

Spinal Nerves.—The diaphragm consists of a central tendon and two strong muscular crura which connect with the lumbar vertebrae,

Foramen venae cavae | Pars sternalis diaphragmatis

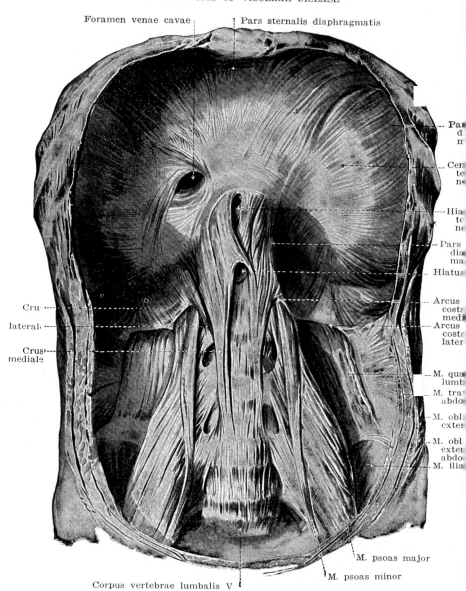

Cru⋯

lateral⋯

Crus⋯
mediale

Pa⋯
d
m

Cer
te
ne

Hia
te
ne

Pars
dia
ma

Hiatus

Arcus
cost⋯
med

Arcus
cost⋯
later

M. qua
lumb

M. tra
abdo

M. obl
exter

M. obl
exter
abdo
M. ilia

M. psoas major

M. psoas minor

Corpus vertebrae lumbalis V

Fig. 45.—Diaphragm viewed from below and in front. The diaphragm is made up of central fleshy tendons (pars lumbalis) and thinner fibers running to the ribs (pars costalis) and sternum (pars sternalis). The contraction of the diaphragm consists in shortening of both the crura (pars lumbalis) and the pars costalis and pars sternalis. With the abdominal viscera as a fulcrum, the contraction of the diaphragm widens the lower portion of the thorax as shown in Fig. 47,A. In inflammations of the lungs its motion is restricted. It is probably in tonic contraction for the reason that the neck and chest muscles are in contraction, having its nerve supply in part from the cervical portion of the cord. This restricted action seems to be confined to the side involved. In some cases the limited motion does not seem to be present, but where it is present there is probably an actual shortening of the fibers, the same as in the surface muscles when they are contracted.

and a peripheral or costal portion which joins it to the lower costal margin. The central tendon of the diaphragm with its crura is innervated largely by the phrenics which take their origin from the IIIrd and IVth, sometimes the IVth and Vth, cervical segments of the cord. The phrenics also send some fibers to the costal portion of the diaphragm. They pierce the diaphragm and are distributed to the falciform ligament and peritoneum, covering the upper surface of the liver, also the peritoneum in relationship to the stomach and pancreas; and some fibers go to the tissue about the adrenal gland and upper pole of the kidney. The costal portion of the diaphragm, on the other hand, is largely supplied by the lower six intercostal nerves, which also send some fibers to the central tendon. The diaphragm is shown in Fig. 45 in which the relative importance of the crura and the costal portion may be seen.

II. THE DIAPHRAGM: CLINICAL CONSIDERATION

The diaphragm has not received the careful clinical study that its physiologic importance warrants. The diaphragm is the most important muscle of respiration. Its acts are both voluntary and involuntary. It is connected reflexly through the sympathetics, with both thoracic and abdominal viscera, a fact which affords opportunity for many viscerogenic reflexes.

Sympathetic Reflexes

Diaphragmatic Visceromotor Reflex.—The diaphragmatic visceromotor reflex is not easily recognized, because the same sympathetic nerves which supply the diaphragmatic pleura come from the pulmonary plexuses, and the lower intercostals. Therefore, reflexes occur through the same spinal nerves and in the same tissues that are affected when the pulmonary parenchyma or the lower costal pleura is inflamed. The same may be said of the reflexes which originate from inflammation of the peritoneal surface of the diaphragm. They occur through the same nerves and in the same tissues as reflexes caused by inflammation of the abdominal viscera. Consequently, these diaphragmatic reflexes of sympathetic origin cannot be differentiated by their location in the tissues from reflexes of sympathetic origin arising in the thoracic and abdominal viscera.

Diaphragmatic Viscerosensory Reflex.—The same may be said of the diaphragmatic viscerosensory reflex as was said of the viscero-motor reflex. Inflammation of the pleural surface of the diaphragm reflects through its sympathetic nerves in two areas: first, the same area that shows the sensory reflex from the lung, which is particularly the IIIrd to Vth cervical sensory zones; second, the areas which show the sensory reflex arising from inflammation of the lower portion of the costal pleura, the thoracic zones, VIth to XIIth.

The viscerosensory reflex arising from the peritoneal surface of the diaphragm likewise cannot be differentiated from reflexes arising in the abdominal viscera, because reflexes from both sources express themselves in abdominal tissues supplied by the lower six thoracic neurons. It can be said, however, that as a rule when the peritoneal surface of the diaphragm is inflamed, both sensory and motor disturbances of reflex origin usually occur near that portion of the diaphragm which is involved instead of in the median line, in the more peripheral distribution of the nerves.

Parasympathetic Reflexes

It is somewhat difficult to describe definite parasympathetic reflexes originating in the diaphragmatic pleura and diaphragmatic peritoneum, although any reflex that can arise from the pleura in general through irritation of vagus nerve endings, might arise when vagus endings in the diaphragmatic pleura are irritated. Thus, we find a cough very often as a symptom of diaphragmatic pleurisy. Arising from the peritoneal surface of the diaphragm, we have at times a slowing of the pulse, and parasympathetic reflexes arising in the organs of the enteral system. This is particularly true when there is a definite, inflamed area involving both neighboring organs and the peritoneal surface of the diaphragm. This is not wholly due to the peritoneal involvement, but probably is due partly to it, and partly to the inflammation in adjoining structures. Inflammation of the diaphragm is a common cause of hiccough.

Reflexes Through the Spinal Nerves

There are both motor and sensory reflexes which take place from stimuli arising in the diaphragm, the afferent impulses traveling centralward through both the phrenics and the lower intercostal spinal nerves. The phrenic motor reflex, if it could be differentiated from that from the lung, would show as an increased tonus of the muscles which arise from the IIIrd and IVth, or IVth and Vth cervical segments of the cord; thus the scaleni, levator anguli scapulae and rhomboidei would be particularly affected. The phrenic sensory reflex also shows itself in the IIIrd and IVth, or IVth and Vth

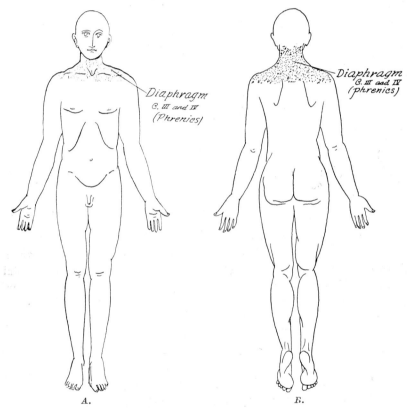

A.   *B.*

Fig. 46.—Site of diaphragmatic viscerosensory reflex. *A*, anterior view; *B*, posterior view. Afferent impulses travel centralward through the phrenics, producing reflex sensory disturbances, particularly in the IIIrd and IVth cervical zones. Note that these are the same areas involved in pulmonary viscerosensory reflex, and on the right side the same as that of the hepatic viscerosensory reflex.

cervical segments of the cord. This sensory reflex is the most constant symptom in that form of diaphragmatic pleurisy in which the central tendon is involved. It may appear as a superficial pain, in which case it is acute; or as a deep pain in the muscle, above enumerated, in which case it is dull. Fig. 46, *A* and *B*, shows the common site of diaphragmatic pain reflected through the phrenics.

When this phrenic diaphragmatic reflex is on the right side, it is located in the same areas as pain from the gall bladder. I have seen instances of cholecystitis in tuberculous patients where differentiation was all but impossible. Auscultatory findings sometimes aid in differentiation.

It can be seen readily, therefore, that from the tissues involved alone, it is difficult to differentiate these reflexes from those which occur through the sympathetic nerves when the pulmonary parenchyma is involved. In the latter, however, other segments are often stimulated, bringing other tissues under the reflex action. The diaphragm being innervated by spinal nerves in which the sensory neurons are more sensitive than those of the sympathetics, shows reflex sensory disturbance more plainly than the pulmonary parenchyma.

Motor and sensory reflexes also take place through the lower six spinal (intercostal) nerves as well as through the phrenics. These show as a spasm of those muscles which receive their innervation from the VIth to XIIth thoracic spinal nerves, the lower six intercostals, and the abdominal muscles. The sensory disturbance (pain) manifests itself somewhere in the path of the sensory spinal nerves which take their origin from these segments, usually near the lower costal margin; sometimes, however, extending well down over the abdomen, and now and then even in the median line of the abdomen. Thus it can be seen that these motor and sensory reflexes originating through the lower intercostals cannot be differentiated, by the tissues involved, from the visceromotor and viscerosensory reflexes which originate from the lower portion of the costal pleura, as shown in Figs. 58 and 59, pages 337 and 339.

Many errors in diagnosis arise from the fact that the costal portion of the diaphragmatic pleura often transfers the pain below the costal arch. Oftentimes the gall bladder and appendix are suspected when the pleurisy is at the right base and gastric ulcer when it is at the left base. Operations on abdominal viscera are not infrequently done because of a misinterpretation of basal pleurisy (Pottenger,[1, 2] Neumann[3]). Every year I see patients who have been so operated upon without relief because the pleural involvement was the cause. Atrophy over the lower intercostals makes it necessary to consider the pleura.

Reflexes Shown in the Diaphragm, the Afferent Impulse Coming From Other Organs

The diaphragmatic muscle proper, receiving its innervation through the phrenics from the IIIrd and IVth, or IVth and Vth, cervical segments of the cord, and from the lower six intercostal nerves, is bound reflexly to all organs which send afferent sensory impulses to the particular segments from which these spinal nerves arise.

The importance of the diaphragm and the relationship which it bears to the health of the individual, is not sufficiently appreciated by medical men. It is not only the most important muscle of respi-

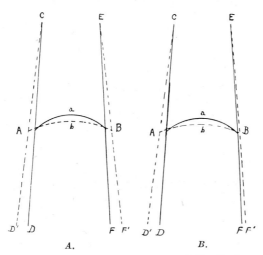

Fig. 47.—Schematic illustration of the influence of the diaphragm in enlarging the intrathoracic space. *A*, normal respiration; *B*, illustrating the effect when the movement of one side of the diaphragm is lessened. The intrathoracic space fails to be enlarged to the extent that motion of the chest and abdominal wall *EF*, in Fig. *B*, is limited.

ration, but a normal action of the diaphragm affords a very necessary aid to the circulation of the blood. Disturbance in its action is followed by many functional disturbances, such as weakness, loss of endurance, dizziness, faintness, and other symptoms of the cardio-neurotic group. These have been carefully studied by Wenckebach[4] and Eppinger,[5] whose works are very valuable and suggestive.

When the diaphragm contracts, it starts a whole train of action. It descends, enlarging the thorax from above downward, at the same time compressing the abdominal viscera, increasing the intraabdominal tension, and forcing the large abdominal muscles outward. The main factors in causing this major contraction are the crura which are supplied by the phrenic nerves. While they are contracting, however, the costal portion, which is supplied by the lower six intercostal nerves, also contracts, shortening this portion of the muscle. The effect of this is to raise the lower arch of the thorax which brings the anterior portion of the ribs upward so that they come nearer to the horizontal plane. This increases the anteroposterior diameter of the thorax. In this the lower external intercostals and intercartilageni also have a hand, as well as in the next movement of the ribs, which is to turn and raise them like a bucket bail, enlarging the lateral diameter. As a result of these movements, the thorax is greatly enlarged. The action of the diaphragm in enlarging the thorax laterally is schematically shown in Fig. 47. The blood is aspirated from the large veins by the enlarging thoracic cavity and literally squeezed from them by the compressing force exerted upon the abdominal viscera. The importance of this action to the health of the individual should be apparent. The influence of pathologic conditions in both the thoracic and abdominal cavities, which interfere with this normal diaphragmatic action, deserves careful study. Reflexes which result in diminished diaphragmatic movement deserve most careful study not only from a diagnostic standpoint, but also from the general standpoint of understanding the effect of disease upon the human organism.

The piston action of the diaphragm is interfered with in diseases of the parenchyma of the lung; in diseases of the pleura, whether due to fluid or air in the cavity or to adhesions; and sometimes by subdiaphragmatic inflammation. It is also inhibited as a result of artificial pneumothorax and operations on the phrenic nerve as frequently used today in the treatment of pulmonary tuberculosis. No patient with an adherent or paralyzed diaphragm, or one in which the motion is greatly interfered with by other causes, can measure up readily to the extra demands made on the respiratory and circulatory mechanism by the necessity for a greatly increased physical activity. This lack of freedom in diaphragmatic activity often adds to the dyspnea of patients suffering from either thoracic or abdominal lesions.

Lungs.—When the pulmonary parenchyma is inflamed, as in pulmonary tuberculosis, a very important motor reflex shows itself in the diaphragm. The impulses from the lung course over the afferent fibers of the sympathetic system which arise from the upper five or six thoracic segments of the cord. The impulse is then carried upward by intercalated neurons to the cervical segments of the cord, particularly to the IIIrd, IVth, and Vth, where it is transferred to the motor neurons which innervate the various muscles of respiration, as described in Chapter XXII. This is the portion of the cord which gives origin to the phrenic nerve, which is especially involved in the pulmonary reflex. The reflex shows in the diaphragm as a limited motion, and is described clinically either as lagging or as diminished motion of the hemothorax. The muscle, being already in a state of partial contraction, responds with a lesser movement to the normal respiratory impulse. In limiting the movement of the chest, the contraction of the diaphragm below is aided by the contraction of the neck muscles above, particularly the subclavius and scaleni, which are attached to the first and second rib. In unilateral disease this motor reflex is confined to the side of involvement, while the healthy side gives normal respiratory movement; consequently, it is of great value in the diagnosis of pulmonary inflammations. This reflex shows early in pulmonary tuberculosis, before the disease is widespread. Another factor on the part of the lung in producing diminished motion of the diaphragm is the lessened elasticity of the pulmonary tissue caused by disease processes. It also may result from pleurisy and inflammation of mediastinal structures.

Fig. 48A shows the paths through which stimuli arising in the lung effect a motor reflex in the diaphragm.

Pleura.—When the pleura is inflamed, particularly the lower portion, afferent impulses are carried centralward either through the afferent fibers of the sympathetic system or through the sensory fibers of the intercostal nerves which supply it; and, on reaching the cord, are transmitted to motor neurons in the same segments, which produce a reflex spasm of the intercostal muscles, the costal portion of the diaphragm, and sometimes also of the superficial muscles. Sometimes this tension involves a considerable portion of the muscles of the abdomen, but usually is confined largely to that portion near the

costal margin. The costal portion of the diaphragm, which is innervated by these same lower intercostal nerves, being involved in
the motor reflex and being aided by the superficial muscles, causes
diminished respiratory motion.

Fig. 48*B* shows the paths through which stimuli arising in the lower
portion of the pleura or in the abdominal viscera effect a motor reflex
in the diaphragm.

Abdominal Organs.—Inflammation of the various abdominal viscera, stomach, intestine, appendix, liver, pancreas, or kidney, may
produce a motor reflex which particularly affects the costal portion

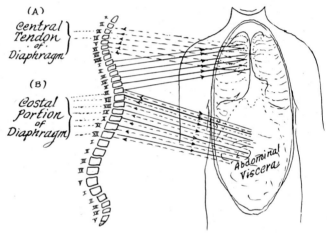

Fig. 48.—Showing diaphragmatic reflex from other organs. *A*, lungs; *B*, abdominal viscera.

A. The motor reflex in the diaphragm which arises from the lungs is shown
in the central tendon of the diaphragm. The impulses travel through the sympathetic afferent system to the cord and are transmitted upward to the cervical
segments where they join with the phrenics, arising from the IIIrd to Vth cervical
segments. The path shown in the figure is schematic. Instead of returning directly
from the lung to the cervical segments as shown, the impulse travels back to the
upper six thoracic segments, then upward to the cervical segments through intercalated neurons in the cord.

B. The diaphragmatic visceromotor reflex which originates from the abdominal
viscera is produced by impulses traveling centralward to the lower seven thoracic
segments, the efferent impulse being expressed through the lower seven intercostal
nerves which supply the costal portion of the diaphragm.

of the diaphragm, the afferent impulse traveling centralward to the
thoracic segments, Vth to XIIth, through the afferents of the sympathetic system which supply these various viscera. When the impulse
reaches the cord, it mediates with the motor neurons in the lower

six thoracic segments and is expressed in action through the intercostal nerves which supply the costal portion (particularly) of the
diaphragm. While the increased tension (spasm) of the muscle cannot be detected as such, it shows as a decreased motility, the same
as the reflex through the phrenics from the lung and through the
intercostals from the pleura. There is another diaphragmatic motor
reflex which affects the crura and central tendon. The impulses
causing it arise in those organs lying below the diaphragm which are
supplied by fibers from the phrenic nerve. The result is that we may
have a limited respiratory motion on the side of involvement, the
same as we have from the thoracic viscera, the difference being that
the lung shows particularly through the phrenics, the pleura through
the lower intercostals, and the abdominal viscera in a reflex less
marked, through both intercostals and phrenics.

Sale has described such a reflex as this in connection with acute
abdominal conditions as mentioned on page 260. It is probable that
the diaphragm, the intercostals, and the superficial muscles all take
part in this reflex diminution of respiratory movement the same as
was mentioned in the preceding paragraph in reference to the reflex
from the pleura.

The innervation of the liver, the small intestine, the appendix,
the ascending colon, and the right kidney is such that they reflect
largely on the right side of the diaphragm, while the stomach, pancreas, descending colon, and left kidney reflect largely on the left
side of the diaphragm.

Peritoneum.—The peritoneum when inflamed produces a motor
reflex in the diaphragm and in the muscles of the abdominal wall,
the impulse going through the afferents of the sympathetic system
to the cord, where it is transferred to the efferent neurons which
are found in the lower intercostal nerves which supply the costal
portion of the diaphragm, on the one hand, and the abdominal
muscles on the other.

References

1. Pottenger, F. M.: Pain and Muscle Tension Caused by Inflammation of the
   Diaphragmatic Costal and Lower Parietal Pleura Simulating That From
   Abdominal Viscera, Surg., Gynec. & Obst. 40: 62, 1925.

2. Pottenger, F. M.: Neuere Methoden zur Diagnose von Lungen- und Pleuraer-
krankungen. Diskussion und Klassifikation der durch Lungen- und
Pleuraentzündungen verursachten sympathischen und parasympathischen
Reflexe; Beschreibung der Palpationsmethode zur Bestimmung von Or-
gangrenzen und Differenzierung pathologischer Zustände, die verschiedene
Dichte in den Organgeweben erzeugen, hauptsächlich in den Lungen und der
Pleura (Leichte Tastpalpation), Beitr. z. klin. d. Tuberk. **60:** 25-604.

3. Neumann, Wilhelm: Die Phrenikusdruckpunkte bei der Lungentuberkulose
und ihre Bedeutung für die Erkennung der blutende seite der Hämoptoe,
für die Frühdiagnose der Lungentuberkulose und die Erkennung der
larvierten Tuberkulose. Beitr. z. klin. d. Tuberk. **45:** 206.

4. Wenckebach: Ueber Pathologische Beziehungen Zwischen Atmung und Kreis-
lauf in Menschen. Sammlung Klinischer Vorträge (Volkmann) Innere
Medizin, 1907, Nos. 140 and 141.

5. Eppinger: Allgemeine und Specielle Pathologie des Zwerchfells, Wien, 1911,
Holder.

CHAPTER XXIII

THE BRONCHI AND LUNGS

I. INNERVATION OF THE BRONCHI AND LUNGS

The bronchi and lungs are developed from a diverticulum from the gastrointestinal canal, hence have the same innervation as other parts of the enteral system. They are activated by the vagus and receive inhibitory fibers from the sympathetics, as shown in Plate I, page 46.

Parasympathetics.—Connector fibers to the smooth musculature surrounding the bronchi and to the glands of the mucous membrane, come from the visceral nucleus of the vagus and join the motor cells in the walls of the bronchi.

According to Larsell[1, 2, 3] these end in plexiform terminations in the epithelium of the primary bronchi and at the point of bifurcation of all orders of bronchi as far as the alveolar ducts. He has also shown that sensory fibers terminate in the muscles of the bronchi. He has been able to distinguish three different and distinct types of terminations of afferent nerves which he describes as being suggestive of three different afferent functions. As in the intestines and the heart, the motor cells of the parasympathetic system lie within the walls of the bronchi, while the vagus supplies the connector fibers which unite them with the central nervous system.

Stimulation of the afferent fibers which course in the nervi laryngeus superior, tracheales and bronchiales and whose cells lie in the sensory nucleus solitarius of the vagus, carries impulses to centers in the brain which have an inhibiting influence on the respiratory center and cause the reflex act known as cough. They also carry afferent impulses which are responsible for many parasympathetic reflexes in other organs.

In order to understand the parasympathetic reflexes from the lung it is necessary to remember that afferent vagus fibers bear a relationship to motor and sensory neurons of other cranial nerves and to its own motor neurons, similar to that of the afferent sympathetic system

301

to the efferent neurons both spinal and sympathetic which arise from the same spinal segments. This gives a basis for a wide distribution of reflexes.

The relationship to the spinal accessory is very important inasmuch as the spinal portion of this nerve, along with certain cervical spinal nerves, is responsible for motor reflexes in the sternocleidomastoideus and trapezius muscles when the pulmonary tissue is inflamed.

Sympathetics.—The lungs are supplied by connector fibers which arise from the upper five or six thoracic segments of the cord. They pass to the stellate ganglion and there end in motor cells of the sympathetic system which send out true sympathetic fibers through the plexus pulmonalis to the lungs. Sympathetic fibers course with the blood vessels and bronchi throughout the pulmonary tissue.

Sympathetic fibers carry vasoconstrictor impulses to the vessels of the lungs. This was long disputed but now seems to have been definitely proved. They also carry impulses which are inhibiting to the vagus, whose function is to relax the bronchial musculature and depress bronchial secretion; and further, there are sympathetic fibers which influence respiration.

II. THE LUNGS: CLINICAL CONSIDERATION

I first described the motor reflex from the lung in 1909,[4] and since that time have described many reflexes which are produced by impulses which arise in the pulmonary parenchyma.[5-12] While these various reflexes are definite, as far as their clinical manifestations are concerned, I at first found great difficulty in tracing the paths through which they are produced, owing to the paucity of knowledge of the vegetative neurology of the lung.

Clinically, we have reflexes, some of which, according to present knowledge and our best reasoning, have their afferent components in the sympathetic, and others in the parasympathetic system. It was necessary first to approach the study and development of the subject of pulmonary reflexes from the clinical standpoint and leave the detailed physiologic study to follow later.

There are certain controversial points which relate to the afferent fibers which mediate the motor and trophic reflexes in the muscles, subcutaneous tissue, and skin and cause the referred pain in areas supplied by the cervical spinal nerves. There are very excellent clinical reasons, as well as reasons of analogy, which make it appear that these phenomena are due to impulses carried over afferent neurons belonging to the sympathetic system as I have discussed elsewhere.[13] There is histologic evidence, on the other hand, which indicates that many afferent fibers from the lung belong to the vagus nerve. (Larsell,[3] Rasmussen.[14, 15]) The experiments of Heinbecker,[16] as described on page 349, in reference to cardiac pain, might also suggest the possibility of afferent impulses from the lung being carried back to the central nervous system via the Vth cranial nerve, the rami communicantes, and the dorsal roots of the upper cervical nerves.

That the pulmonary reflexes are expressed in somatic structures through the midcervical spinal nerves is proved by clinical experience. The course of the impulse from the lung to the efferent fibers, however, will have to await further investigation. It seems to me that the transfer of the impulse from the upper thoracic segments to the midcervical over intracentral paths has both embryology and clinical observation to recommend it.

The path of these reflexes will have to be left to the future, although their existence has been established clinically and their importance is gradually demanding a free and frank discussion.

In order for impulses arising in the lung and coursing in the sympathetic system to produce reflexes in tissues supplied by cervical spinal nerves, it is necessary for them to depart from the usual law of afferent impulses mediating most readily in the segment of the cord which the afferent fiber enters, as laid down by Sherrington, see page 169. Since, however, the lungs embryologically, belong far cephalad in the body, and since intercalated neurons are interposed normally in such a manner as to make such reflex paths possible, it requires no breach of physiologic principles to accept such as the normal path for the viscerosomatic reflexes. For these reflexes to be caused through the parasympathetics (vagus), on the other hand, there would have to be a complete departure from the reflex paths found in other viscera of the enteral system.

For these reflexes to be produced by impulses transmitted over afferents of the sympathetic system, the following would be the course: the impulses from the lungs course in the afferents of the sympathetic system to the same segments of the cord (Ist to VIth thoracic) as those from which the connector fibers originate; but in producing reflex motor, sensory, and trophic reflexes, they mediate with mid-cervical spinal nerves. Therefore, intercalated fibers must transmit the impulses from the upper thoracic to the midcervical segments where they mediate reflexes with the cervical spinal nerves. Fig. 49 from Villiger illustrates the intercalated neurons, their axons, and collaterals over which such impulses may be carried.

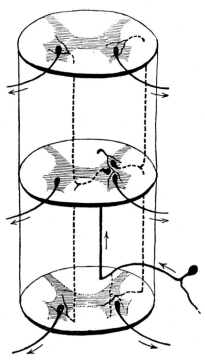

Fig. 49.—Reflex paths in the spinal cord showing the manner in which impulses are distributed to other levels by intercalated neurons. (Villiger.)

Solid lines represent neurons going to and from the cord. Broken lines represent neurons distributing impulses to other levels.

Inasmuch as the sensory, motor, and trophic reflexes from the lung belong to the more complex reflexes, I desire to make plain the difference between these and the simple reflex, and cannot do better than quote from Villiger:[17]

"The simplest reflex path is established by the *reflex collaterals.* In this case only two neurons share the entire path, the transference from the centripetal to the centrifugal neuron being accomplished by means of the collaterals given off directly from the centripetal or afferent neuron.

"The release of the reflex may be induced, however, by intercalated neurons. Thus, between the centripetal and the centrifugal neuron a third neuron may intervene, thereby making possible the transference of the impulse conveyed by a single centripetal neuron to several centrifugal ones. Such intercalated neurons, for example, are the association-cells of the spinal cord, which distribute, by means of their axons and collaterals, impulses to many cells within the cord-segments of higher and lower levels. To this category belongs, further, the posterior longitudinal bundle. Impulses carried to Deiters' nucleus by the vestibular nerve may be distributed to the nuclei of the eye-muscles and to the motor cells of the cord by means of fibers, which proceed from Deiters' nucleus and run within the posterior longitudinal bundle. In consequence of the introduction of several neurons between the centripetal and the centrifugal conduction, the entire reflex mechanism may become very complex."

In this quotation, Villiger terms afferent fibers, centripetal, and efferent, centrifugal.

It has been my pleasure to describe a number of new reflexes from the lung, and further to offer an explanation for many of those described by others. In recent papers I have classified pulmonary reflexes into four groups.[18, 19] This grouping will, I hope, make clear the function of the vegetative system as a correlator of action and show the importance of understanding the visceral relationships.

It will be seen that some of these reflexes have diagnostic importance attached to them, while others have none. Some of them apparently do the patient no harm but others are extremely harmful.

Tables IV and V contain the reflexes for which the impulses from the lung are carried over afferent neurons of the sympathetic system. In Table IV the activating arm of the reflex is found in the spinal nerves, particularly those which take their origin from the midcervical segments of the cord. In Table V, I have arranged reflexes in which the impulse from the lung is carried centralward over neurons of the sympathetic system and is expressed in other tissues by sympathetic neurons. The reflexes in Table IV are expressed in skeletal structures; those in Table V, in visceral structures. In Tables VI and VII, I have arranged reflexes in which the impulses from the lung are carried over afferent parasympathetic fibers. Table VI contains those involving skeletal tissues, which are expressed through cranial nerves; while Table VII contains those in which the impulse from the lung courses over afferent parasympathetic fibers and is expressed peripherally in tissues and structures innervated by parasympathetic neurons. Table VI contains skeletal reflexes while Table VII contains those of a visceral nature.

TABLE IV

PULMONARY REFLEXES IN SKELETAL STRUCTURES IN WHICH STIMULI COURSE CENTRALWARD OVER THE AFFERENT FIBERS OF THE SYMPATHETIC SYSTEM AND PRODUCE REFLEXES IN THE CERVICAL SPINAL NERVES PRINCIPALLY CIII, CIV AND CV

I. Motor reflexes when the disease is active, as follows:
   1. Spastic contraction of the muscles of the shoulder girdle (sternocleidomastoideus, scaleni, pectorales, subclavius, trapezius, levator anguli scapulae and rhomboidei) and the crus and central tendon of the diaphragm.
   2. Limited motion of the half of the thorax, on which the diseased lung is found, through reflex spastic contraction of the sternocleidomastoideus, scaleni, and subclavius above, and the crus and central tendon of the diaphragm below.

II. Trophic reflexes when the disease becomes chronic, or has healed, as follows:
   1. Atrophy of the muscles of the shoulder girdle.
   2. Atrophy of the skin between the second rib and angle of the jaw anteriorly; and the spine of the scapula and the base of the skull posteriorly.
   3. Atrophy of the subcutaneous tissue between the second rib and the angle of the jaw anteriorly; and the spine of the scapulae and base of the skull posteriorly.

III. Sensory reflexes as follows:
   1. Altered sensation, both superficial and deep, usually in the form of discomfort or aching rather than sharp pain; noted both when the disease is acute and when chronic.
   2. Vasomotor phenomena producing flushing of the ear through the IIIrd cervical sensory nerve, when the disease is active.

TABLE V

VISCERO-VISCERAL PULMONARY REFLEXES IN WHICH BOTH AFFERENT AND EFFERENT STIMULI COURSE OVER THE SYMPATHETICS

I. Motor and secretory visceral reflexes when the disease is active, such as:
   1. Dilatation of pupil.
   2. Inhibition of motor and secretory activity in gastrointestinal canal.
   3. Spasm of sphincters in gastrointestinal canal.
   4. Increased heart action (tachycardia).
   5. Probably decreased motility and decreased secretory activity in ducts and glands of gall bladder, liver, and pancreas, although not readily proved.

II. Probably trophic reflexes in structures subject to reflex action, when the disease is chronic or has healed.

TABLE VI

PULMONARY REFLEXES IN SKELETAL STRUCTURES IN WHICH STIMULI COURSE
CENTRALWARD OVER THE PARASYMPATHETICS (VAGUS) AND PRODUCE
REFLEXES IN VARIOUS CRANIAL NERVES

I. Motor reflexes when the disease is active, as follows:
1. Spasm of the sternocleidomastoideus and trapezius, through the spinal accessory. (Possibly spasm of all muscles of the shoulder girdle, through cervical nerves, as suggested by Rasmussen.)
2. Motor reflexes in the facial muscles through the facialis and trigeminus.
II. Trophic reflexes when the disease becomes chronic or has healed, as follows:
1. In the facial muscles through the facialis and trigeminus.
2. In the tongue, causing atrophy and sometimes deviation toward affected side, through the hypoglossus and lingual nerve.
III. Sensory reflexes as follows:
1. Headache, face ache, etc., through the sensory branches of the trigeminus, when the disease is both acute and chronic.
2. Vasomotor phenomena producing flushing of the face, through the sensory fibers of the trigeminus when the disease is active.

TABLE VII

VISCERO-VISCERAL PULMONARY REFLEXES IN WHICH BOTH AFFERENT AND
EFFERENT STIMULI COURSE OVER THE PARASYMPATHETICS

I. Motor and secretory visceral reflexes when the disease is active, such as:
1. Increased secretion in the mucous glands of the nasal and nasopharyngeal mucous membranes (catarrh) through the VIIth cranial nerve.
2. Disturbances in the motility of the vocal cords through the superior and inferior laryngeal nerves.
3. Probably motor reflexes in the lingual muscles through the hypoglossus since this atrophies when the disease becomes chronic.
4. Slowing of heart through the vagus.
5. Increased motility and increased secretory activity in gastrointestinal canal through the gastric and intestinal fibers of the vagus, favoring appetite and digestion in early nontoxic lesions.
6. Probably increased motility and increased secretory activity in the ducts and glands of liver, gall bladder, and pancreas, favoring digestion, although not readily proved.
7. Cough, the afferent impulse being carried over the vagus to a center from which efferent impulses go out producing sensation in the larynx over the superior laryngeal nerve, action in the abductor muscles of the larynx over the inferior laryngeal nerve, and in all expiratory muscles through the various spinal nerves; and simultaneously producing inhibition of action in the adductor muscles of the larynx and the muscles of inspiration.
The cough reflex is produced through spinal nerves more than through parasympathetics.
II. Trophic reflexes in structures subject to reflex action when the disease is chronic or has healed.
1. In the tissues of the nasopharynx through the facialis.
2. In larynx through superior and inferior laryngeal nerves.
3. Probably in heart, gastrointestinal tract, liver, and pancreas, though not readily proved.
III. Sensory phenomena.
1. Laryngeal irritation through the superior laryngeal nerve.

The importance of these various reflexes will appear as the discussion proceeds. This classification furnishes a basis for grouping reflexes which arise in other viscera, as well as those arising in the lung; hence its importance. There are many other reflexes, some evident, others only probable with our present state of knowledge of vegetative activity, which may be worked out and classified in one of these four groups. It is quite probable also that we have impulses which travel over the afferents of the sympathetic system which may be transferred to the parasympathetics for action, and also impulses which course over the parasympathetics, which may be transferred to the sympathetics for completion of the action. All of these possibilities must be considered in our future study of reflex relationships.

Sympathetic Reflexes

Pulmonary Visceromotor Reflexes.—When the lung is inflamed, impulses course centralward to the upper thoracic posterior root ganglia; but instead of being directly transferred to the spinal nerves in the corresponding segments, they are carried upward in the cord through intercalated neurons, as previously mentioned, and transferred to motor and sensory spinal nerves in the midcervical segments. Therefore, we have a different distribution of visceral reflexes when the stimulation arises in the lungs from what we have when it arises in most other organs—as for example, the reflexes which occur from stimuli in the intestines. In intestinal reflexes impulses seem to be carried strongest in the spinal nerves emerging from the same segments that receive the impulses over the afferents sympathetic fibers. See Tables IV and V (page 306) for the grouping of the sympathetic pulmonary reflexes.

The visceromotor, viscerosensory, and viscerotrophic reflexes which arise from stimuli originating in the lungs seem to manifest themselves in tissues supplied by nerves arising in most of the cervical segments, but to be more marked in those tissues supplied by neurons arising in the IIIrd to Vth segments. They appear as motor and sensory changes in the tissues supplied by the cervical spinal nerves; and, if the disease becomes chronic, as trophic changes.

In the lung and pleura we have an opportunity to prove clinically that there is a differentiation in innervation between the anterior and posterior portions of the lung and pleura, for, if there is an inflammation in the anterior portion of the lung or pleura, the motor, and later, the trophic changes in the tissues manifest themselves in the anterior muscles and other soft tissues; while if the posterior part of the lung is involved, the posterior superficial soft structures show the reflex changes. It is not at all uncommon to find spasm in the anterior muscles, and degeneration in the soft tissues anteriorly, and none or little posteriorly, and vice versa.

The visceromotor reflex which is caused by inflammation in the lung shows itself in the contraction of the fibers of those muscles which receive their origin from the cervical portion of the cord and particularly from the IIIrd to Vth segments. This is recognized clinically as an increased tone or spasm. The muscles which show this

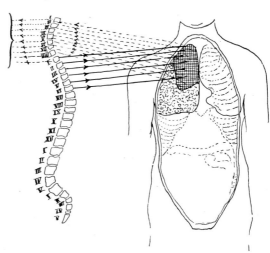

Sterno Cleido mastoideus
Scaleni
Pectorales
Diaphragm
Trapezius
Levator Anguli Scapulae
Rhomboidei

Fig. 50.—Schematic illustration of pulmonary visceromotor reflex.
Lines running between the lung and the spinal cord represent sympathetic connectors. Solid lines carry innervation to the lung. Broken lines carry the impulses from the lung to the cord, where they are transmitted upward to the cervical portion to engage spinal motor nerves, which complete the reflex. The muscles involved in this reflex are shown in the cut. The path of the reflex is not, as shown in the cut, directly from the lung to the cervical portion of the cord, but back to the upper six thoracic segments, from which it is carried upward to the cervical portion by intercalated neurons as shown in Fig. 49, page 304.

best (Fig. 50) are the sternocleidomastoideus, scaleni, pectoralis, trapezius, levator anguli scapulae, rhomboidei and diaphragm;[6, 7] receiving innervation from the cervical segments from the IInd to the VIIIth. While the spasm cannot be seen or felt in the diaphragm, the increased tension in this muscle may be inferred from the diminished motion of the side of the chest from which the visceromotor reflex arises.

It is characteristic of the visceromotor reflex, as well as the viscero-sensory and viscerotrophic reflexes, that it is confined largely to the side of involvement. It readily will be understood that increased tonus or spasm in the muscles of respiration, would have a tendency to fix the side involved, resulting in a lessened respiratory movement.

The muscles which take the greatest part in limiting the respiratory movement, unless the intercostals are also in spasm as a result of an underlying pleuritis, are the diaphragm below, as may be inferred from Fig. 47, page 295, and the scaleni above which fix the upper portion through their attachments to the first and second ribs. They are aided, however, by the sternocleidomastoideus and subclavius. The effect of the diaphragm in limiting motion may be appreciated readily because it is the most important muscle of respiration.

The motor reflex (spasm) on the part of these various muscles, sometimes appears as an increase in size; at other times as an increased prominence and augmented tonus because of their shortening. It may sometimes be seen on inspection and may usually be determined more or less readily by palpation.

The readiness with which the motor reflex is determined will depend upon the character of the muscles in a given patient prior to the pulmonary inflammation; that is, whether naturally well developed or not; whether hypertrophied as a result of the character of work pursued; or degenerated as a result of previous occupation or previous chronic inflammation. Individuals whose vocation does not call for an unusual use of the arms, generally have a lengthening of the muscles of the shoulder girdle, and a dropping of the shoulder on the side of the hand which they use most. This affects particularly the sternocleidomastoideus, pectoralis, and acromial portion of the trapezius. The levator anguli scapulae and rhomboidei, on the other hand, are usually larger than on the other side. It is only those who do strenuous work who show enlargement of all these muscles. This must always be taken into consideration in the examination of patients. Reflex muscle tension is of great diagnostic value, but all conditions which normally produce increased muscle tension must be considered if we would correctly interpret palpation and auscultatory findings.

It is difficult to determine the motor reflex in individuals with poorly developed muscles, also in those whose muscles are firm from use. If the palpable muscles in the latter type of cases are in reflex tension as a result of inflammation in the lung, the same reflex increased tonus will be present in the crus of the diaphragm and together with the scaleni and other neck muscles above, will produce a diminished motion of the corresponding hemothorax.

A word regarding the method of palpating for reflex muscle tension is in order at this time. Many who fail to find this important reflex do so because of faulty technique. The groups of muscles to be palpated should be *actively* relaxed. If the muscles are held in a thoroughly relaxed condition for some little time before they are palpated, it will be found that those particular fasciculi or bundles that are in reflex spasm will show their tension by contrast with the thoroughly relaxed bundles which are not affected.

In preparing for palpating the muscles, the patient should thoroughly relax his shoulders. Preliminary to this, however, the patient should sit erect with the feet flat on the floor, and in such a way that the trunk is supported on the pelvis in a perfectly easy manner, the anterior and posterior muscles, likewise the muscles of each side, being thoroughly relaxed. Relaxation of the muscles to the fullest extent is necessary in order to avoid error.

It must be remembered that flat muscles may show reflex spasticity in certain fasciculi or bundles, while the remaining fasciculi or bundles show normal tone. For this reason I have found that palpating by slight pressure of the finger pulps, followed by rapid release similar to the movement used in playing the piano, enables one to recognize the tension best. The fasciculi rebound against the palpating finger as it is released in the same manner that the string of a bow rebounds.

Pulmonary Viscerosensory Reflex.—The viscerosensory reflex resulting from inflammation in the lungs is expressed by the nerves which arise from the same cervical segments that show the visceromotor reflex. The fact that inflamed pulmonary tissue does not cause referred acute pain, such as accompanies acute inflammation of hollow viscera, such as the intestines, is often taken as proof that there is no referred pain from the lung; but such conclusion is unwarranted. Pain is only one of many sensory phenomena found in somatic and visceral structures. The sensory reflex from the lung manifests itself more often as an altered reaction to sensations of heat and cold in the skin and a sensation of soreness in the deep tissues. The areas in the skin which show the greatest departure from normal in sensation are those supplied by the IIIrd to Vth cervical nerves, as shown in Fig. 51, *A* and *B*, the same areas that show the viscerosensory reflex from the liver and the diaphragm through the phrenics. These nerves supply the skin and subcutaneous tissue over the neck and shoulder down as low as the second rib

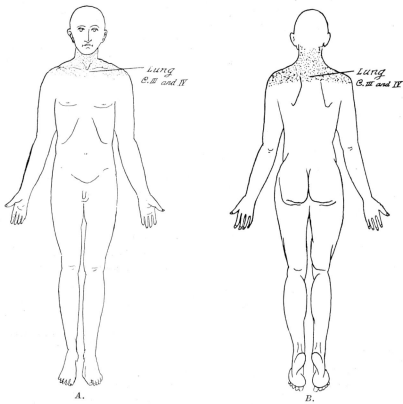

A.   B.

Fig. 51.—Pulmonary viscerosensory reflex. *A*, anterior view; *B*, posterior view. Note that the IIIrd and IVth cervical sensory zones are involved, the same as are shown in the phrenic sensory reflex from the diaphragm; and on the right side the same as found in the hepatic viscerosensory reflex. Cutaneous pain from the lungs is for the most part, if not wholly, expressed above the 2nd rib (*A*) and the spine of the scapulae (*B*). Deep pain is expressed in all the muscles of the shoulder girdle, Fig. 50.

anteriorly and the spine of the scapula posteriorly, and out over the deltoid muscle. The deep soreness may involve all muscles of the shoulder girdle, hence appear down over the chest.

This viscerosensory reflex is extremely common in tuberculosis, in both its acute and chronic forms. Patients with tuberculosis do complain of pain in the interscapular region and over the anterior surface of the chest, but more often of a soreness. These particular sensory reflexes are deep pains expressed by the cervical sensory nerves which supply the muscles. The mediastinal tissues and those about the hilum of the lung, which are extrapulmonary, produce their reflex effects particularly in the interscapular region, and to a lesser extent along the border of the sternum. The pleura may produce hyperesthesia or hyperalgesia of the superficial tissues anywhere in the areas supplied by the thoracic spinal nerves. I have noticed a very interesting viscerosensory reflex complained of in the fingers in a few instances. This is important because it shows that, while the greatest degree of sensory change seems to be in the IIIrd and IVth cervical segments, changes in sensation may also take place through the lower cervical segments. One case was a man who had a chronic tuberculosis which had left him with large cavities in the right lung. Every now and then an increase in the inflammatory process was experienced. At such times he felt a peculiar sensation in the ends of his fingers, which must have been brought about through the VIIth and VIIIth cervical and Ist thoracic sensory nerves.

It will be noticed that the skin areas and muscle areas which show pain from the lungs are not coextensive, yet they have an innervation in common. The cervical cutaneous zones which are particularly involved in the sensory reflexes, when the pulmonary parenchyma is inflamed, do not extend below the second rib anteriorly and the spine of the scapula posteriorly. Sensory nerves, however, from the same cervical segments supply the muscles belonging to the shoulder girdle, which include the pectoralis, trapezius, and rhomboidei which extend far down over the chest wall. This offers an explanation for the fact that the pulmonary sensory reflexes show in the skin of the neck, shoulders, and the chest above the second rib anteriorly and the spine of the scapula posteriorly; while the pain or soreness which affects the muscles may extend down over the chest itself. This later expresses itself clinically as a "deep pain." The basis for this explanation lies in the difference in distribution of the cervical nerves going to the skin and those going to the muscles, as shown in Figs. 19, A and B, and 20, A and B, pages 150 to 153, from Dejerine.

Pulmonary Viscerotrophic Reflex.—The viscerotrophic reflex from the lung likewise expresses itself in all tissues affected by the viscero-motor and viscerosensory reflexes. The nutrition of tissues depends upon both sensory and motor nerves. The nutrition of the skin and subcutaneous tissue is influenced by the sensory spinal nerves, through which the sympathetic nerves which supply the blood vessels course. Both sensory and motor nerves belonging to the spinal system and the vasomotors of the sympathetic system enter into the nutritional control of muscles and other skeletal structures. We find that the pulmonary viscerotrophic reflex shows itself best in the IIIrd to Vth cervical sensory zones. It is most marked in the skin and subcuta-neous tissue of the neck, extending downward over the chest to the second rib anteriorly and to the spine of the scapula posteriorly. It also affects all muscles which are brought into action by the viscero-motor reflex as detailed above; but particularly those receiving in-nervation from the anterior roots of the IIIrd to Vth segments, thus: sternocleidomastoideus, scalenus anticus and medius, trapezius, leva-tor anguli scapulae, and rhomboidei. The muscles affected are shown in Fig. 50, page 309. Thus the viscerotrophic is much wider in the extent of tissue involved than visceromotor, and coextensive with vis-cerosensory reflexes.

There is a condition present in most people which proves to be very confusing in determining the trophic reflex changes which arise from the lung in the soft tissues immediately below the clavicle on the side of the arm that is used more. As previously mentioned, the shoulder on the side which is used more, is lower than the other because of a lengthening of the muscles which support it. As the acromion drops, the insertion of the pectoralis in the upper arm is lowered. This lowers the entire pectoral muscle mass and accentuates the subclavicu-lar groove. This must not be mistaken for the reflex degeneration of subcutaneous tissue and muscle which results from inflammation of pulmonary tissue. Careful examination will reveal the difference and show the lessening of the subcutaneous tissue as well as the changes in its texture which denote atrophy.

While innervation follows the body segmentation for the most part, yet it is not exact, and extension beyond the usual limits of a given nerve may now and then be found. Roughly speaking, however, it may be said that a viscerotrophic reflex affecting the skin and sub-cutaneous tissue above the second rib anteriorly and the spine of the scapula posteriorly and extending up into the neck, is of pulmonary origin; while that extending from these areas downward to the lower costal margin, is of pleural origin. It must be remembered, however, that the visceral pleura has the same nerve supply as the lung, and,

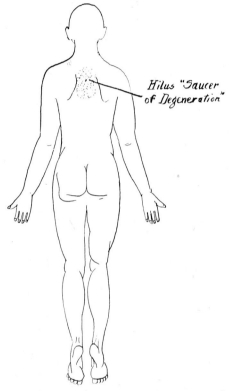

Hilus "Saucer of Degeneration"

Fig. 52.—Hilus viscerotrophic reflex. "Hilus saucer of degeneration."
This reflex shows as a dengeration and wasting of the skin and subcutaneous tissue in the interscapular space. In some cases this degeneration is so marked that it appears hollowed out like a saucer.

consequently, reflects above the second rib and spine of the scapula the same as the lung. Since a tuberculous pleuritis of severe degree rarely occurs without involvement of the underlying lung, degenera-tion of the soft tissues in these areas may be taken to mean an inflam-matory process, chronic or healed, in the corresponding lung. It is also possible that mediation to a limited extent might take place between the afferents of the sympathetic system of the lung and the efferent spinal neurons in the upper five or six thoracic segments although this is difficult to establish.

The viscerotrophic reflex from the lung, as it manifests itself in the skin and subcutaneous tissues on the anterior surface of the chest, often appears as what I have termed a "collar of degeneration." This degeneration affects both skin and subcutaneous tissue and shows in the same tissues which are the seat of superficial pain when the pulmonary parenchyma is inflamed (Fig. 51, page 312). At a glance it is

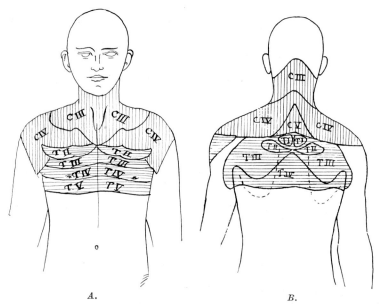

A.   B.

Fig. 53.—*A*, Anterior view, showing the cutaneous and subcutaneous areas which are affected by pulmonary viscerosensory and viscerotrophic reflexes.

This viscerotrophic reflex is shown particularly as a degeneration of the skin and subcutaneous tissue supplied by the IIIrd and IVth, and slightly by the Vth, cervical sensory roots. It will be seen that anteriorly this includes the tissues of the neck, shoulders, and chest down as far as the second rib.

B, Posterior view, showing the cutaneous and subcutaneous areas which are affected by the pulmonary viscerosensory and viscerotrophic reflexes. This includes the neck, shoulders, and that portion of the chest above the spine of the scapula. The interscapular tissues involving T.I, T.II, T.III, and T.IV show the "hilus saucer of degeneration."

often noticed that the skin gives a different appearance. There seems to be different pigmentation in the area which is degenerated from that which is not. Posteriorly, in the interscapular space, I have called attention to what I have termed the "hilus saucer of degen-

eration," as shown in Fig. 52, likewise affecting both skin and subcutaneous tissue. This, I believe, indicates that there has been at
some time a marked inflammation of the hilar tissues. The hilar
glands are extrapulmonary structures, hence reflect in different cutaneous zones from the lung. On palpation the wasting of the subcutaneous tissue in the areas of the reflex is readily determined.
It is thinner than normal, has lost its elastic tone, and feels lifeless
and doughy.

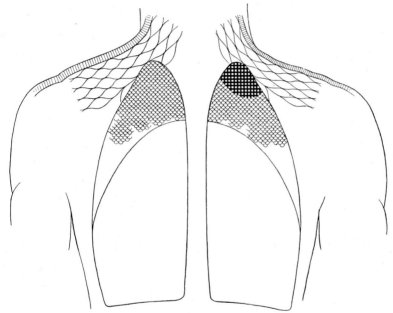

Fig. 54.—Illustrating schematically the degenerative effects upon soft tissues
produced reflexly by a chronic inflammation in one lung. The subcutaneous tissue
and muscle mass is much smaller than on the other side. This materially influences the percussion note, and must be considered in interpreting findings, on
palpation, percussion, and auscultation.

The viscerotrophic reflex furnishes particularly convincing proof
that the innervation of the anterior and posterior portions of the
lungs are supplied by distinct and separate groups of nerve fibers,
which likewise mediate with spinal neurons which are confined in
their distribution to anterior and posterior areas on the body surface.
As previously stated inflammation in the anterior portion of the lung,
if it becomes chronic, reflects on the anterior surface of the neck and
upper chest; while that in the posterior part of the lung, particularly

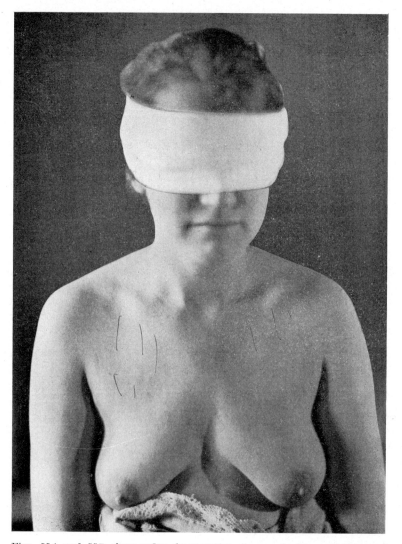

Figs. 55A and 55B show reflex degenerative changes in the soft tissues of a patient with extensive chronic tuberculosis of the right lung and pleura and a slight lesion of the left lung.

Fig. 55A.—Anterior view. On the right side it will be noted that the degeneration of the soft tissues extends from the angle of the jaw to the fourth or fifth rib. This indicates that both the underlying lung and pleura are involved.

The trophic reflex from the lung and visceral pleura is expressed between the angle of the jaw and second rib, which is very marked in this case.

The trophic reflex from the parietal pleura extends from the second rib down over the chest, at times even a little below the lower costal margin. Inasmuch as the degeneration is very evident between the second and fourth or fifth ribs, it shows that the parietal pleura is extensively involved.

Aside from the trophic changes it will be seen that the sternocleidomastoideus stands out somewhat prominently, which is indicative of increased tension due to the motor reflex, indicating an active inflammation in the corresponding lung at the time the picture was taken.

On the left side very slight degeneration is shown above the second rib. Apparently none below. This is indicative of a comparatively smaller healed or chronic lesion than that on the right, without any marked pleural involvement.

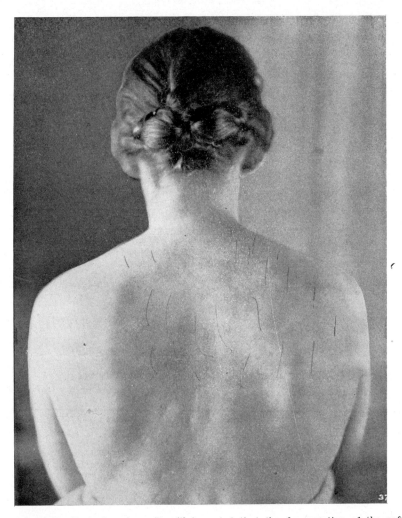

Fig. 55B.—Posterior view. It will be noted that the degeneration of the soft tissues extends down over the right shoulder and back. This is the result of both the trophic reflex from the lung, which expresses itself in the skin and subcutaneous tissue from the base of the skull to the spine of the scapula, and the parietal pleura, which expresses itself from the spine of the scapula down over the chest wall.

On the left side it will be noted that there is very little degeneration, it being practically confined to the areas above the spine of the scapula, indicating a smaller involvement than that on the right, but also chronic or healed.

The trophic changes are also marked in the interscapular space, indicative of an old chronic hilar lesion (hilar saucer of degeneration). These hilar tissues are extrapulmonary and show their reflexes in the interscapular region.

that in the lower lobe, reflects in the posterior soft tissues. The IIIrd and IVth cervical sensory zones which show the viscerotrophic reflex best are indicated in Fig. 53, A and B.

It can be seen that a recognition of the visceromotor, viscerosensory, and viscerotrophic reflexes may be of great advantage in the diagnosis of diseases of the lung, because the changes are evident on examination by inspection and palpation. It can further be seen that the visceromotor and viscerotrophic reflexes may be utilized as a basis for differential diagnosis between inflammation of the lungs and pleura. These reflexes have a further very important bearing upon percussion and auscultation, because the results of percussion and auscultation are greatly modified by the amount and condition of these soft structures through which the percussion blow and auscultatory sound must pass. In some instances on the side of an old chronic pulmonary involvement, the soft tissues will be so degenerated that they are reduced from 30 to 50 per cent in volume as compared with those on the normal side. This is shown schematically in Fig. 54 and as it actually appears in Figs. 55, A and B. One can readily see that such a condition must greatly modify the comparative percussion and auscultatory findings. At other times, the visceromotor reflex causes such a tension of the musculature that it raises the pitch of the percussion note and increases the resistance to the finger. This same condition also modifies the respiratory sound as elicited by auscultation. The photographs shown in Fig. 55, pages 318 and 319, illustrate the trophic changes in the muscles and subcutaneous tissues on the right side of the chest and spasm of the neck muscles on the left.

Parasympathetic Reflexes

As parasympathetic pulmonary reflexes we describe reflexes in other tissues resulting from impulses which travel centralward over the sensory fibers of the vagus and express themselves peripherally in other organs or tissues of the body, as shown in Tables VI and VII, page 307. Likewise we must classify reflexes which express themselves in the bronchial musculature and secretory glands, through the efferent branches of the pulmonary vagus, the impulse originating in the lung itself, or in other viscera, such as, at times, are responsible for asthma and bronchitis.

PARASYMPATHETIC REFLEXES SHOWN ON THE PART OF OTHER VISCERA,
THE IMPULSES ORIGINATING IN THE LUNG

Vagus.—Inflammatory conditions in the lung may influence reflexly the smooth musculature and secreting glands in all structures
supplied by the vagus nerve. In some of these the effect is very
evident.

In the *larynx* we have motor, sensory, and secretory reflexes shown
through the superior laryngeal nerve. The parasympathetic sensory
reflex in patients suffering from pulmonary disease is expressed
through the superior laryngeal nerve as an irritation in the pharynx
and larynx and a sensation which is followed by coughing. There is
also a motor reflex shown through this nerve, which manifests itself
in a condition in which the cords are relaxed and baggy in the center
instead of approaching each other as they should. This comes from
an interference with the innervation of the cricothyroid muscle. The
inferior laryngeal nerve supplies the remaining muscles of the larynx;
and many disturbances in muscular action, which manifest themselves
in an abnormal approach of the cords, are found as a result of the
pulmonary reflex. These two reflexes produce various degrees of
hoarseness and aphonia, which may be noted at any period from the
time that the pulmonary tissue is first irritated until the disease ends.
They are shown in Figs. 71 and 72, page 378.

The glands of the pharynx and larynx also receive innervation
from the two laryngeal branches of the vagus and an *increased
secretion* is frequently noted as a reflex phenomenon.

On the part of the gastrointestinal tract, motor and secretory
disturbances are extremely common as a result of the reflex which
arises from the inflamed lung.

Hypersecretion and hypermotility on the part of the *stomach* and
intestines are frequently produced reflexly by inflammation in pulmonary tissue. On the part of the stomach there may be a hyperchlorhydria—a symptom which may be found in all stages of tuberculosis. This manifests itself at times even during marked toxemia
with high fever. When marked toxemia is present, the sympathetics
are centrally stimulated, and in those structures normally activated by the parasympathetics and inhibited by the sympathetics,
the inhibitory action should predominate; so, throughout the en-

tire gastrointestinal tract, with the exception of the sphincters, we should expect a general relaxation of the musculature and a decreased secretion.

When the pulmonary tissue is involved, however, this does not always occur. In many instances, the prolonged irritation and inflammation in the lung either stimulate reflexly the parasympathetics to such an extent that there is still a marked increase in motility and secretory activity in the gastrointestinal tract in spite of the marked stimulation of the sympathetics produced by the toxemia, or the sphincters are contracted by sympathetic action and cause retention of the stomach contents with acid accumulation. It is extremely common, therefore, to find in our patients suffering from chronic pulmonary tuberculosis, various degrees of hyperacidity and hypermotility. Reflex nausea and vomiting are frequently found during the stages of activity with prolonged toxemia in this disease. Some degree of spasm of the pylorus with an open cardia may be present which permits the regurgitation of food. These are partly reflex, partly nutritional, effects and not wholly due to toxemia, as formerly explained. These symptoms appear very commonly when cavities are being formed and marked irritation of the pulmonary tissue is present; also in many patients when the disease has lasted for a long period of time. Increased tonus is also produced in other branches of the vagus nerve. Spastic constipation, intestinal stasis, colicky pains, and colitis are common. Motor and secretory disturbances on the part of the larynx are found, and a pulse slower than would be expected for the condition is frequently present.

In the intestines the hypermotility affects both the circular and longitudinal fibers. If it affects the circular the more, constriction of the bowel takes place, interfering with the onward passage of the ingesta, resulting in colicky pains, spastic constipation, and more or less stasis. If the increased muscular tonus affects the longitudinal instead of the circular fibers, then the ingesta hasten on and a loosening of the bowels and diarrhea may result.

In the intestinal tract we also infer that there is an increased secretory activity, because the stools commonly show an increased water content.

The *spastic constipation,* which is commonly found in pulmonary tuberculosis, may be due to reflex stimulation most marked in the circular muscles. This causes contracture, and the contracture as a rule is uneven, leaving points of constriction and areas between which are in a less degree of tonus. This explains the fact that is well known, that spastic constipation is usually attended by more or less gas and often by colicky pains. The spasticity varies so in degree that it may cause either slight interference, or great difficulty, in emptying the bowel. Some degree of *intestinal stasis* as a result of reflex stimulation is commonly found accompanying pulmonary tuberculosis. It is closely related to spastic constipation in its etiology. Owing to the fact that the ingesta is delayed in its passage through the bowel, an opportunity for increased bacterial action is offered, decomposition takes place with a liberation of toxins and gas. This results in a more or less temporary toxemia, the symptoms of which appear as malaise, headache, and sometimes general aching. There are other symptoms which do not necessarily belong to the toxic group which are also commonly present, such as nausea and vomiting. The condition may relieve itself if the stimulation of the sympathetics which results from the toxemia is sufficient to inhibit the action of the parasympathetics and permit the muscular tonus to lessen. Such conditions, however, are usually treated by cathartics. This moves the ingesta onward and removes the symptoms for the time being.

That form of *colitis* in which there is one or more soft stools a day, is also very common in pulmonary tuberculosis, and could be readily produced by an extra stimulation of the parasympathetics producing increased motility and increased secretory activity, as mentioned above.

That the disturbed equilibrium in the gastrointestinal tract may be of local origin caused by an altered ion content of the cells or an increased cellular permeability due to a relative decrease in the calcium content of the cells may be assumed from the fact that both the hypermotility and hypersecretion may be improved or relieved by the administration of calcium intravenously. Another explanation for the fact might be that the calcium ions increase the normal sympathetic inhibitory effect on the gastrointestinal musculature. It also forms an astringent calcium soap.

Open Cardia.—A common gastric syndrome in chronic diseases of all important internal viscera—the heart, gall bladder, appendix, kidney, and lung—is slow digestion, the accumulation of large quantities of gas with eructations frequently acid in character. The cause usually is a weakened gastric musculature, deficiency of digestive juices, constricted pylorus, and open cardia. The acid eructations are frequently of an organic nature. This syndrome is readily classified as a condition of excessive sympathetic action. Since it is present in nontoxic conditions it seems to be explained best as a sympathetic reflex.

The action of the *heart* may be markedly disturbed in pulmonary tuberculosis. There are numerous conditions present which, acting through the sympathetics, have a tendency to increase the rapidity of the heartbeat, such as toxemia, insufficient oxygenation, and an interference with the normal circulation of the blood as well as the condition of the blood itself, and the various emotional and psychic states to which the patient is subject. On the other hand, there is a continuous stimulation of the pulmonary vagus which produces reflex action and has a tendency to slow the pulse. This makes for a very unstable condition of the pulse in pulmonary tuberculosis. While this may not manifest itself as long as the patient is at rest, when called upon for extra exertion the disturbance in innervation is often evident.

At one time sympathetic action may predominate and at another time vagus action; while in different individuals one may show a predominance of vagus action and the other a predominance of sympathetic action. The effect of vegetative instability on the pulse is shown when the patient is called upon to exert himself; for not only will the heart increase its rate of contraction more than it would under normal conditions, but also it will return to its average beat much more slowly.

The influence of the vagus upon the pulse in pulmonary tuberculosis is often evident even when marked toxemia with high fever is present. Under such circumstances, as a rule, a considerable area of lung tissue is involved and necrosis is usually occurring. The absorption of toxins should be sufficient under ordinary circumstances to stimulate the sympathetics sufficiently to cause a very rapid contraction of the heart, but under these circumstances the irritation to the pulmonary ends of the vagus is often sufficient to produce a reflex action in the cardiac branch of the vagus and cause the pulse rate to be much slower than would be expected from the degree of toxemia present. Sometimes when an acute cavity is forming, instead of the pulse increasing in rate in proportion to the rise of temperature, it remains markedly slower, as illustrated in Fig. 56A.

The patient whose chart is shown here was suffering from a rapidly destructive process in the lung. The inflammation was quite severe, as is indicated by the accompanying temperature chart.

Beginning about the twenty-eighth of July the temperature began to go higher and continued until a maximum of 103° was reached on the first days of August. At this time the patient's cough increased and was accompanied by a very free expectoration, resulting from destruction of tissue and cavity formation.

It will be noticed that the pulse did not follow the temperature; either in the lesser rise during the middle of July, or in the more marked one during the early days of August.

During the first days shown in the chart the temperature was only a little over 99°, and the pulse was about 75. During the early days of August the temperature reached 103° but the pulse only went to 90, making an increase of 4° in temperature but only 15 beats in pulse.

This reflex bradycardia was due to the inflammation in the lung stimulating the afferent pulmonary branches of the vagus which mediate in the medulla with the efferent cardiac branches of the vagus, producing an inhibitory effect on the heart.

Another evidence of reflex vagus stimulation upon the heart is shown in Fig. 56B. The chart is that of a patient suffering from active tuberculosis with accompanying toxemia, who improved readily when put under treatment. The chart shows the pulse to be twenty beats higher at the end of the month with a maximum daily temperature of 99.5° than it was at the beginning with a temperature of 101°. The patient was at rest during the entire time. An explanation of this phenomenon is offered by visceral neurology as follows: At the beginning of the chart toxins were stimulating the sympathetics centrally and exerting an accelerating influence on the pulse; but the accelerating influence was overcome by the inflammation in the lung which was, at the same time, stimulating the pulmonary endings of the vagus, and producing a reflex-inhibiting action upon the heart through the cardiac branches of the vagus. At first the

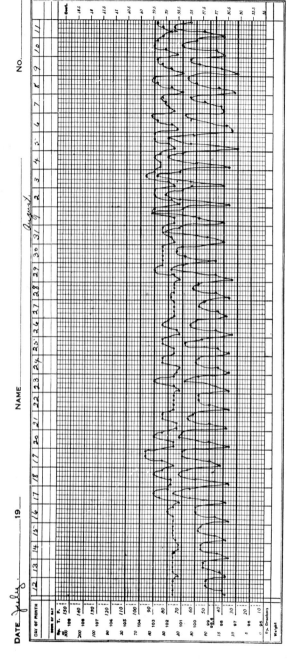

Fig. 56A.—Showing bradycardia in presence of severe allergic reaction and cavity formation in the lung.

This chart represents one month's temperature and pulse of a patient suffering from chronic active ulcerative tuberculosis. During the period from July 29 to August 5, it will be noted that the temperature became very much higher than it had been on the preceding days. This was accompanied by increased cough and expectoration, and a definite cavity formation.

It will be noted that the pulse rate did not increase in proportion to the rise in temperature. The first few days of the chart show a temperature between 99° and 100°, with a pulse between 70 and 80, which was about the same as this patient had been previously running. During this period of cavity formation, the maximum temperature was between 101½° and 103°, yet the pulse range was between 72 and 96, being most of the time below 90. This relatively slow pulse was due to the reflex stimulation of the heart through the vagus by afferent impulses coming from the inflamed lung.

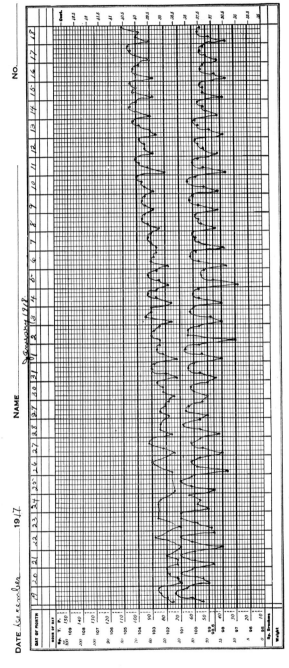

TEMPERATURE CHART

Sp.—Sputum.

Fig. 56B.—Chart showing how inflammation in the lung reflexly slows the heart. The afferent impulse courses through the pulmonary and the efferent through the cardiac branches of the vagus nerve.

At the beginning of the month with a temperature of 101° the maximum pulse for the day was between 80 and 90. The inflammation gradually subsided and at the end of the month the temperature was between 90° and 100° but the pulse had increased, the maximum for the day being between 100 and 110. This chart shows the pulse becoming progressively more rapid as the inflammation in the lung progressively decreases and the reflex stimulation of the vagus lessens.

inhibiting action maintained a relatively slow pulse. But as the inflammation in the lung lessened, as indicated in the chart by the gradual fall in temperature, the reflex-inhibiting effect upon the heart decreased and the pulse became markedly accelerated.

Oculomotor Nerve.—It is quite possible that there are distinct reflex effects which are carried to the IIIrd cranial nerve when the lung is inflamed. An unbalanced *pupil* is present in a great many of our tuberculous patients. Sometimes contraction is in evidence, and sometimes dilatation. Dilatation is a reflex in which both afferent and efferent impulses course in the sympathetic system. The afferent impulse follows the usual course from the lung to the cord and mediates with nerve cells in Budge's center in the lower cervical and upper thoracic segments. From this center efferent stimuli pass out to the cells in the superior cervical ganglion from which arise the dilator fibers for the pupil. Dilatation is commonly recognized but the fact that this symptom is so irregular, being found at one time and not at another, although the observation is made on the same day; and the fact that it is found so irregularly in the disease, can be accounted for by the fact that the dilator fibers of the sympathetics are opposed by the IIIrd cranial nerve which may be reflexly influenced as a result of afferent impulses traveling centralward through the sensory fibers of the vagus.

Patients with pulmonary tuberculosis also suffer a great deal from disturbance in *accommodation*. Oculists often complain that they have difficulty in fitting glasses to patients with tuberculosis, and the patients themselves complain a great deal of the glasses not fitting them. The condition of instability in this instance is much the same as we find in cases of neurasthenia and psychasthenia, where there is disturbance in accommodation except that it is reflex in nature.

Trigeminus.—One of the reflexes which it has been heretofore difficult to explain is that of *hectic flush*. It has generally been considered as being due to toxemia; but that does not explain it. It is a one-sided phenomenon and found on the side of the pulmonary involvement where one lung only is affected; or, on both sides, but varying in degree according to the degree of activity, where both lungs are affected. It seems therefore that reflex action alone can explain this phenomenon.

It has been shown that stimulation of sensory spinal roots either before or after they have passed through the posterior root ganglia causes dilatation of the vessels in the area supplied by the roots, no matter what the character of the stimulus. To explain this Starling[20] says: ''We must assume that the axons of the peripheral sensory nerves branch, some branches going to the surface, others to the muscle cells of the cutaneous arterioles.''

The sensory fibers of the fifth cranial nerve are analogous in their function to the sensory fibers of the spinal nerves; and they stand in the same relationship to the afferent fibers of the vagus in the production of reflexes as the spinal sensory nerves do to the afferent fibers of the sympathetic system.

Dastre and Morat[21] traced the dilator fibers contained in the cervical sympathetics from the spinal nerves and showed that most of them unite in their course with the trigeminus. They showed further, that, by cutting the trigeminus before it is joined by the sympathetics and stimulating the latter, very slight vasodilatation effects are produced; but that, after cutting the cervical sympathetics and permitting the fibers to degenerate, stimulation of the trigeminus was still able to produce vasodilatation of the vessels of the face. ''This proves that there are some dilator fibers in the trigeminus which are of cerebral origin.''

This fact, together with the further fact that the vagus afferent fibers mediate with the sensory efferent neurons of the trigeminus in the medulla, affords a satisfactory explanation for the production of hectic flush as it manifests itself in the areas supplied by the trigeminus nerve.

The most common seat of hectic flush is in the upper portion of the cheek, although in certain cases I have observed it to extend over the side of the nose and over the forehead near the median line.

The flushing of the ear, which is also frequently seen in tuberculosis, has an entirely different path for its production. Here the afferent impulse courses in the sympathetics and is transferred in the cord to the third cervical nerve.

Herpes is a common pulmonary parasympathetic reflex expressed through the trigeminus nerve. It is particularly common in pneumonia, but it is sometimes found in other affections of the lung. It also occurs in common colds and some gastrointestinal conditions. The afferent impulse, in the case of the lung, travels centralward over the sensory fibers of the vagus; the efferent passes outward over the sensory fibers of the trigeminus.

Tooth decay which is so common in pulmonary tuberculosis could be partly accounted for as a pulmonary reflex through the trigeminus.

Facialis.—The vegetative fibers of the VIIth nerve supply the mucous membranes of the *nasal cavities,* mouth, and soft palate. Patients with pulmonary tuberculosis often suffer from an increased secretion of the nasal mucous membrane, which might be due to a parasympathetic reflex. The catarrhal condition of these mucous membranes has long been known in pulmonary tuberculosis. It was taught that the catarrh "ran into" tuberculosis; but now we see it is more probably a parasympathetic reflex, expressing itself through the secretory fibers of the VIIth cranial nerve.

Atrophy of the facial muscles occurs occasionally as a result of stimuli arising in the lung. It is best seen in chronic one-sided lesions accompanied by marked destruction. The facialis has the major part in the production of this reflex, although the trigeminus plays a lesser rôle.

Facialis and Glossopharyngeal.—The *salivary glands* are supplied by the chorda tympani from the VIIth and Jacobson's nerve from the IXth cranial nerves. An increased salivary secretion is noticed in patients suffering from pulmonary tuberculosis every now and then, and particularly is this noticed if the larynx is involved. This also occurs at times in angina pectoris and in stomach disturbances.

Accessorius.—A parasympathetic motor reflex through the accessorius evident when the pulmonary tissue is inflamed is shown in the muscular branches which go to the *sternocleidomastoideus* and *trapezius.* These two muscles have a double source of stimuli which is capable of giving a motor reflex, one from the sympathetics, the other from the parasympathetics. The esophagus and larynx are also affected reflexly through the accessorius.

Hypoglossus.—I noted a few years ago that the tongue of patients suffering from chronic tuberculosis, largely limited to one side, occasionally shows a deviation from the median line when protruding, the tongue sometimes pushing over to the side on which the greater amount of inflammation had occurred. This is a trophic reflex in which the sensory impulse travels through the vagus and the efferent impulse is carried over the trigeminus and hypoglossus. It results in an atrophy of the side of the tongue on which the pulmonary lesion exists, so that the muscle is smaller and weaker than on the other side. When the tongue is protruded, it may be forced to the side on which the disease is found. This is illustrated in Fig. 57.

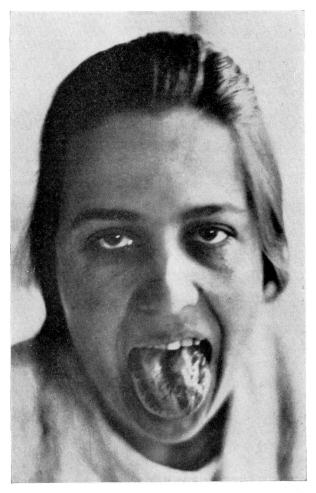

Fig. 57.—Reflex atrophy of the tongue in patient with chronic extensive left-sided pulmonary tuberculosis. It will be noted that the left half of the tongue is degenerated, is smaller than the right half, and that the tongue when protruded turns toward the left. The trophic changes on the left give the appearance of ulceration, but no ulcer exists. The reflex takes place through the trigeminus and hypoglossus.

Pelvic Nerve.—Reflexes from the pulmonary parenchyma expressed in the pelvic nerve are not so readily determined, although it is possible that there is a definite influence exerted upon the generative organs, the bladder, and rectum, which are activated by the parasympathetics.

One cannot understand the reactions which take place in the body unless he bears in mind that organs which are widely separated in the body have their activity closely integrated through the nervous system. Patients with tuberculosis, particularly women, suffer a great deal from a relaxation of the *vesical sphincter.* This might readily be produced by a reflex action, the afferent impulse being carried centralward through the vagus, or more likely the sympathetics, and then through intercalated fibers, being transmitted to the neurons which arise from the sacral portion of the cord, which carry dilator impulses to the bladder sphincter.

Parasympathetic Reflexes Shown on the Part of the Lung, the Impulses Originating Either in the Lung or in Other Viscera

The only two parasympathetic reflexes which can arise in the lung as a result of impulses coming from stimuli originating either in the lung or in other viscera, are increased bronchial tonus or spasm (asthma) and increased bronchial secretion (bronchitis).

We may thus have an *asthma* or a *bronchitis* arising from stimuli in the lung or in other organs. It has long been thought that asthma is frequently of reflex origin, and the seat of the stimulus has been placed in many organs. Pulmonary tuberculosis, eye strain, nasal irritation, polyps, septal spurs and deflections, hay fever, sinus infection, stomach and intestinal irritation, heart affections, and affections of the genitourinary tract, have all been suggested as causes; and all have the physiologic reflex connection through the parasympathetics to produce it. No doubt some cases of bronchitis are also of reflex origin, the afferent impulse arising either in the lung or in other viscera. What the difference in stimulation is that will produce a bronchial spasm at one time and an increased bronchial secretion at another, we cannot answer satisfactorily at this time. It is quite possible that the difference may be a quantitative one in an individual who is a potential asthmatic.[22] I have seen cases of asthma, however, which developed coincidentally with healing of pulmonary tuberculosis with the formation of dense scar. In the bronchitis which accompanies such an asthma the secretory stimulus for the glands may act directly upon the motor cells in the plexuses in the bronchial walls.

It has long been known that patients suffering from pulmonary tuberculosis can eat and digest large quantities of food. Oftentimes, when suffering from a marked degree of toxemia which has a tendency to lower the appetite and digestive capacity, the patients are still able to eat large quantities and digest it. This is probably due to the influence of the parasympathetic reflexes which heighten the muscular contractility and secretory activity of the digestive tube. Even though the sympathetics are markedly stimulated, they are not able to inhibit the vagus activity because of the fact that it is reinforced by the reflex stimulation from the inflammation in the lung.

References

1. Larsell, O.: The Ganglia Plexuses and Nerve Terminations of the Mammalian Lung and Pleura Pulmonalis, J. Comp. Neurol. 35: 97, 1922.
2. Larsell, O.: Some Aspects of the Innervation of the Lung, Northwest Med. 22: 311, 1923.
3. Larsell, O., and Mason, M. I.: Experimental Degeneration of the Vagus Nerve and Its Relation to the Nerve Terminations in the Lung of the Rabbit, J. Comp. Neurol. 33: 509, 1921.
4. Pottenger, F. M.: A New Physical Sign Found in the Presence of Inflammatory Conditions of the Lungs and Pleura, J. A. M. A. 52: 771, 1909.
5. Pottenger, F. M.: Die Rigidität der Muskeln und die leichte Tastepalpation als wichtige Zeichen zur Erkennung der Lungenkrankheiten, Deutsche med. Wchnschr. 1910, No. 16.
6. Pottenger, F. M.: Muskelspasmus und Degeneration. Ihre Bedeutung für die Diagnose intrathoracischer Entzündungen und als causativerer Faktor bei Veränderungen am knöchernen Thorax. Brauer's Beiträge zur Klinik der Tuberkulose 22: No. 1, 1912.
7. Pottenger, F. M.: Muscle Spasm and Degeneration in Intrathoracic Inflammation and Light Touch Palpation, St. Louis, 1912, The C. V. Mosby Co.
8. Pottenger, F. M.: The Relationship of Pulmonary Tuberculosis to the Vegetative Nervous System, Tr. Sect. Practice Med. J. A. M. A., 1917, pp. 173-186.
9. Pottenger, F. M.: The Importance of the Study of Symptoms, With a Discussion of Mackenzie's Law Governing Their Production, Tr. Sect. Practice Med., J. A. M. A., 1921, p. 230.
10. Pottenger, F. M.: Pain and Muscle Tension Caused by Inflammation of the Diaphragmatic Costal and Lower Parietal Pleura Simulating That From Abdominal Viscera, Surg., Gynec. & Obst. 40: 62, 1925.
11. Pottenger, F. M.: Neuere Methoden zur Diagnose von Lungen- und Pleuraerkrankungen, Brauer's Beiträge zur Klinik der Tuberkulose 60: No. 5, 1925.
12. Pottenger, F. M.: The Most Dependable Symptoms for Making a Diagnosis of Early Clinical Pulmonary Tuberculosis, Am. Rev. Tuberc. 15: 194, 1927.
13. Pottenger, F. M.: The Motor, Sensory, and Trophic Reflexes From the Lung, Am. Rev. Tuberc. 15: 477, 1927.

334   SYMPTOMS OF VISCERAL DISEASE

14. Rasmussen, A. T.: The Pathways for Nervous Reflexes From the Parenchyma of the Lung, Am. Rev. Tuberc. **13**: 545, 1926.
15. Rasmussen, A. T.: The Innervation of the Chest, Chap. X, The Normal Chest, by J. A. Myers, Baltimore, 1927, The Williams and Wilkins Company, p. 247.
16. Heinbecker, Peter: Anatomic and Physiologic Criteria for Surgical Relief of Cardiac Pain, J. Thoracic Surg. **2**: 517, 1933.
17. Villiger, Emil: Brain and Spinal Cord, Philadelphia, 1912, J. B. Lippincott Co., p. 192.
18. Pottenger, F. M.: Disturbances in the Vegetative System in Diseases of the Lungs and Visceral Pleura. Proceedings of the Association for Research in Nervous and Mental Disease, 1930, Vol. IX, p. 587.
19. Pottenger, F. M.: Ueber Lungenreflexe mit einem Vorschlag zu deren Einteilung. Festschrift für A. Biedl, Ztschr. für Experimentelle Medizin, 1929.
20. Starling, E. H.: Human Physiology, Philadelphia, 1915, Lea & Febiger, p. 1000.
21. Dastre and Morat: Recherches sur le système nerveux vasomoteur, Paris, 1884, quoted by Luciani, Human Physiology, London, 1911, Macmillan & Co., p. 354.
22. Pottenger, F. M.: The Potential Asthmatic, J. Lab. & Clin. Med. **13**: 913, 1928.

CHAPTER XXIV

THE PLEURA

I. INNERVATION OF THE PLEURA

The pleura receives its nerve supply from the sympathetics, parasympathetics, and the spinal nerves.

Parasympathetics.—The parasympathetic nerves have the same origin as those supplying the lung. The connector motor fibers come from the visceral nucleus of the vagus, and the afferents from the nucleus solitarius of the same nerve. These afferent fibers are particularly in close communication centrally with the sensory fibers of the larynx which course in the superior laryngeal nerve, as is shown by the sensation of irritation with the desire for cough when the pleura is involved. Both visceral and parietal pleura are supplied with parasympathetic fibers from the same source.

Sympathetics.—The sympathetics which supply the pleura are from two different sources. Those which innervate the visceral pleura belong to the pulmonary supply. Their connector neurons arise from the upper five or six thoracic segments and their motor cells lie in the stellate ganglion. The parietal pleura, on the other hand, receives its sympathetic supply partly from the same source as the visceral pleura and partly from filaments which course in the intercostal nerves. The motor fibers originate in the vertebral ganglia and are connected with each thoracic segment from the Ist to the XIIth by its respective connector fibers. The afferent fibers carry impulses to the ganglia on the posterior roots of their respective thoracic segments and mediate reflexes in the same segments. The diaphragmatic pleura also probably receives sympathetic innervation from both sources.

Spinal Nerves.—The spinal nerves which supply the pleura are the phrenics, which furnish motor and sensory fibers to the diaphragm, particularly the central tendon, and two small branches to the apical pleura as the phrenics cross it; and the intercostals (Ist to XIIth inclusive) which supply every portion of the costal pleura.

335

II. THE PLEURA: CLINICAL CONSIDERATION

It will be noted that the pleura differs from most other viscera in that it has a plenteous supply of fibers from the spinal nerves as well as from the sympathetics and parasympathetics. This affords an opportunity for motor, sensory, and trophic reflexes through all three systems. In one the impulse travels centralward through the afferent neurons of the sympathetic system, in another through the parasympathetics, and in the third through the spinal nerves.

Sympathetic Reflexes

Pleural Visceromotor Reflex.—The pleural visceromotor reflex, Fig. 58, has been known for a long time, but it has not received the clinical recognition that it deserves, as witnessed by the frequency with which the diagnosis of intercostal neuralgia is made when acute pleural inflammation is present. It should be recognized by the motor reflex (spasm) in the underlying intercostal muscles which produces a feeling of boardiness.

It is impossible, and only of theoretical value, if possible, to separate the motor reflexes caused by stimuli coursing in the afferent neurons of the sympathetic system and those coursing in the spinal intercostal nerves; therefore no attempt will be made.

The best known motor reflex arising from the pleura is that which expresses itself in the lower intercostal muscles when the underlying pleural surface is the seat of inflammation. That which is found at times in the upper abdominal muscles near and immediately below the costal margin, is usually due to an inflammation of the lowest portion of the parietal or the costal portion of the diaphragmatic pleura, or both. The possibility of its existence should always be borne in mind, when rigid muscles and pain are found in this region. Such signs are usually taken as being due to subdiaphragmatic pathology, but the possibility of their being of lower parietal and diaphragmatic pleural origin should not be forgotten.

The involvement of the upper abdominal wall in the pleural visceromotor and viscerosensory reflexes is an indication that the afferent stimuli have spread to neurons other than those which are usually involved in the reflex. In the same manner we sometimes find pain in angina pectoris in the neck (IIIrd and IVth cervical zones) or over the right side of the chest.

Motor reflexes of pleural origin exist in the upper intercostal muscles more commonly than in the lower, but are rarely recognized. Much of the feeling of resistance that is felt on palpation and percussion over the first and second interspaces in pulmonary tuberculosis, when the disease is acute, may be due to an underlying pleural reflex in the intercostal muscles; or when the disease is chronic, to a thickening of the pleura and advanced pathologic change in the muscles as described by Coplin.[1] The importance of this increased tension of muscles should be impressed on all who have witnessed the frequency of thickening of the pleura over the apices on postmortem examination of bodies with limited apical involvement; and from this, the importance of its recognition as a clinical diagnostic factor should be emphasized.

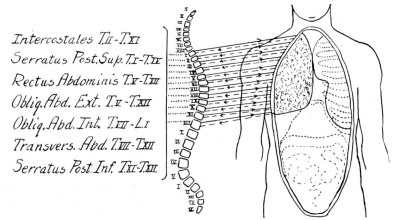

Intercostales T.II-T.XII

Serratus Post.Sup.T.I-T.IV

Rectus Abdominis T.V-T.XII

Oblig.Abd. Ext. T.V-T.XII

Oblig.Abd.Int. T.VIII-L.I

Transvers. Abd. T.VII-T.XII

Serratus Post.Inf. T.XI-T.XII

Fig. 58.—Pleural visceromotor reflex.
Lines connecting the pleura with the segments of the cord from Ist to XIIth, represent sympathetic connectors. Solid lines represent the sympathetic nerves supplying the pleura. Broken lines represent afferent nerves which carry impulses to the cord from the pleura. Dotted lines on the other side of the cord represent corresponding spinal nerves which receive the impulses from the pleura and transmit them to the muscles shown, producing the pleural visceromotor reflex.
When the impulse is strong, the abdominal muscles may also be involved in the pleural visceromotor reflex. At times, particularly when the lower portion of the pleura is involved, this shows as a marked spasm which is sometimes considered as indicating acute disease of abdominal viscera.

The path of the motor reflex involving the intercostal and upper abdominal muscles as a result of pleural involvement, is clear. The afferent impulses travel centralward through the neurons of either the sympathetic or the intercostal systems; and the efferent impulses leave the cord in the spinal nerves arising from the thoracic segments which receive the afferent stimulus. The result is a spasm of the muscles, or that portion of the muscles, which are in reflex relation with the afferent neurons in the cord.

There is another group' of muscles which, from the standpoint of their physiologic reflex relationship, could be the seat of a pleural motor reflex, the afferent impulse traveling through the sympathetic system. This is the same group that shows the visceromotor reflex when the pulmonary tissue is involved, and takes its innervation from the cervical portion of the cord. (See Chapter XXIII.) This is evident from the fact that the visceral pleura is supplied by sympathetic fibers from the pulmonary plexuses. Such a reflex, however, cannot be differentiated from that arising in the pulmonary parenchyma when the latter is inflamed, and is of no value as a differential sign between inflammations of the lung and pleura.

Pleural Viscerosensory Reflex.—The sensory reflexes arising from the pleura are very important from a clinical standpoint. I shall not attempt to separate those which arise from afferent impulses which course centralward through the sympathetic and spinal systems. However, I shall discuss separately those pains which are found in the cervical zones of the neck and shoulder, caused by afferent impulses which course through spinal (phrenic) nerves. We must not forget, however, that it is possible to have pleural viscerosensory reflexes in the cervical zones, the afferent impulse coursing in the fibers derived from the pulmonary plexuses.

The viscerosensory reflex which expresses itself in the skin of the thoracic and upper abdominal zones, may be caused, like the motor reflex from the costal pleura, by irritating stimuli which course centralward in either the sympathetic or the spinal systems which supply the pleura. The reflex may express itself in any zone supplied by sensory fibers which arise from the spinal segments from the Ist to the XIIth thoracic inclusive (Fig. 59). Pleural pain then may be expressed over the entire surface of the chest, over the skin of the entire abdomen, or in the chest and abdominal muscles. This has been critically discussed by Neumann.[2]

The pain over the abdomen is most common at the costal margin, yet I have seen it over the entire abdominal surface (Pottenger[3]). When it is situated in the upper right quadrant, it is frequently mistaken for inflammation of the gall bladder; when in the lower right quadrant, for inflammation of the appendix; and when in the upper left quadrant, for ulceration of the stomach. When low down over the abdomen, it is sometimes even mistaken for disease of the pelvic viscera. In this connection it must be remembered that the extent of tissue involved in the pleural viscerosensory reflex depends greatly upon the strength of the stimuli, which means upon the severity of the inflammation.

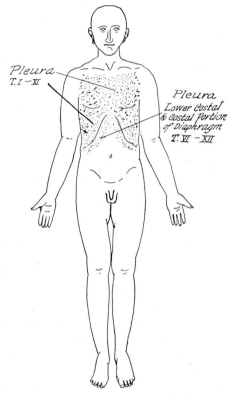

Fig. 59.—Pleural viscerosensory reflex.
As shown in the figure, pleural pain may occur over any portion of the chest wall; and, if the lower costal pleura and costal portion of the diaphragm are involved, the pain may extend down over the upper surface of the abdomen.

Pleural Viscerotrophic Reflex.—The tissues which show motor and sensory changes when the inflammation is acute, show degenerative changes when it becomes chronic. This fact should always be borne in mind when considering diseases of the lungs and pleura. Any reflex trophic change in muscles or other soft tissues whose innervation depends upon nerves arising from the cervical portion of the cord, is due most often to inflammation of pulmonary tissue or of the visceral pleura. Since the latter rarely occurs without lung tissue being inflamed, it is safe to say that degeneration of these structures means chronic inflammation of the underlying lung. On the other hand, degenerative changes of reflex origin which are found in the muscles or other soft tissues which receive their innervation from the thoracic portion of the cord are most likely due to impulses which have come from the parietal or costal pleura; and means that that portion of the pleura which is situated so as to send afferent impulses to the cord and reflect in the atrophied tissues, has been the seat of chronic inflammation.

The viscerotrophic reflex from the lung is expressed for the most part in the neck and upper chest muscles and the skin and subcutaneous tissue above the second rib anteriorly and the spine of the scapula posteriorly; while that from the parietal or costal pleura is expressed almost entirely in the intercostals and in the skin and subcutaneous tissue between the second rib anteriorly and the spine of the scapula posteriorly, on the one hand, and the lower margin of the ribs on the other. See Fig. 55, *A* and *B*, pages 318 and 319.

Degeneration of the soft tissues over the bony thorax is of great diagnostic value. Aside from the degeneration above the second rib anteriorly and the spine of the scapula posteriorly, which nearly always indicates previous or chronic inflammation in the underlying lung, frequently there are areas of degeneration below this which indicate previous pleural inflammation.

It is of particular clinical importance to recognize degeneration when present in the area over and above the diaphragm, because of the tendency for chronic pain to be expressed in the same areas as the degeneration. Degeneration is permanent and pain may persist long after the acute inflammation of the pleura has passed away. Sometimes, particularly in individuals who show pain easily and stand it poorly, this pain recurs under many conditions, such as tiring, weather changes, at the menstrual cycle in women, and under emotional and physical strain; and may be incapacitating in its effect. Examination of these areas may show nothing unless one is able to recognize the degeneration of the tissues caused by the previous pleurisy. The physician is often confounded by his inability to satisfy himself or the patient that there is nothing serious the matter. In case the pain extends down over the abdomen, as it often does, then inflammation of the gall bladder and ulcer of the stomach are often suspected. The recognition of degeneration of the soft tissues in the same area as the pain will often furnish the best clue to its cause.

Spinal Nerve Reflexes

As spinal nerve reflexes we designate those which arise from impulses which are carried from the pleura to the cord through afferent fibers of either the intercostals or the phrenics. The former cannot be distinguished from the visceromotor, viscerosensory, and viscerotrophic reflexes caused by impulses carried central ward from the parietal or costal pleura by afferents of the sympathetic system. The phrenics, however, while not producing a motor reflex that is recognizable, produces a very important viscerosensory reflex which expresses itself as pain in the neck and shoulders in the IIIrd, IVth, and Vth cervical sensory zones.

This sensory reflex is present either when the apical pleura or the pleura covering the central tendon of the diaphragm is inflamed. The latter expresses itself in the same zones as the pain from the lung, but as a rule is more severe, and usually comes on acutely. Fig. 51, page 312, shows the position of the reflex pain which results from afferent impulses coursing through the phrenics and is usually found in the presence of diaphragmatic pleurisy. The same areas are involved as in the pulmonary viscerosensory reflex.

In accounting for the pain in the neck and shoulder which patients suffering from chronic pulmonary tuberculosis experience, we must not forget the small branches of the phrenic nerve which are given off to the pleura when the phrenics cross it in the neck.

There are three sources of origin for the sensory reflex (pain) felt in the neck by patients suffering from pulmonary tuberculosis: 1, the pulmonary tissue; 2, the diaphragmatic pleura; and 3, the portion of the apical pleura which is supplied by the twigs given off from the phrenics.

A pain in the shoulder is experienced every now and then when the pleura is suddenly filled with air as occurs in spontaneous or induced pneumothorax. This is probably a result of stretching or breaking up of adhesions which irritate the sensory fibers of the phrenics; or it might possibly be due to irritation of the afferents of the sympathetic system supplying the visceral pleura, for these would express the pain in the same tissues as the fibers from the lung—the neck and shoulder.

The neurons expressing pain as a result of inflammation in the lung, inflammation in the visceral pleura, and inflammation of those portions of the apical pleura or diaphragmatic pleura which are supplied by the phrenics, are practically the same. They are the cervical spinal nerves arising from the IIIrd, IVth, and Vth segments of the cord. While impulses from the lungs and visceral pleura may express pain in other cervical segments, yet the IIIrd, IVth, and Vth are the segments usually affected. Hiccough sometimes occurs as a result of intrathoracic disease through irritation of the sensory fibers of the phrenics. I have seen several cases of intractable hiccough follow spontaneous pneumothorax.

Parasympathetic Reflexes

The pleura gives origin to one very important parasympathetic sensory reflex. I refer to the irritation experienced in the larynx when the pleura is inflamed. This is expressed through the superior laryngeal nerve. Cough, which is a complex act, is caused reflexly by stimuli which course centralward over the sensory parasympathetics from the pleura.

REFERENCES

1. Coplin, W. M. L.: Changes in the Intercostal Muscles and the Diaphragm in Infective Processes Involving the Lungs and Pleura, Am. J. M. Sc., May, 1904.
2. Neumann, Wilhelm: Die Phrenikusdruckpunkte bei der Lungentuberkulose und ihre Bedeutung für die Erkennung der blutende Seite bei Hämoptoe, für die Frühdiagnose der Lungentuberkulose und die Erkennung der larvierten Tuberkulose, Beitr. z. Klin. d. Tuberk. 45: 206, 1920.
3. Pottenger, F. M.: Pain and Muscle Tension Caused by Inflammation of the Diaphragmatic Costal and Lower Parietal Pleura Simulating That From Abdominal Viscera, Surg., Gynec. & Obst. 40: 62, 1925.
4. Pottenger, F. M.: Neuere Methoden zur Diagnose von Lungen- und Pleuraerkrankungen. Diskussion und Klassifikation der durch Lungen- und Pleuraentzündungen verursachten sympathischen und parasympathischen Reflexe; Beschreibung der Palpationsmethode zur Bestimmung von Organgrenzen und Differenzierung pathologischer Zustände, die verschiedene Dichte in den Organgeweben erzeugen, hauptsächlich in den Lungen und der Pleura (Leichte Tastpalpation). Beitr. z. Klin. d. Tuberk. 60: 25-406, 1925.

CHAPTER XXV

THE HEART

I. INNERVATION OF THE HEART

Although the heart of higher vertebrates consists of striated muscle, it is beyond the control of the will and belongs to the so-called vegetative structures. It is activated by the sympathetics, which cause increased rapidity of contraction when stimulated. The innervation of the heart is shown in Fig. 60.

Sympathetics.—The sympathetics which supply the heart arise from the Ist to the VIIth thoracic segments of the cord. They pass upwards through the lateral to the inferior middle and superior cervical ganglia. Three trunks—the superior, middle, and inferior cardiac nerves—one from each of these ganglia, pass to the heart through the deep cardiac plexus. There are also fibers which pass to the heart directly from the lateral ganglia.

When stimulated, they increase the rate of contraction of the heart muscle without increasing blood pressure; in fact, at times the pressure may fall. There are also fibers in the sympathetics which increase the force of the heartbeat, shorten the time of systole, increase the ventricle output, and raise blood pressure without a general change in vasomotor tonus.

Parasympathetics.—The vagus supplies the heart with three separate bundles of nerves: first, from the superior laryngeal; second and most important, from the recurrent laryngeal; and, third, a branch from the thoracic portion of the vagus.

The right vagus cares particularly for the deep layers of the heart muscle, while the left vagus goes to the plexus cardiacus superficialis. When the vagus is stimulated, it inhibits the action of the heart and slows the pulse. When vagal effects are inhibited, as by atropine, the heart action may be accelerated.

Vagus fibers enter the heart as medullated fibers and connect with motor nerve cells which lie in the heart itself. It has been shown that all of those cells lying in the organ itself belong to the vagus and none to the sympathetics.

343

The inhibitory influence upon the heart may be produced reflexly by stimulating the vagus in many different organs. Brodie and Russel[1] found that the pulmonary vagus produces the strongest reflex inhibitory influence upon the heart. Irritation of the pulmonary branches produces a reflex slowing of the heart almost equal to that caused by stimulation of the vagus in the neck. Irritation of the larynx will also slow the heart.

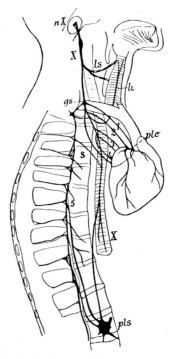

Fig. 60.—Innervation of the heart, *nX*, vagus center; *X*, nervus vagus; *gs*, ganglion stellatum; *ls*, N. laryngeus superior; *li*, N. laryngeus inferior; *s*, nervus sympathicus; *pls*, plexus solaris; *plc*, plexus cardiacus; *1*, the superior central branch to the heart; *2*, the ascending nerve; *3*, the inferior central branch to the heart; *4*, the superior and inferior external branch to the heart; *5*, ansa vieussenii. (Bechterew.)

The effect of irritation through the gastrointestinal branches has long been recognized, also that from the appendix, the gall bladder, the gastric, and intestinal walls.

Not only is the reflex inhibitory influence of the parasympathetics upon the heart shown when the branches of the Xth nerve are stimulated, but when fibers of other sensory nerves in reflex communication with the parasympathetics are concerned. Pressure on the eyeball and irritation in the nose will both slow the pulse, the afferent stimuli being carried by the sensory branches of the Vth cranial nerve.

When both vagus and sympathetic fibers to the heart are similarly stimulated, inhibition prevails (Bechterew[2]).

Peculiarities of Heart Innervation.—In some of the lower forms of animal life, such as the tortoise, both striated and unstriated muscle are found. There is a strong layer of unstriated muscle next to the endothelium of the auricle which extends out into the sinus venosus and the beginning of the large veins.

The innervation of this unstriped layer is different from that of the rest of the heart. It is activated by the vagus and receives inhibitory fibers from the sympathetics, while the striated muscle is activated by the sympathetics and receives inhibitory fibers from the vagus. This unstriped muscle acts toward atropine and muscarine in the same manner as the bronchial and enteral unstriped musculature. Gaskell[3] calls attention to this fact and says further that the striated heart muscle behaves like the enteral sphincter muscles, is activated by the sympathetics, and receives inhibitory fibers from the vagus. As the unstriped muscle has disappeared from the higher vertebrates, it has withdrawn its innervation and left the heart with the same innervation as the sphincters of the gut.

The nerve cells which lie in the heart muscle are associated only with vagus fibers. They are massed in three ganglia: Remak's, along the superior vena cava; Ludwig's, along the interauricular septum; and Bidder's, at the auriculoventricular junction. The vagus fibers, therefore, enter the heart as medullated fibers having their motor cells within the heart muscle. The sympathetics, on the other hand, enter the heart as nonmedullated fibers, having their motor nerve cells in extracardiac ganglia. After the vagus fibers enter the heart, they send off collaterals to many ganglion cells lying within the muscle substance, which are inhibitory cells to the heart musculature.

II. HEART: CLINICAL CONSIDERATION

Cardiac Visceromotor Reflex.—The heart, being supplied by sympathetics whose connector fibers arise from the Ist to VIIth thoracic segments, has no important superficial neck or chest muscles in which

to show a motor reflex regularly. (See Fig. 61.) The upper intercostals are sometimes in spasm and give a sense of constriction during
attacks of angina; under certain circumstances the muscles of the
arm become somewhat affected through the Ist thoracic nerve; and,
occasionally, the muscles of the neck, particularly the sternocleidomastoideus and trapezius, may show increased tension. In affections
of the heart, however, the motor reflex is not as well known as the
sensory reflex.

Cardiac Viscerosensory Reflex.—The cardiac viscerosensory reflex
is one of the best known sensory reflexes in clinical medicine. It is

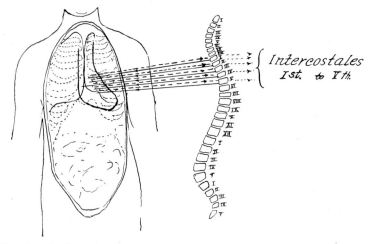

Fig. 61.—Cardiac visceromotor reflex.
    Lines connecting the heart with the segments of the cord from Ist to VIIth
thoracic segments, represent sympathetic connectors. Solid lines represent the
sympathetic nerves supplying the heart. Broken lines represent afferent sympathetic nerves which carry sensory impulses from the heart to the cord. Broken
lines on the other side of the cord represent spinal nerves which receive the impulses from the afferent sympathetic nerves and transmit them to the muscles
shown, producing the cardiac visceromotor reflex.

usually found in the upper half of the left chest, running out and
down the inner surface of the arm and hand to the ends of the little
and ring fingers (Fig. 62). This pain in the arm under certain conditions becomes very severe; and, at times, a hyperalgesia of the skin
and deep soreness occur which, as in the case of John Hunter as
quoted by Mackenzie,[4] became "so severe that he could not bear to be
touched."

At times the pain in diseases of the heart is not confined to the
usual seat—upper left chest and inner side of the arm—but extends

over on the right side, also lower down over the thorax and up into the neck. After the acute pain has subsided, the skin sometimes remains in a state of hyperalgesia for a period of time as previously mentioned and the left sternocleidomastoideus and trapezius muscles may also become tender, as mentioned by Mackenzie.[5] The explanation of this extension of the painful skin areas, is probably furnished by the

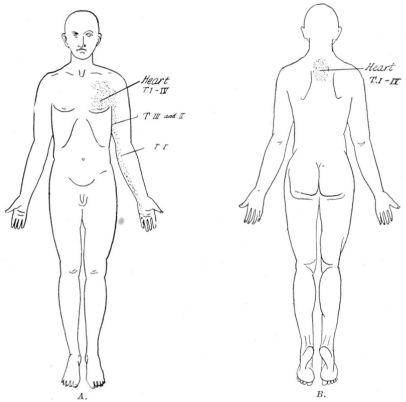

A.

B.

Fig. 62.—*A,* Cardiac viscerosensory reflex. Anterior view. As will be noted by the shaded areas above, the cardiac viscerosensory reflex may show both anteriorly and posteriorly. The anterior area takes in the upper portion of the chest, particularly the Ist, IInd, and IIIrd thoracic zones, and the inner side of the arm; this also being supplied by the first, second, and the third thoracic segments.

B, Cardiac viscerosensory reflex. Posterior view. The area of pain on the posterior surface of the chest is over the vertebrae in the Ist to IVth thoracic segments.

observations on reflexes due to impulses of varying strength, as discussed on page 53. It requires a certain stimulus to produce pain, or a motor reflex, through a given nerve fiber. If the stimulus is greater than that required to bring about this result, it does not increase the contraction of the given muscle fibers or increase the pain perceived through the given sensory fibers, but the greater stimulus manifests itself by the efferent impulse being conveyed to a greater number of neurons, which causes the reflex to show in wider areas.

The explanation of the tenderness noted in the sternocleidomastoideus and trapezius muscles may not be so certain. It may be possible that the afferent vagal fibers transfer the sensory stimuli downward into the upper cervical segments, but it seems more rational that the sensation should be transmitted centralward over the sympathetic system and be transferred upward in the cord through intercalated neurons to mediate with the spinal nerves emerging from the second, third, and fourth cervical segments from which the sternocleidomastoideus and trapezius receive their sensory nerve supply. This latter would seem to be the rational explanation, and, if correct, shows that the reflexes from the heart may have under severe stimulation the same indirect mediation with the cervical spinal nerves as those from the lungs. This path for the heart is not usual, but follows the law governing the spread of reflexes.

It is necessary to call attention to the difference in location of pain which originates in the auricle from that originating in the ventricle. Following the development of the heart from lower forms of life to man, we find that in the lower forms the position is reversed from what we find it in man. The apex is situated anteriorly and the auricles posteriorly. The innervation being segmental, the apex receives its nerves from segments lying more anteriorly in the cord than those supplying the auricles. This accounts for the fact that pain arising in the ventricle, as in angina, extends down the inner aspect of the arm, and over the upper portion of the chest, areas supplied by the Ist, IInd, and IIIrd thoracic segments, while pain arising in the auricle is found lower down on the chest wall in areas supplied by the IVth, Vth, and VIth thoracic segments.

Owing to the recent attempts to relieve anginal pain by operation on the cervical sympathetics, there arises a need for a more careful study of anginal pain and its method of production.

To date there has been no uniformity in operative procedure nor in the results obtained. Jonnesco[6] removed the left sympathetic chain, including the middle, inferior, and stellate ganglia. Coffey and Brown[7, 8] removed not only the superior cervical ganglion but, also a portion of the sympathetic trunk. They also injected the ganglion with triple distilled water. In a few instances the right superior cervical ganglion has also been removed. White and White[9] injected the upper five vertebral ganglia with alcohol, and reported satisfactory relief of pain.

The experiments of Heinbecker,[10] may require us to change our opinion regarding the paths of cardiac pain. He states: "Pain fibers from the human heart and first portion of the aorta are found in all sympathetic nerve trunks supplying efferent fibers to these structures. These fibers enter the central nervous system via the fifth cranial nerve, via the rami communicantes, and by the dorsal roots of the eight cervical and upper six or seven thoracic spinal nerves. It is probable that pain fibers from heart in small numbers also ascend in the vagus nerve trunk."

The results of these operations have been variable, as would be expected from the nature of the malady which they are attempting to relieve. The operation proves conclusively that interruption of the sympathetics will relieve the pain, whether by relieving a tension or spasm in the aorta and coronary arteries from which the pain impulses arise, as Coffey and Brown believe, or by severing the connection with the central nervous system by cutting the afferent nerves is not clear. Leriche and Fontaine[11] state: "The object is to cut the ascending fibers from the heart and the aorta. Section of the motor fibers is not only useless but may prove dangerous. . . . The most important group of sensory fibers coming from the heart are those which enter the stellate ganglion. It is possible to interrupt this without any damage to the motor fibers by cutting the rami communicantes of this ganglion. This seems the most important part of the operation. When this section has been done, the operation may be completed in one of several ways, varying from simple suprastellate sympathicotomy to the complete removal of the superior part of the cervical sympathetic system, avoiding in so far as possible ganglionary removals which frequently produce very disagreeable postoperative complications."

Cardiac Sympathetic and Parasympathetic Reflexes.—Of parasympathetic reflexes from the heart, I would mention the nausea which at times occurs in patients suffering from heart disease. Heart patients also very often complain a great deal of their digestive systems. The disturbance in function may be that of either an increased or a decreased tonus throughout the digestive tube. The impulses which produce these reflexes are carried centralward through either the sympathetics or the cardiac vagus and express themselves through their corresponding neurons in the gastric and intestinal structures. We hear very much of cardiac asthma. Such a condition may exist, being brought about through reflex stimulation of the pulmonary vagus. In this manner, bronchitis might also be produced aside from that which is due to the weakness of the heart.

The Manner in Which the Heart Is Influenced by Stimuli From Other Organs.—More interesting than the manner in which the other organs are reflexly affected by the heart, is the way the heart is influenced by diseases of other structures. The heart is an organ which responds quickly to all kinds of stimuli, either physical or psychic. Its beat can be slowed by pressure upon the eyeball, the afferent impulses going through the Vth cranial nerve, the efferent through the cardiac vagus. It can also be slowed by irritation in the nasal mucous membrane, the afferent impulses going through the Vth cranial nerve, the efferent through the cardiac branches of the vagus. Bradycardia can also be produced by stimulation of the larynx, by inflammation in the lung, in the gall bladder, the stomach, the intestinal wall, or the appendix. In all of these organs supplied by the vagus, the afferent impulses course through the respective branches of the vagus from the organ in which the stimuli originate; and the efferent impulses travel peripherally through the cardiac branch of the vagus.

A slowing of the pulse is a very common symptom in many cases of intestinal tuberculosis (Fig. 40, page 272). I have called attention to this repeatedly in my writings, and have shown charts illustrating it.[12, 13] The slowing of the pulse rate as found in pulmonary and intestinal tuberculosis is often marked in spite of the fact that the patient is suffering from marked toxemia with high temperature, conditions which, under ordinary circumstances, stimulate the sympathetic and increase the pulse rate. The effect of toxemia upon the heart is to increase the pulse rate. The same condition is brought about through fear, anxiety, worry, pain, and malnutrition; also by many of the internal secretions, such as adrenalin, by the increased metabolic activity caused by the secretion of the thyroid, and by the secretion from the pituitary. All of these measures which increase the heart rate do so by directly or indirectly stimulating the sympathetic neurocellular mechanism or acting in conjunction with it, or depressing the action of the vagus.

REFERENCES

1. Brodie and Russel: Reflex Cardiac Inhibition, J. Physiol. **26**: 92, 1900.
2. Bechterew: Die Funktionen der Nervencentra, Jena, 1908, Gustav Fischer.
3. Gaskell: Involuntary Nervous System, London, 1916, Longmans, Green & Co., pp. 82 and 102.
4. Mackenzie: Symptoms and Their Interpretations, London, 1909, Shaw & Sons, p. 59.
5. Mackenzie: Loc. cit., pp. 229-232.
6. Jonnesco, T.: Operative Cure of Angina, Bull. Acad. de méd., Paris, Oct. 5, 1920; ibid. **86**: 67, 208, 1921; ibid. **90**: 168, 1923.
7. Coffey, W. B., and Brown, Philip King: The Surgical Treatment of Angina Pectoris, Arch. Int. Med. **31**: 200, 1923.
8. Coffey, W. B., Brown, Philip King, and Humber, John Davis: Angina Pectoris, New Orleans, 1927, A. J. Dickerson.
9. White, James C., and White, Paul D.: Angina Pectoris, Treatment With Paravertebral Alcohol Injections, J. A. M. A. **90**: 1099, 1928.
10. Heinbecker, Peter: Anatomic and Physiologic Criteria for Surgical Relief of Cardiac Pain, J. Thoracic Surg. **2**: 517, 1933.
11. Leriche, René, and Fontaine, René: The Surgical Treatment of Angina Pectoris. What It Is and What It Should Be, Am. Heart J. **3**: 649, 1928.
12. Pottenger, F. M.: Clinical Tuberculosis, St. Louis, 1917, The C. V. Mosby Co., Vol. II, p. 42.
13. Pottenger, F. M.: Tuberculosis in the Child and in the Adult, St. Louis, 1934, The C. V. Mosby Co.

CHAPTER XXVI

THE AORTA

I. INNERVATION OF THE AORTA

Embryologically the aorta is formed high in the pharynx; as it descends it leaves the anterior (upper) part of the arterial system, which remains in adult life, to care for the portion of the body anterior to (above) and including the upper extremities, while that portion which becomes the aorta travels backward (downward) with the heart until it reaches the position found in adult mammals and man.

Sympathetics.—The upper aorta is supplied by sympathetic nerves from the aortic plexus. The motor cells from which these fibers originate lie in the upper four or five vertebral ganglia. The motor cells for the remaining portion of the aorta come from the plexuses nearest the part innervated.

The blood vessels of the body are innervated by fibers coming from all segments of the cord in which sympathetic connector fibers originate. Those anterior (superior) to the aorta are supplied by connector neurons whose sympathetic motor cells lie in the superior cervical and stellate ganglia. The former sends fibers to the arteries of the head and the latter to the subclavian.

From the fact that aortic pain in case of aneurysm of the thoracic aorta is expressed mainly in the left half of the body, it would seem that, like the heart, it is innervated mainly by neurons which arise in the left half of the cord.

Parasympathetics.—Depressor fibers from the vagus supply the aorta and reflexly slow the heart and cause general vasodilatation. How generally this parasympathetic supply is distributed to the aorta has not been fully determined.

II. THE AORTA: CLINICAL CONSIDERATION

The arch of the aorta, the portion which is best known for furnishing pathologic conditions, being supplied with sympathetic fibers from the upper vertebral ganglia, and being bound reflexly with the

352

upper spinal thoracic nerves produces pain which is most commonly expressed in the upper thoracic segments, and seems to show its maximum effect either near the sternum and vertebral column in the Ist, IInd, IIIrd, and IVth thoracic sensory zones or in the arm and on the anterior surface of the chest in the peripheral distribution of the nerves arising from those segments.

This peripheral pain, like that from the heart, I have found most commonly on the left side. In dilatation or aneurysm of the arch, it may extend over the Ist and IInd sensory thoracics out and down the inner aspect of the arm, and over the upper five or six thoracics to the surface of the chest wall. We may find also, at times, that the impulse is transferred by intracentral neurons in the cord to both higher and lower levels, the pain showing in the cervical sensory zones and in the intercostals below those mentioned. In this the aorta is like the heart. The pain, being due to distention of a hollow viscus, is precipitated and increased by conditions such as strain and exertion which call for greater distention of the arterial wall. Unlike pain produced by acute inflammatory processes, the condition stimulating the nerves is often present for a long time, consequently the pain may be present over long periods of time.

It is impossible to differentiate by location, the pain caused by inflammation of the arch and that from the heart. (See Fig. 62, page 347.)

Since the depressor fibers from the vagus which supply the heart also extend into the aorta, we would expect the same parasympathetic reflexes from those portions of the aorta which receive these fibers as occur in case of the heart (see page 349). These fibers also have a very important function in regulating blood pressure. When the blood pressure rises in the aorta, it stimulates the endings of the vagus and reflexly slows the heart and also acts upon the centers in the central nervous system and sends out stimuli over the sympathetics which produce general vasodilatation.

CHAPTER XXVII

THE BLOOD VESSELS

ARTERIES

The arteries of the body possess the all important quality of contractility which is indispensable to maintaining blood pressure and normal circulation. Contractility depends upon the smooth circular muscles found in the arterial walls. The smaller the vessel, the greater the relative muscular development of its walls and the greater the arterial force upon the circulation.

Small ganglion cells like those found in the heart and in the intestines have been described as being in the vessel walls. Kuntz,[1] however, does not think that the evidence is sufficient to establish their presence, although he accepts the evidence for parasympathetic innervation as being quite convincing, citing Kuré's[2] work in support of the idea.

Contractility is an inherent property of cells independent of nerve action, and, as such, belongs to all of the muscle tissues of the body. While it is a property which may exist without nerve action being called into play, nevertheless it is influenced and modified by impulses which course over the nerves which supply these tissues.

The nerves which supply the arterial walls contain both motor and sensory fibers. The sensory fibers exert an influence upon the heart and also upon the vessels themselves, which reflexly influence blood pressure.

THE VASOMOTOR NERVES

The musculature of the blood vessels is usually described as belonging to the group of tissues which is supplied by the sympathetic nerves alone, and to them is ascribed both constrictor and dilator effects (Fig. 63). According to this view the sympathetics are unopposed in nearly every portion of the body in their vascular control. Now that evidence is being produced which shows the possibility or even probability of a more general parasympathetic distribution to vessels, we must bear this in mind in our study of circulatory effects.

Dale,[3] in a discussion of the activity of the capillaries, quotes approvingly the works of Rouget[4] and Mayer,[5] which show that active contraction takes place in the smallest arterioles and capillaries, and accepts the work of Steinach and Kahn[6] as show-

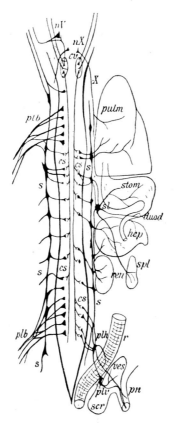

Fig. 63.—Distribution of vasomotor centers and nerves. *cv*, chief vasomotor center in medulla ; *cs*, spinal vasomotor centers; *s*, nervus sympathicus ; *nX*, vagus center ; *X*, nervus vagus ; *nV*, trigeminus center ; *plb*, plexus brachialis ; *plh*, plexus hypogastricus ; *plv*, plexus vesicalis ; *pulm*, the lungs ; *stom*, stomach ; *duod*, duodenum ; *hep*, liver ; *spl*, spleen ; *ren*, kidney ; *r*, lower portion of colon ; *ves*, urinary bladder ; *scr*, scrotum ; *pn*, penis. (Bechterew.)

ing that the capillaries possess motor nerves derived from the sympathetic system. This gives the capillaries a much more active part in circulation than had been previously assigned to them. Krogh[7] has shown by actual count that the relative participation of the capillaries in guinea pig's muscle is 85 per square millimeter in resting muscle and 2,500 in contracting muscle. From this we may understand the compensatory shifting of the blood in the capillaries of the tissues to meet the various demands made upon them.

According to the accepted opinion not only are the sympathetics the vasoconstrictor nerves which reduce the lumen of the vessels and raise the blood pressure when stimulated, but they also produce dilator effects as well and hold a control over the normal *tonus* of the vascular musculature. There has been considerable discussion in literature in recent times as to whether adrenalin under normal conditions aids the sympathetic system in maintaining the tonus of blood vessels. A great many writers assume that adrenalin is continuously present in the circulating blood and that it is a large factor in maintaining the tonus of the blood vessels. That this is questionable is suggested by the contributions of Hoskins,[8] Vincent,[9] and Stewart.[10] The experiments of these physiologists indicate that under normal conditions there is considerable doubt whether adrenalin is found in the blood stream at all; and further indicate that under normal physiologic conditions it has little effect upon the body economy. In an emergency, however, when the sympathetics are markedly stimulated, the chromophil cells of the medulla of the adrenals are stimulated and adrenalin is poured into the blood stream. Its effect, except upon the sweat glands, is the same as that of stimulation of the sympathetic nerves, and wherever acting it seems to fortify and prolong the sympathetic action. It must not be thought, however, that adrenalin acts upon the blood vessels alone. It acts upon practically all structures innervated by the sympathetics, the sweat glands being a known exception. Adrenalin does not, as is generally believed, always produce vasoconstriction. The effect varies with dosage and demands. It produces a vasoconstriction in one set of vessels and a compensatory vasodilatation in others.

The vasomotor nerves leave the cord by the anterior roots throughout the length of the thoracicolumbar segments which give origin to sympathetic fibers (Ist thoracic to the IVth lumbar). Therefore, their connector fibers are found in all white rami.

The motor cells which give origin to the nonmedullated fibers which supply the vessels, are found in both lateral and collateral ganglia. The *lateral ganglia* send nonmedullated fibers to care for all the blood vessels which go to structures supplied by spinal and cranial segmental nerves, and to the thoracic viscera. Thus the vessels going to all the skeletal tissues, those of the head, neck, and thorax, are supplied by motor cells which lie in the lateral ganglia.

The *collateral ganglia* supply motor cells which give origin to the fibers which control the vessels of the abdominal and pelvic viscera. These vessels are called the splanchnic vessels, and are of the greatest importance in the maintenance of blood pressure and the circulation of the blood. The splanchnics are the storehouse for surplus blood when not required by body activity. When special activity on the part of any organ is required, more blood is needed, and the splanchnics are called upon to deliver it. This action is brought about through the splanchnic nerves working in harmony with the part undergoing activity.

By histologic studies and electrical conductivity tests, Bishop, Heinbecker, and O'Leary[11] have demonstrated vasodilator fibers which leave the cord over its posterior roots which they believe belong to the parasympathetic system.

The vessels of different areas of the body are supplied by nerves from particular sections of the cord, as follows: .

Head and Neck.—Vasomotor connector fibers for the head and neck leave the cord by the first four or five thoracic segments. They pass through their corresponding lateral ganglia, the stellate, inferior and medium cervical to the superior cervical ganglion, where they end in motor cells which send out nonmedullated fibers along the carotid artery to the entire region of the head and neck. The IInd, IIIrd, and IVth segments give maximal effect when stimulated, as shown in Fig. 64.

Anterior Extremity.—The connector fibers for the anterior extremity arise from the IVth to the Xth thoracic segments. These pass through the various lateral ganglia on the way to the stellate ganglion, where they find the motor cells which give origin to the nonmedullated fibers which pass in the gray rami to the various nerves of the brachial plexus, and go to all the vessels of the anterior extremity, as shown in Fig. 65.

Posterior Extremity.—The connector fibers for the posterior extremity arise from the XIth, XIIth, and XIIIth (cat) thoracic, and Ist, IInd, and IIIrd lumbar segments. These fibers pass downward to the VIth and VIIth lumbar (cat), and first sacral ganglia, where they end in motor cells which give origin to nonmedullated fibers which go to the sacral plexus, and are thence distributed throughout the vessels of the lower extremity, as shown in Fig. 66.

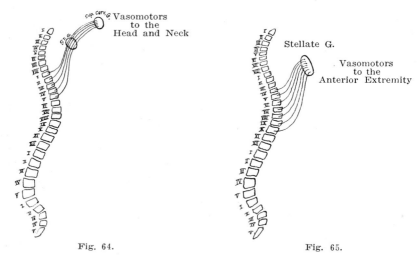

Fig. 64.   Fig. 65.

Fig. 64.—Schematic illustration of vasomotor supply for head and neck. The connector neurons which supply the vasomotor control for the head and neck arise from the Ist to Vth thoracic segments of the cord. They pass upward through the stellate ganglion to the superior cervical ganglion and then on to supply the vessels going to the head and neck.

Fig. 65.—Schematic illustration of vasomotor supply for anterior extremity. The connector neurons which supply vasomotor control for the upper extremities arise from the IVth to the Xth thoracic segments of the cord. They pass upward to the stellate ganglion in which originate the true sympathetic fibers which supply vasomotor control for the vessels of the arm.

Abdominal and Pelvic Viscera.—Most of the connector fibers from the lower seven thoracic and upper three lumbar segments, join to form the splanchnic nerves. The splanchnic nerves find their motor cells for the vessels of the abdominal and pelvic viscera in the semilunar, superior mesenteric, renal, ovarian or spermatic, and inferior mesenteric ganglia, as shown in Fig. 67.

Reciprocal Stimulation of Viscera and Somatic Structures Through Vasomotors.—The distribution of vasomotor nerves offers a path through which stimuli from the peripheral nervous system may influence the viscera and through which visceral stimuli may influence peripheral structures.

Vasomotor Control.—The blood vessels are controlled by one chief center in the medulla, and by subsidiary centers in the spinal cord. Vasomotor control from the center in the medulla courses in part through the vagus (Xth), hypoglossus (IXth), facialis (VIIth), and trigeminus (Vth), but for the most part the connection is through spinal centers.

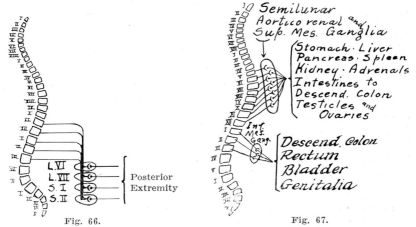

Fig. 66.   Fig. 67.

Fig. 66.—Schematic illustration of vasomotor supply for posterior extremity. The connector neurons from which originate vasomotor control for the lower extremities, arise from the XIth and XIIth thoracic, and Ist, IInd, and IIIrd lumbar segments of the cord. They pass downward to the lower lumbar and upper sacral ganglia, and then on to supply the posterior extremity.

Fig. 67.—Schematic illustration of vasomotor supply of abdominal and pelvic viscera.

The vasomotor supply for the upper abdominal viscera comes from the Vth to XIIth thoracic segments and passes through the superior mesenteric ganglion. The vasomotor supply for the descending colon and pelvic viscera comes from the Ist to the IIIrd lumbar segments and passes through the inferior mesenteric ganglion.

Vasomotor effects in the body walls and limbs take place through the sympathetic nerves. Vasoconstrictor effects are produced experimentally when the motor nerves are stimulated or when the central end of a cut sensory nerve, such as the sciatic, is stimulated. On the other hand, vasodilator effects are produced through the same sensory nerves when the intact nerve is centrally stimulated. An excellent and well-known example of this is the flushing of the face in pulmonary tuberculosis. The reflex vasodilatation is caused by the impulse which arises in the inflamed lung, being carried centralward over the vagus to the medulla, where it is transferred to the cells which give origin to the sensory fibers of the trigeminus (Vth), through which the vasodilator supply for the cheek courses.

THE SPLANCHNIC NERVES

The splanchnic nerves are the most important vasomotor nerves of the body. They arise from the Vth to XIIth dorsal, and Ist to IIIrd lumbar segments. These connector fibers end in the semilunar, superior, and inferior mesenteric, renal, ovarian and spermatic ganglia; and there give origin to the nonmedullated fibers which supply all of the vessels of the important abdominal and pelvic viscera.

Every ganglion which supplies an organ with sympathetic fibers also supplies the vessels of that organ with vasomotor nerves. Table VIII, from Gaskell,[12] based largely upon the work of Bradford and Langley, is useful for ready reference for the vasomotor supply of various parts of the body.

TABLE VIII

SITUATION OF BLOOD VESSELS	SITUATION OF MOTOR GANGLION CELLS	ROOTS CONTAINING CONNECTOR NERVES
Head and neck	Superior cervical ganglion	1, 2, 3, 4, 5, thoracic; 2, 3, 4, give maximum effect
Heart	Ganglion stellatum and inferior cervical ganglion	1, 2, 3, 4, 5, thoracic; 2, 3, give maximum
Anterior extremity	Ganglion stellatum	4, 5, 6, 7, 8, 9, thoracic and 10 slightly
Posterior extremity	6th lumbar, 7th lumbar, and 1st sacral ganglion	11, 12, 13, thoracic; 1, 2, lumbar and 3, lumbar slightly
Kidney	Renal ganglion	4, 5, 6, 7, 8, 9, 10, 11, 12, 13, thoracic; 1, 2, 3, 4, lumbar
Spleen	Semilunar ganglion	3, 4, 5, 6, 7, 8, 9, 10, 11, 12, 13, thoracic; 1, 2, 3, lumbar
Abdominal viscera	Superior mesenteric ganglion and semilunar ganglion	6, 7, 8, 9, 10, 11, 12, 13, thoracic; 1, 2, lumbar
Pelvic viscera	Inferior mesenteric ganglion	1, 2, 3, 4, lumbar

There has been some question whether the vessels to the brain, lungs, and coronary vessels, have vasoconstrictor nerves, but this has been finally decided affirmatively. Gaskell commenting on this says: "I for one cannot believe that muscles exist without motor nerves."

VASODILATOR NERVES

The question of vasodilatation is one that has received much attention at the hands of physiologists. It is generally taught that vasodilatation is governed by the sympathetics through vasomotor centers in the medulla and cord. The requirements of different parts of the body are met by different degrees of stimulation of the sympathetics; but whether there are genuine dilator fibers in the sympathetics or whether these are of parasympathetic origin, is not definitely settled. There are, however, some definitely parasympathetic dilator nerves, such as those which course in the *chorda tympani* (VIIth cranial), which, when stimulated, causes dilatation of the vessels in the submaxillary glands; in the *small petrosal* (IXth cranial), which carries dilator fibers to the parotid gland; in the *lingual,* which dilates the vessels of the tongue, and in the *nervus erigens,* which dilates the vessels of the penis. Nor must we forget the possibility of parasympathetic dilators emerging from the posterior roots, as suggested by Bishop, Heinbecker and O'Leary.[11]

Tissues produce chemical products during the stage of activity which are acid in nature and are spoken of as *acid metabolites.* These have the property of acting locally upon the musculature of the vessels in the part affected and producing vasodilatation. Krogh[7] does not consider that this has been proved. All organic extracts influence the tonus of the vessel walls and produce lowered blood pressure (Swale Vincent[13]).

Fibers which produce vasodilator effects are described as passing to ganglia in or near the tissues innervated before they end in the true dilator fibers, the same as the parasympathetic fibers in connection with the heart.

Stimulation of the posterior spinal sensory roots either before or after passage through the root ganglia or of the Vth cranial nerve, no matter what the stimulation used, causes dilatation in the area supplied by the sensory root affected. This is exceedingly interesting because the impulses pass outward contrary to the direction of the usual impulse in sensory nerves. Bayliss,[14] who made this discovery, called these impulses *"antidromic"* or reversed impulses. The fibers which transmit these impulses seem to be identical with the protopathic fibers described by Head. Starling[15] in commenting on this action says:

"So far this phenomenon of a nerve-fiber functioning (not merely conducting) in both directions is almost without analogy in our knowledge of the other nerve-functions of the body. There is no doubt, however, that similar antidromic impulses are involved in the production of the so-called trophic changes, such as localized erythema or the formation of vesicles (as in *herpes zoster*) which may occur in the course of distribution of a sensory nerve, and is always found to be associated with changes, inflammatory or otherwise, in the corresponding posterior root ganglia. Moreover, evidence has been brought forward that these fibers may take part in ordinary vascular reflexes of the body, that in fact they are normally traversed by impulses in either direction."

VESSEL TONE

Until further proof, we assume that changes in vessel tone are produced, with few exceptions, through sympathetic nerves only. This differs from that of the heart, respiratory system, and gastrointestinal systems, where tonus is altered by the action of antagonistic nerves: one activating, the other inhibiting. If vessels for the most part are supplied by the sympathetics alone, this change is affected by variation in the point of application and probably in the strength of the stimulation. The degree of stimulation is determined by the vasomotor centers in the medulla and cord. The vasomotor control is such that the tonus in one vascular area may differ greatly from that in another. Compensation takes place between various organs so that a vasoconstriction in one is met by a vasodilatation in another, and the normal blood pressure maintained. The vasomotor balance is very delicate and is subject to changes caused by physical forces acting upon the body or by psychic stimuli; but it is always modified by the requirements of the various tissues. It is necessary to maintain a fairly stable blood pressure; so when one large area of vessels contracts, another must dilate, and vice versa.

Action of Adrenalin Upon the Vasomotors.—In a discussion of vasomotor control, it is important to cite the results of the action of adrenalin upon blood pressure. This has been summarized by Hartman[16] in a paper in which he cited his own and other important experiments which show that the prevailing idea as to the universal constrictor action of adrenalin upon blood vessels, regardless of dosage, is no longer tenable.

Adrenalin acts differently in different structures and differently according to the size of the dose administered. In the blood vessels in some structures it produces a dilatation. The steps in this discovery are stated by Hartman thus:

"Cannon and Lyman[17] demonstrated that cats respond to small doses of adrenalin (intravenous) by a fall in blood pressure in a majority of cases. To be sure, other more or less isolated observations of this sort had been made previously, but the credit belongs to them for establishing the fact. Because this was opposed to the generally accepted idea of adrenalin action it appeared attractive for further research. An attempt was made by me to account for the fall in blood pressure. By tying off the arteries of the splanchnic area or of the head and limb area and then determining the blood pressure response to adrenalin, I was led to the discovery that there was a shifting of the blood from the splanchnic area to the outlying skeletal muscles.[18] This was accomplished by active dilatation of skeletal muscle areas attended simultaneously by active constriction of the splanchnic area. At the same time it was observed by use of the nasal plethysmograph that the nasal mucosa constricted.

"Later, Hoskins, Gunning, and Berry,[19] using the plethysmographic method, confirmed my observation that there was active dilatation in the 'peripheral' regions, but they went further and demonstrated that the skin constricts while the muscle dilates. Hoskins and Gunning[20] and ourselves[21] working independently, made a study of the spleen, kidney, and intestine by the use of oncometers. On the whole, the observations of both of us agreed with the first observations on the differential action of adrenalin;[18] i.e., depressor doses of adrenalin cause constriction of the splanchnic area. However, we did differ from each other to a certain extent in our findings on the intestine. While Hoskins and Gunning frequently obtained dilatation of the intestine with small doses, we found constriction to be the more common and that dilatation usually resulted from larger doses and was preceded by constriction.''

While it is broadly stated that adrenalin acts peripherally at the myoneural juncture on the same tissue that is supplied by sympathetic fibers, Hartman's experiments indicate that this is not a universal fact, and show it to be untrue as far as the vasomotor mechanism is concerned. The fact that peripheral vessels may contract while splanchnic vessels dilate, indicates that the factors which control the vasomotor mechanism for different parts of the body must differ. On this point Hartman[16] says:

''We believe that we have proved that the mechanism causing vasodilatation in the intestine, when adrenalin is injected into the general circulation, is located in the collateral sympathetic ganglia, probably in the superior mesenteric ganglion.''

Further:

''Thus far our work indicates that the limb mechanism is located in both the dorsal root ganglia and the sympathetic ganglia.''

Recapitulating, he says:

''In the adult, adrenalin poured into the blood in small quantities, causes, by its peripheral effects, constriction of the vessels in the skin, mucous membranes, and abdominal organs, driving the blood into the vessels supplying the skeletal muscles which are actively dilated for its reception through the effect on the sympathetic and dorsal root ganglia mechanisms. But as the quantity of adrenalin liberated increases, the peripheral effect begins to overcome the gangliar effect in skeletal muscle, the intestinal vessels by action on the sympathetic ganglia begin to dilate and the blood is reversed in its path.

''Although the effect of adrenalin on blood pressure, a fall with small doses and a rise with larger doses—is the more evident, the differential effect is after all the more important.''

The clinical importance of these experiments upon the vasomotor nerves is evident. Early in the writer's attempt to explain the effects of toxemia upon the nervous system as manifested in clinical medicine, he was impressed by the fact that the syndrome of toxemia is a double one.[22] Part of the effect of toxins is expressed upon nerve cells in general as a part of the general injury to body cells.

The cellular system of the body including the endocrines and the entire nervous system are rendered unstable, producing such symptoms as malaise, lack of endurance, and nerve irritability. It was further noticed, however, that the peripheral expression of toxins is a sympathetic syndrome: lack of appetite, coated tongue, hypochlorhydria, hypomotility throughout the intestinal tract (constipation), increase in pulse rate, and rise in temperature. The latter symptoms were all, except rise in temperature, so clearly those of increased activity of the sympathetic nerves, that I was forced to classify it as such, although I was not able to explain it until later.[23]

My opinion that pathologic hyperpyrexia, or fever, belongs partly to the syndrome of sympathetic stimulation and is due to an interference with the elimination of heat as well as an increased amount of heat production, was based upon both physiologic facts and clinical observation, as follows: (1) the effect of toxins acting directly through the sympathetic nerves and probably indirectly through an increase in adrenalin production, is to produce vasoconstriction in the blood vessels of the skin, which interferes with heat elimination; (2) the greatest amount of body heat, 85 per cent, is eliminated through the skin; (3) that preceding and at the beginning of a rise of temperature as a result of toxemia, the superficial blood vessels are constricted; (4) that pathologic hyperpyrexia, known as fever, occurs when the extra heat produced in the body fails to be eliminated; and (5) that physiologic hyperpyrexia, such as occurs during active physical exercise, a game of tennis for example, is not followed in the normal individual by a fever of more than temporary duration, because dilatation of the superficial blood vessels and sweating take place, which favor the rapid elimination of the surplus amount of heat which has resulted from the exercise, and a rapid return to normal.

Now that we understand that adrenalin can affect the superficial and splanchnic vessels differently, and that small amounts of it produce cutaneous vasoconstriction, we are further strengthened in our explanation that fever, pathologic hyperpyrexia, is partly due to and maintained by the toxins acting upon the cutaneous vasomotor nerves in such a way as to cause constriction and the interference with heat dissipation, as well as to an appreciable increased heat production. This vasoconstrictor effect is probably produced both by direct stimulation of the sympathetics and also by the action of small amounts of adrenalin, the production of the latter being stimulated by the action of the toxins upon the sympathetics.

The better understanding of the action of adrenalin upon the vasomotor mechanism may help solve some of the problems connected with shock.

Nearly all of the sensory nerves of the skin when stimulated cause stimulation of the splanchnics, the result varying with the stimulus. The close connection between the nerves of the surface of the body and the connector fibers for the sympathetics in the thoracicolumbar segments of the cord, suggests the effect that surface sensory stimuli may have upon the vasomotor nerves of the body.

THE BLOOD VESSELS: CLINICAL CONSIDERATIONS

There are many conditions met in the clinic which cannot be understood until we complete our anatomic and physiologic knowledge of the capillaries, venules, and arterioles. Much impetus has been given to this study by recent correlation of our knowledge by such master minds as Bayliss, Krogh, and Lewis.[24]

Skin Temperature and Color.—Skin temperature depends not on the amount of blood in the skin but on the rapidity of flow. A skin may be pale and yet be warm. Ebbecke[25] concludes that in the warm pale hand the arteries are dilated while the capillaries are not. In the cold blue hand the capillaries and venules are dilated while the arteries are contracted. Redness and paleness depend upon the amount of blood in the capillaries and venules.

Dermographia.—This condition may now be explained as being a capillary and venule reaction, depending upon the local contracting mechanism in the vessel walls. The light stroke with a blunt instrument, as well as light pressure, produces a *white line.* Under the microscope Krogh found that there was at first an opening of many capillaries following the stimulus, which was quickly succeeded by a closure of particularly the venules which caused the reaction.

If the stimulus is sufficiently strong to produce a *red line bordered by white,* the primary reaction is the same as above, but the capillaries and venules in the central area quickly dilate giving the blush while the borders contract as in the white line. For further discussion of this subject, see Chapter XXXIV.

Urticaria.—Urticaria is a local manifestation of increased permeability of capillaries. Why it localizes as it does is difficult to say. The eruptions of herpes zoster, on the other hand, are definitely located by the nerves whose central cells are irritated.

There are also certain hemorrhages in tissues, and certain pulmonary hemorrhages, which are best explained on the basis of the action of a local capillary poison, the walls being so injured that they are rendered sufficiently permeable for the largest blood elements to pass out of the vessel walls. In my opinion many of the minor instances of hemoptysis during the course of pulmonary tuberculosis are so caused.

Shock.—One of the controversial subjects of medicine is shock. Much light was thrown on this subject during the World War by work of many independent workers and The Special Investigation Committee on Surgical Shock and Allied Conditions.[26] Krogh accepts the cause of shock as being a capillary poison which causes the capillaries to dilate. The venous radicals are also full, but the heart and arterial system are comparatively empty. The cause of this capillary dilatation is some special capillary poison developed in the wound related to histamine.

Shock is favored by common anesthetics which have a slight capillary dilating effect, but which when added to some other capillary poison may prove disastrous. Nitrous oxide does not seem to have this dilating effect.

Periarterial Sympathectomy.—During recent years there has been an attempt to relieve certain conditions of disturbed circulation and pain in peripheral arteries by operative procedure. This method was suggested and first practiced by Leriche[27, 28] of Lyons. He found that when the adventitial coat of the artery supplying a limb was stripped from it, vasodilatation with increased temperature and pulse volume followed. He claimed that the circulation in the limb was improved and pain was relieved.

Much has been written on this subject recently, and the views expressed vary so much that it is impossible to assess a true value for the procedure at this time. Recent articles by Callander,[29] Lehman,[30] White,[31, 32, 33] Adson,[34] Adson and Brown,[35] and Livingston[36] should be consulted by those who are particularly interested in this subject.

Frostbite.—The Russian experience in successfully treating severe frostbite in their Finnish campaign, according to Burdenko,[37] was based on knowledge of the vasomotor control of the extremities. Freezing was accompanied by vasoconstriction of peripheral vessels extending to the arteries of secondary size—the subclavian and brachial and common iliac. It was found that blocking the afferent nerve paths in the posterior roots, in a large percentage of instances, was followed by vasodilatation, rise in temperature of the limb, and return of circulation.

In treating frostbite of the lower extremities paravertebral anesthesia was produced by injecting 40-50 c.c. of 0.5 per cent novocain solution into the intervertebral ganglia, second to the fifth lumbar. For the upper extremity, the solution was injected into the areas of the neck, as in vagosympathetic blocking, or into the cervical plexus. The injections may be repeated on several successive days if necessary. The action of novocain may be prolonged by adding one drop of 1:1,000 adrenalin to each 10 c.c. of the solution, or 20 c.c. of 2 per cent potassium sulphate and 12 drops of adrenalin 1:1,000.

References

1. Kuntz, Albert: The Autonomic Nervous System, Philadelphia, 1929, Lea & Febiger, p. 136.
2. Kuré, K., Nitta, Y., Tsuji, M., Shiraishi, K., and Sunoga, B.: Die histologische Darstellung der parasympatischen Fasern in den hintern Rückenmarks wurtzeln der Lumbalsegmente, Pflüger's Archives **218**: 573, 1928. Quoted by Kuntz, A.: The Autonomic Nervous System, Philadelphia, 1929, Lea & Febiger, p. 136.
3. Dale, H. H.: The Activity of the Capillary Blood Vessels, Brit. M. J. **1**: 959, 1923.
4. Rouget: Memoire sur le développenant de la tunique contractile des raisseaux, Compt. rend. Acad. d. sc., Paris **79**: 559, 1873.
5. Mayer: Die Muskularisierung der capillaren Blutgefässe, Anat. Anz. **21**: 442, 1902.
6. Steinach and Kahn: Echte Contractilität und motorische Innervation der Blutcapillaren, Pflüger's Arch. f. d. ges. Physiol. **97**: 105, 1903.
7. Krogh, August: The Anatomy and Physiology of the Capillaries, The Silliman Lectures, New Haven, 1922, Yale University Press.
8. Hoskins: Relation of Adrenal Glands to Circulation of the Blood, Endocrinology **1**: 292, 1917; also comment on Prof. Vincent's paper, Endocrinology **1**: 151, 1917.
9. Vincent: Recent Views as to the Function of Adrenal Bodies, Endocrinology **1**: 140, 1917.
10. Stewart: Comment on Prof. Vincent's paper, Endocrinology **1**: 151, 1917.
11. Bishop, G. H., Heinbecker, P., and O'Leary, J. L.: The Function of the Nonmyelinated Fibers of the Dorsal Roots, Am. J. Physiol. **106**: 647, 1933.
12. Gaskell: The Involuntary Nervous System, London, 1916, Longmans, Green & Co., p. 36.
13. Vincent, Swale: Endocrinology **1**: 140, 1917.

14. Bayliss: Principles of General Physiology, London, 1915, Longmans, Green & Co., pp. 473 and 690.
15. Starling: Human Physiology, ed. 2, Philadelphia, 1915, Lea & Febiger, p. 999.
16. Hartman: Adrenalin Vasodilator Mechanisms, Endocrinology 2: 1, 1918.
17. Cannon, W. B., and Lyman, H.: Depressor Effect of Adrenalin on Arterial Pressure, Am. J. Physiol. 31: 376, 1913.
18. Hartman, F. A.: Differential Effects of Adrenin on Splanchnic and Peripheral Arteries, Am. J. Physiol. 38: 438, 1915.
19. Hoskins, R. G., Gunning, R. E. L., and Berry, E. L.: Volume Changes and Venous Discharge in the Limb, Am. J. Physiol. 41: 513, 1916.
20. Hoskins, R. G., and Gunning, R. E. L.: Volume Changes and Venous Discharge in the Spleen, Am. J. Physiol. 43: 298, 1917; Volume Changes and Venous Discharge in the Kidney, Am. J. Physiol. 43: 304, 1917; Volume Changes and Venous Discharge in the Intestine, Am. J. Physiol. 43: 399, 1917.
21. Hartman, F. A., and McPhedran, L.: Further Observations on the Differential Action of Adrenalin, Am. J. Physiol. 43: 311, 1917.
22. Pottenger: The Syndrome of Toxemia, an Expression of General Nervous Discharge Through the Sympathetic System, J. A. M. A., 1916.
23. Pottenger: Fever, a Part of the Syndrome of Toxemia, New York M. J., August, 1916.
24. Lewis, Thomas: The Blood Vessels of the Human Skin and Their Responses, London, 1927, Shaw and Son, Ltd.
25. Ebbecke, U.: Die lokale vasomotorische Reaktion (L. V. R.) der Haut und der inneren Organen, Pflüger's Arch. f. d. ges. Physiol. 169: 1, 1917.
26. Wound Shock and Hemorrhage, Special Reports (I-VII) of Medical Research Committee, London, 1919.
27. Leriche, R.: De l'élongation et de la section des nerfs périvasculaires, Lyon chir. 10: 378, 1913.
28. Leriche, R., and Policard, R.: Étude de la circulation capillaire chez l'homme pendant l'excitation des nerfs sympathiques périartériels et la ligature des artères, Lyon Chir. 17: 703, 1920.
29. Callander, C. L.: Arterial Decortication, Ann. Surg. 77: 15, 1923.
30. Lehman, E. P.: Periarterial Sympathectomy, Ann. Surg. 77: 30, 1923.
31. White, James C.: Diagnostic Blocking of Sympathetic Nerves to Extremities With Procaine, J. A. M. A. 94: 1382, 1930.
32. White, James C.: Raynaud's Disease (Studies on Postoperative Cases Bearing on the Etiology of the Disease and the Efficiency of Sympathetic Ganglionectomy, New England J. Med. 206: 1198, 1932.
33. White, James C.: Progress in the Surgery of the Sympathetic Nervous System, New England J. Med. 205: 449, 1931.
34. Adson, A. W.: The Results of Sympathectomy in the Treatment of Peripheral Vascular Diseases, Hirschsprung's Disease, and Cord Bladder, Ann. Int. Med. 6: 1044, 1933.
35. Adson, A. W., and Brown, G. E.: Thoracic and Lumbar Sympathetic Ganglionectomy in Peripheral Vascular Diseases, J. A. M. A. 94: 250, 1930.
36. Livingston, W. K.: The Clinical Aspects of Visceral Neurology, Springfield, Ill., 1935, Charles C. Thomas.
37. Burdenko, Nikolai N.: The Effect of Frostbite on the Sympathetic Nervous System, Am. Review of Soviet Medicine 1: 15, 1943.

CHAPTER XXVIII

THE SALIVARY GLANDS

I. INNERVATION OF SALIVARY GLANDS

The secretion of saliva is a double process. The secretion of the watery elements and the salts is increased by stimulation of the parasympathetics, while secretion of the organic substances depends upon stimulation of the sympathetics. The secretion of saliva may be reflexly stimulated through mechanical contact with the endings of the trigeminus (Vth cranial) and chorda tympani of the facial (VIIth cranial) nerves; and through the taste nerves of the glossopharyngeal (IXth cranial nerve). It is also stimulated by the thought of, the sight of, and odor of food. Thus afferent stimuli which cause the reflex secretion of saliva may course in any one of the sensory cranial nerves.

Whether the sympathetics have a direct inhibitory influence on the secretory activity of the glands which is produced by the parasympathetics (nervus tympanicus and chorda tympani); or whether they decrease the watery elements of the secretion, simply through producing a vasoconstriction, thus limiting the blood supply to the glands, is not definite; but, clinically, we find that conditions which stimulate the sympathetics, such as fear, anger, and toxemia, depress salivary secretion and may be accompanied by a dryness of the mouth, while patients who are strongly vagotonic may have an abnormal amount of saliva.

The secretion of saliva depends upon three separate glands. The innervation of each is shown in Fig. 68, also in Plate IV, page 72.

Parotid Gland.—The parotid gland is supplied with *sympathetic* fibers from the superior cervical ganglion through the plexus meningeus medius. These, when stimulated, produce vasoconstriction in the vessels of the gland, and a thick, tenacious secretion of saliva with the watery elements wanting. The sympathetics activate the blood vessels and, by causing constriction reduce the amount of watery elements of the saliva and make the mouth dry.

This gland is also supplied by the *parasympathetics* from the nervus tympanicus (Jacobson's nerve) of the glossopharyngeal (IXth cranial), the fibers of which course through the nervus auriculo temporalis of the trigeminus (Vth cranial). Stimuli applied to these fibers cause a dilatation of the blood vessels of the gland and a free flow of thin watery saliva.

Submaxillary and Sublingual Glands.—These two glands like the parotid, are innervated by both sympathetic and parasympa-

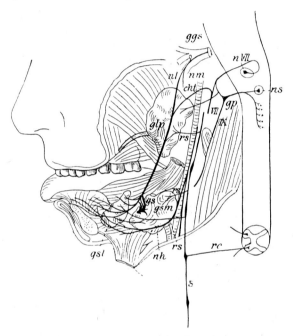

Fig. 68.—Innervation of salivary glands. *glp,* parotid gland; *gsm,* submaxillary gland; *gsl,* sublingual gland; *ggs,* Gasserian ganglion; *nl,* nervus lingualis; *nm,* nervus mandibularis; *nVII,* nervus facialis; *cht,* chorda tympani; *IX,* nervus glossopharyngeus; *ns,* center for salivary secretion in medulla; *gp,* ganglion petrosum; *s,* sympathetic nerves; *rs,* sympathetic branch to salivary glands; *gs,* submaxillary ganglion; *nh,* nervus hypoglossus; *rc,* ramus communicans. (Bechterew.)

thetic nerves. The sympathetic fibers arise from the superior cervical ganglion and reach these glands by way of the external carotid and external maxillary arteries. They produce, when stimulated, a constriction of the vessels of the gland and a thick, tenacious secretion the same as in the parotid gland.

The *parasympathetic* fibers come through the chorda tympani of the facial (VIIth cranial) and join the lingual of the trigeminus (Vth cranial) and pass with it to the glands. When stimulated the chorda tympani produces dilatation of the vessels of the glands and an abundant watery secretion.

II. SALIVARY GLANDS: CLINICAL CONSIDERATION

Such psychic conditions as fear and anger, and conditions of marked toxemia, such as accompany the acute infectious diseases or exacerbations in chronic infections, are usually accompanied by a salivary secretion far below normal. There are also conditions present at times in which the amount of saliva is so great as to greatly annoy the patient. Paralysis of the cervical sympathetics, such as follows operation on the cervical ganglia or cord, removes their opposition to the parasympathetics and an increase in salivary secretion on the affected side follows.

There is at times a marked increase in salivary secretion in tuberculosis of the lungs and particularly of the larynx. This is partly due to reflex action through the sensory neurons of the vagus and the parasympathetic neurons of the VIIth and IXth cranial nerves, and partly to the pain caused by swallowing. Increased flow of saliva is often seen in cases of gastric disturbances, and at times in severe attacks of angina pectoris.

CHAPTER XXIX

THE NASAL AND PHARYNGEAL MUCOUS MEMBRANES AND ACCESSORY SINUSES

I. INNERVATION OF NASAL AND PHARYNGEAL MUCOUS MEMBRANES AND ACCESSORY SINUSES

The mucous membrane of the nose, pharynx, and accessory sinuses is supplied with both sympathetic and parasympathetic fibers; also with sensory fibers from the Vth cranial nerve as shown in Fig. 69.

Sympathetics.—The sympathetic fibers come from the superior cervical ganglion and pass through the nervus petrosus profundus to the sphenopalatine ganglion, whence fibers go to the tissues. They cause vasoconstriction in the vessels which supply these structures.

Parasympathetics.—The parasympathetic motor fibers which supply the nasal, palatine, and pharyngeal mucous membranes, and the accessory sinuses come from the sphenopalatine ganglion. They arise in the vegetative nucleus of the facial (VIIth cranial) nerve; and, after entering the sphenopalatine ganglion, they emerge and course with branches of the *trigeminus* (Vth cranial) nerve; the nervi nasalis posteriores to the mucous membrane of the nose, and the nervi palatini to the hard and soft palate, and nasopharynx. They activate the secreting glands and furnish dilator fibers to the vessels. The pharynx also receives innervation from the glosso-pharyngeal and vagus.

II. NASAL AND PHARYNGEAL MUCOUS MEMBRANES AND ACCESSORY SINUSES: CLINICAL CONSIDERATION

Disturbance in Secretion

Dryness of the Mucous Membrane of the Nose and Throat.—Dryness of the mucous membrane of the nose and throat occurs in several acute conditions in which the sympathetics are stimulated. A dryness of these mucous membranes is noticed during high fever. It is not the fever, as usually suggested, which produces the drying, but the same condition that stimulates the vasomotor nerves and produces cutaneous vasoconstriction and interferes with the elimination of heat, stimulates the sympathetics which supply the mucous membranes and inhibits secretion.

Excessive Secretion.—Excessive secretion of the glands of the nose occurs in hay fever and in acute and chronic rhinitis. It may be increased reflexly by irritation in the eye, and the teeth; and I have often noticed that some patients suffering from pulmonary tuberculosis and certain gastrointestinal irritations complain at times of an unusual amount of secretion from the mucous membranes of the upper air passages. This same excessive secretion is

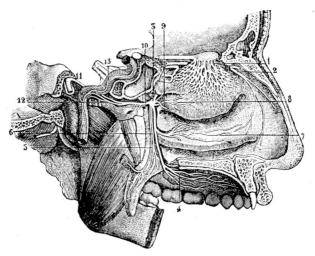

Fig. 69.—Nerve supply of nasal mucous membrane. Nerves of outer wall of nasal cavity. 3/5. (Sappey, from Hirschfeld and Leveille.) *1*, network of branches of olfactory nerve descending into the region of the upper and middle turbinals; *2*, external branch of nasal nerve; *3*, sphenopalatine ganglion; *4*, ramifications of great palatine nerve; *5*, small palatine nerve; *6*, external palatine nerve; *7*, branch to region of lower turbinal; *8*, branch to region of upper and middle turbinals; *9*, nasopalatine branch to septum (divided). (Luciani.)

seen at times in asthma. The afferent sensory stimulus in such cases travels in the vagus, and the efferent through the vegetative fibers of the VIIth cranial nerve.

Motor, Sensory, and Secretory Disturbances

Many motor and sensory reflexes originate in the nasal mucous membrane. *Sneezing*, which is a powerful expiratory effort, is produced by afferent impulses through the sensory fibers of the Vth cranial nerve. These may come from irritation of the cutaneous and ocular branches, or from the nasal mucous membrane itself. *Rhinitis* may be due to a direct irritation of the nasal mucous membrane, the afferent impulses coursing in the Vth cranial, the efferent in the vegetative fibers of the VIIth cranial. Pressure in the nose at times will produce reflex *asthma,* the afferent sensory impulse traveling through the fibers of the Vth cranial nerve, the efferent motor effect being discharged through the Xth (vagus) cranial nerve. Such a reflex may be inhibited by anesthetizing the nasal mucous membrane by cocaine. The mucous membranes of the nasal sinuses have the same innervation as the nasal chambers themselves. Clinicians have reported asthmatic attacks arising from sinus inflammation. This is readily explained through the reflex connection of the sensory fibers of the Vth and the motor fibers of the Xth cranial nerves. Irritation of the nasal mucous membranes, at times, will also slow the *heart.* The reflex in this instance travels over the same path as the one just described, except that it manifests itself in the cardiac instead of in the pulmonary branches of the vagus. Reflex action from this same source could easily affect the gastrointestinal branches of the vagus. We have noted a tendency to *hyperacidity* and *spastic constipation* in some patients during attacks of hay fever. While this might be caused by a general unbalancing of nerve equilibrium, resulting in a more or less widespread parasympathetic hyperirritability, yet the connection between the various groups of vegetative neurons in the cranial nerves is sufficiently close to suggest a reflex cause as not at all improbable. Herpes of the lips, or "cold sores," probably result from axon reflexes, the afferent stimulus coursing in the vagus and transferring it centrally to the trigeminus. This may be inferred from the nerve connection shown in Plate IV, page 72.

Secretory disturbances in the nasal cavity are seen following sympathetic paralysis or operation on the cervical ganglia and cord. By removing the sympathetics from the field of activity, parasympathetic effects in the form of increased secretion predominate.

CHAPTER XXX

THE LARYNX

I. INNERVATION OF THE LARYNX

The larynx is supplied by two nerves: the superior and recurrent laryngeal branches of the vagus. The former supplies the entire larynx with sensation, and the cricothyroid muscle with motor power, while the recurrent laryngeal is wholly motor and supplies all of the other muscles of the larynx. Sympathetic fibers supply the vessels and the mucous membrane. Fig. 70 shows the nerve supply to the larynx.

II. THE LARYNX: CLINICAL CONSIDERATION

Injury or paralysis of the superior laryngeal causes hoarseness, interferes with the sensation of the larynx, and produces trophic change; while injury or paralysis of the recurrent laryngeal causes trophic changes and aphonia. Stimulation of the recurrent laryngeal may cause laryngospasm; stimulation of the superior laryngeal may cause sensory phenomena, such as the common irritations which lead to cough.

The clinical aspects of laryngeal reflexes emphasize a fact which is apparent in other divisions of the parasympathetics: viz., that reflexes in the internal viscera occur easiest in those structures which are most closely united by their innervation; thus reflexes expressed in the larynx are most likely to originate in impulses coming from the pulmonary and pleural branches of the vagus, and those expressed in the gastrointestinal tract are most likely to be due to impulses originating in other portions of the gastrointestinal tract. While I see nothing to prevent an impulse arising in the gastrointestinal tract or in the cardiac muscle from expressing itself in a sensory disturbance in the larynx leading to cough, at the same time anyone must recognize that most impulses which lead to the act of coughing arise in the respiratory tract and pleura. Nevertheless there is a physiologic basis for the traditional stomach and heart coughs.

A sensory reflex leading to irritation and cough often arises from the parasympathetics in the lungs, pleura, larynx, tonsils, and pharynx. It sometimes arises from that branch of the vagus supplying the external auditory canal.

Aside from cough caused by sensory stimuli originating in the larynx, there are reflexes arising in other organs, which at times

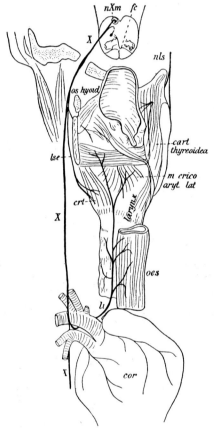

Fig. 70.—Nerve supply of larynx. *nXm*, motor center of vagus; *X*, nervus vagus; *nls*, N, laryngeus superior; *lse*, external branch of the nervus laryngeus superior; *li*, N. laryngeus inferior; *fc*, cerebral laryngeal tract of the vagus; *oes*, esophagus; *crt*, musculus cricothyroideus. (Bechterew.)

assume considerable importance. Among these should be mentioned laryngospasm as often observed in whooping cough and so-called croup; the forms of disturbance which result from pressure of mediastinal glands, heart strain, aneurysms, or other mediastinal tumors upon the recurrent laryngeal nerve; and the motor reflex which results in both recurrent and superior laryngeal nerves from afferent impulses which arise in inflamed pulmonary tissue. This is sometimes seen as an early sign of pulmonary tuberculosis. It is also seen when the tissue is breaking down (cavity formation) and when the mediastinum is shifting as a result of contraction.

The reflex motor disturbance in the larynx when expressed through the recurrent laryngeal nerve appears as a disturbance in adduction, as shown in Fig. 71. The cord on the affected side fails to come up to the center to meet the opposing cord. The motor reflex expressed through the superior laryngeal shows as a bagging of the cords or cord, as shown in Fig. 72. They are not drawn taut and they do not approximate each other at the median line.

These reflexes at times are important signs of early tuberculosis, and at other times accompany marked inflammation during the

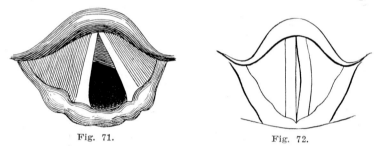

Fig. 71.   Fig. 72.

Fig. 71.—Schematic illustration of motor disturbances in cords through recurrent laryngeal nerves. This form of reflex shows in some form of disturbance in the approximation of the posterior ends of the cords.

Fig. 72.—Schematic illustration of motor disturbance in cords through superior laryngeal nerves. This shows as an inability of the cords to approach in the center, giving a baggy appearance.

course of the disease. Early hoarseness, which, if carefully looked for, will be found in a very large percentage of cases, may be due to this motor reflex. Again when cavity is forming and the inflammation of pulmonary tissue is at its highest point, marked or complete aphonia may be present. This is often mistaken for a tuberculous involvement of the larynx; the diagnosis is rendered somewhat difficult by the fact that coughing is usually severe during these times, and as a result the cords may be injected.

The path of this reflex is plain, the afferent impulses course centralward over the sensory fibers of the pulmonary vagus, and the motor effect is carried out through the inferior and superior laryngeal branches of the vagus.

Parasympathetic Trophic Reflex.—I would like to call attention to reflex atrophy of the tissues of the larynx which occurs as a result of pulmonary tuberculosis. In this, the afferent impulse courses in the pulmonary vagus and the efferent in the laryngeal branches of the vagus and the fifth nerve. The tissue looks pale, loses its resistance, and offers a favorable soil for the implantation of tubercle bacilli. These trophic changes offer a reasonable explanation for the fact that tuberculous lesions in the larynx are usually secondary to chronic infection in the lung; and that if they are unilateral, they usually occur on the side of the pulmonary involvement. The atrophied tissues are less resistant than normal, and when bacilli come in contact with them, whether through the lymph or blood stream, or by the mucus collecting on the surfaces, particularly during sleep, implantation is facilitated and the normal resistance to multiplication is probably reduced.

CHAPTER XXXI

THE EYE

I. INNERVATION OF THE EYE

Many portions of the eye are innervated by vegetative fibers, musculus ciliaris, musculus sphincter pupillae, musculus dilator pupillae, musculus Müller, musculus levator palpebrae, and the lacrimal glands. Some of these are activated by the sympathetic and others by the parasympathetic system. It also receives sensory fibers from the ramus ophthalmicus of the Vth cranial nerve which act as afferent components of parasympathetic reflexes. The innervation of the eye is shown in Fig. 73.

Sympathetics.—The sympathetic fibers to the eye, as far as we definitely know, supply the muscle of Müller, the pupil, and the vessels. The orbital muscle of Müller, when contracted, pushes the eyeball forward. This muscle is a factor in the production of exophthalmos. Sympathetic fibers also supply dilator fibers to the pupil which antagonize the constrictor fibers of the IIIrd nerve, and if able to overcome them, produce dilatation of the pupil.

The sympathetic fibers going to the eye arise from Budge's center in the spinal cord in the region of the VIIth and VIIIth cervical and Ist, IInd, and IIIrd thoracic segments (Fig. 74). The connector fibers pass through the rami communicantes on through the upper thoracic and inferior and medium cervical ganglia, and do not end in sympathetic motor cells for the eye until they reach the superior cervical ganglion. Here they end in motor cells from which they continue as nonmedullated gray fibers, some by way of the internal carotid plexus to the ophthalmic division of the fifth nerve, then by way of the nasociliary and long ciliary nerves to the eyeball; others pass by way of the internal carotid plexus through the ciliary ganglion without interruption into the short ciliary nerves and to the eyeball. Here they unite with the ophthalmic branch of the Vth nerve (trigeminus) and course in the nervi ciliares longi to the vessels of the eye, the dilator muscle of the pupil and the Müllerian muscle.

Parasympathetics.—The vegetative fibers which course in the IIIrd cranial nerve, Plate III, page 70, belong to the parasympathetic division. The oculomotor nerve arises from several nuclei. One of these nuclei is made up of smaller cells than the others. From this nucleus, fibers arise which terminate in the ciliary ganglion. From the ciliary ganglion fibers pass by way of the short ciliary nerves to the circular fibers of the iris, and the muscles which control the nictitating membrane.

The fibers going to the pupil contract it, and, in this, oppose the dilating fibers of the sympathetics.

The ciliary muscle is innervated by parasympathetic fibers which course in the IIIrd nerve. Stimulation of these fibers produces a contraction of this muscle which has the effect of shortening the focal point. There is some question whether or not the parasympathetic

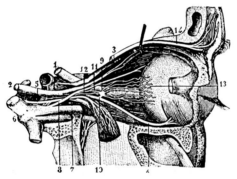

Fig. 73.—Innervation of the eye. Nerves of orbit. Lateral view, reduced three-fourths. The ramus externus is divided and turned back. *1*, optic nerve; *2*, trunk of IIIrd nerve; *3*, its superior division to the levator palpebrae and rectus superior; *4*, its lower and longer branch to the inferior oblique; *5*, sixth nerve joined by branches of the sympathetic; *6*, Gasserian ganglion; *7*, ophthalmic nerve; *8*, its nasal branch; *9*, ciliary ganglion; *10*, its short, *11* long, and *12*, sympathetic roots; *13*, short ciliary nerves; *14*, supra-orbital nerve. (Luciani.)

fibers in this muscle are opposed by sympathetic fibers which tend to relax the muscle and lengthen the focal point. The consensus of opinion is that the eye accommodates itself to distance by a gradual relaxation of the ciliary muscle without the active assistance of a sympathetic inhibitory nerve. When the excitability of the motor cells in this division of the oculomotor nerve is very high, it may result in accommodation spasm.

The musculus levator palpebrae when activated has a tendency to widen the lid slits of the eye and give the appearance of fright. Thus there are two factors which may cause exophthalmos, the Müllerian muscle activated by the sympathetics and the levator palpebrae innervated by parasympathetic fibers from the IIIrd cranial nerve. Activation of the levator palpebrae in exophthalmic goiter results in two common parasympathetic symptoms: von Graefe's sign, in which

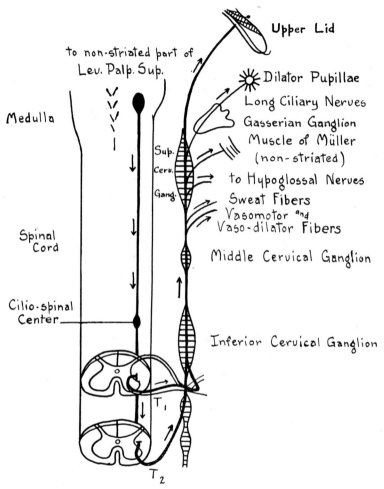

Fig. 74.—Diagrammatic illustration of the ocular fibers of the cervical sympathetic. (After Purves Stewart.)

the contraction of this muscle prevents the upper lid from following the cornea closely as the eye is lowered; and Dalrymple's sign, in which the contraction causes the lid slits to be wider than normal, so that the sclera shows between the pupil and the lids.

II. THE EYE: CLINICAL CONSIDERATIONS

There are many clinical conditions which manifest themselves through stimulation of either one or the other division of the vegetative nerves in and about the eye.

Pupil.—Dilatation of the pupil may occur either as a reflex through the sympathetics; from stimulation of Budge's center in the cord; from peripheral stimulation, as from adrenalin; from general sympathetic stimulation, such as occurs in toxemia; from emotional stimulation by such factors as fear, rage, and pain. Psychic dilatation may be due to cortical action in lessening the excitability of the oculomotorius; or subcortical, in raising the dilator excitability of the sympathetics by stimulating a center which lies in the median portion of the corpus subthalamicum. A reflex dilatation of the pupil takes place on the side of involvement in pulmonary tuberculosis. It probably is due to stimulation of Budge's center in the cord by afferent stimuli from the lung, the efferent impulse coursing over the sympathetics.

Contraction of the pupil follows the impingement of light upon the retina, the impulse being carried through the optic tract. It is carried to the geniculate body and corpora quadrigemina, or, according to some authors, into the gray matter in the floor of the IIIrd ventricle, where collaterals are given off which connect with the parasympathetic motor cells in the nucleus of the IIIrd (oculomotorius) nerve. The brighter the light, the stronger the impulse and the greater the contraction of the pupil.

ARGYLL ROBERTSON PUPIL.—This condition is an early sign of tabes dorsalis and of progressive paralysis. It consists in a preservation of the pupillary reaction to convergence and to accommodation with a loss of reaction to light, but no impairment of sight. The cause of the phenomena has caused differences of opinion. Higier[1] says it could be due to a basilar meningitis involving the fibers from the optic tract which pass between the geniculate bodies through the arms of the anterior corpora quadrigemina.

RIGIDITY OF THE PUPIL TO LIGHT.—When the pupil is completely rigid, the parasympathetics in the oculomotor nerve have no influence upon it; and the sympathetics, whose dilator action normally is not very great, are not able to cause dilatation.

The oculomotor fibers which proceed from the ciliary ganglion normally maintain tonus in the ciliary muscle. While the sympathetics have an inhibiting action, it is not the only influence that dilates the pupil. A lessened stimulation of the oculomotor fibers will permit the pupil to dilate. Damage to the ciliary ganglion, therefore, produces a maximum dilatation of the pupil. In cases of fainting, central lues, epileptic and hysterical attacks, and great fear, a widely dilated and rigid pupil is a result of action in cortical areas; while rigidity with contraction of the pupil is due to increase in the sphincter tonus.

The study of pharmacologic remedies with reference to their action upon the vegetative nerves has shown that they may be used at times with differential diagnostic value as discussed in Chapter VI. According to Higier, the action of cocaine and adrenalin upon the dilator fibers of the pupil may be taken to suggest the character of a lesion. If a dilute solution (1-3 per cent) of cocaine be dropped into the conjunctival sac and dilatation of the pupil fails to appear, it is evidence of a weakening of the sympathetic pupillary control. If evidence of disturbance of the sympathetics is obtained, the next question is to decide where the lesion is located, whether operable or inoperable. This may be determined by adrenalin. Two drops of a 1 per cent solution of adrenalin is dropped into the eye at three different times within five minutes. Normally no effect is evident. If the dilator fibers are rendered sensitive as they usually are in affections which involve the sympathetic fibers distal to the superior cervical ganglion, then after a period of fifteen minutes has elapsed a marked dilatation of the pupil will ensue. This adrenalin mydriasis is common in affections involving the anterior and middle cranial fossae, such as diseases of the orbit and fractures at the base of the skull. Such affections are as a rule limited to one side. If the adrenalin mydriasis is double, then one must think of disturbances in the endocrine glands, which produce a general sympathetic irritability, such as Basedow's disease.

Exophthalmic goiter shows a very interesting eye picture. While the chief eye symptom, that for which the condition is named, a protrusion of the eyeball, may be due either to contraction of the Müllerian orbital muscle, which is activated by the sympathetics, or to contraction of the levator palpebrae, activated by the parasympathetics, there are other eye phenomena which are definitely of parasympathetic origin. Of these von Graefe's and Dalrymple's signs deserve mention.

VON GRAEFE'S SIGN.—This is a condition in which the upper lids do not follow the cornea readily when the eyes are lowered. This phenomenon is due to a heightened tonus of the fibers of the IIIrd nerve which supply the musculus levator palpebrae.

DALRYMPLE'S SIGN.—This sign consists of a widening of the lid slits giving the expression of fright. This is due to the same cause as von Graefe's sign, an increased tonus in the fibers supplying the musculus levator palpebrae.

If both divisions of the vegetative system show symptoms in the same individual in the presence of exophthalmic goiter, it must be due either to some process acting locally on neurons supplying certain structures or to an underlying difference in excitability of the neurons supplying different structures in the same individual, which causes them to become activated when the cell bodies are sensitized by the increased thyroid secretion.[2]

Reflexes in Other Organs Caused by Stimuli Arising in the Eye.— I have called attention in many of the clinical chapters to the reflexes which result from eye strain, particularly those in the gastrointestinal tract. Eye strain will very commonly produce nausea and at times even vomiting, hyperchlorhydria, spastic constipation, and intestinal stasis. The course of these reflexes is most probably through the afferent sensory fibers of the Vth nerve which mediate with the motor fibers of the vagus. In headache, another common symptom of eye strain, both afferent and efferent fibers course through the Vth nerve.

A colleague, Dr. Lyster, called my attention to an unusual cause of reflex cough, in which the impulse arose in the eye. The patient suffered from a contraction of the pupil in one eye. As long as the pupil was contracted the cough persisted; when a mydriatic was used the cough ceased. This cough was so annoying that the patient was referred to me, for she was afraid she might have some pulmonary disease.

References

1. Higier: Vegetative oder Viscerale Neurologie, Ergebnisse Neurologie und Psychiatry, Jena, 1912, Gustav Fischer, p. 90.
2. Pottenger: An Analysis of the Symptoms of Exophthalmic Goiter, Endocrinology 2: 16, 1918.

CHAPTER XXXII
THE LACRIMAL GLANDS

I. INNERVATION OF THE LACRIMAL GLANDS

The lacrimal glands are supplied by both sympathetic and parasympathetic fibers, the former from the superior cervical ganglion, the latter from the VIIth cranial (facial) nerve. They receive sensory fibers from the nervus lacrimalis of the Vth cranial nerve, which carry the afferent impulses in parasympathetic reflexes.

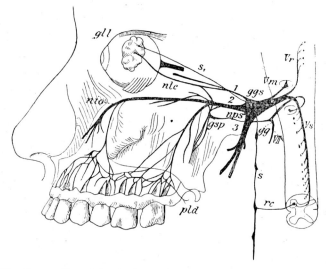

Fig. 75.—Innervation of lacrimal glands. *gll*, lacrimal gland; *rc*, ramus communicans; *s*, nervus sympathicus; *s₁*, sympathetic fibers to the eye (coursing with the first branch of trigeminus); *VII*, root of the facial nerve; *gg*, ganglion geniculi; *nps*, nervus petrosus superficialis, major; *gsp*, ganglion sphenopalatinum; *nlc*, nervus lacrimalis; *Vs*, descending, *Vm*, motor, and *Vr*, reflex roots of the trigeminus; *1, 2, 3*, Ist, IInd, and IIIrd branches of trigeminus; *ggs*, Gasserian ganglion; *nio*, nervus infraorbitalis; *pld*, plexus dentalis. (Bechterew.)

Sympathetic.—The sympathetic system sends fibers to the lacrimal gland, and also controls its blood supply.

Parasympathetic.—The parasympathetic fibers which activate the lacrimal glands, have their origin in the VIIth cranial (facial) nerve. The fibers leave the facial nerve in the geniculate ganglion and pass with the nervus petrosus superficialis major, and reach the nervus subcutaneous malae, a branch of the trigeminus at the sphenopalatine

386

ganglion. This nerve then freely anastomoses with the nervus lacrimalis, a branch of the Vth cranial (trigeminus), and passes to the lacrimal gland. This is shown in Fig. 75; also in Plate IV, page 72.

While the parasympathetic fibers pass to the gland with fibers belonging to the trigeminus (Vth cranial), they do not belong to it in the sense that they originate from a nucleus of the trigeminus; but belong to the facialis (VIIth cranial).

II. THE LACRIMAL GLANDS: CLINICAL CONSIDERATION

Dryness of the Eyes.—There are many conditions in which a dryness of the eyes occurs. This is found particularly in infectious diseases with high fever. During fever, secretion from many of the glandular structures of the body is lessened. This should be expected as a result of the action of the toxins upon the sympathetics.

Epiphora.—Epiphora, or an excess of tears, is found in certain diseases of the eye itself and often as a reflex from diseases of the nasal mucous membrane; also from paralysis of the cervical sympathetics from injury or following operation on the cervical ganglia. Acute rhinitis is commonly accompanied by weeping eyes. Hay fever also has excessive lacrimation as a common symptom. The connection is evident since the parasympathetic fibers of the VIIth cranial nerve supply the lacrimal glands and these are in reflex connection with the sensory fibers in the Vth cranial nerve. I have observed lacrimation as a symptom of abscess at the root of a tooth. Other reflex effects upon the lacrimal secretion will be noted in other diseases producing nasal stimulation. It is not an uncommon symptom in individuals who are strongly vagotonic.

CHAPTER XXXIII

THE UROGENITAL TRACT

I. INNERVATION OF THE UROGENITAL TRACT

The Müllerian and Wolffian ducts are derived from the segmental duct which is of epiblastic origin. Therefore the muscles surrounding these ducts belong to the dermal system, and, as such, are activated by motor cells whose connector fibers belong to the thoracicolumbar or sympathetic outflow.

The Müllerian ducts become the Fallopian tubes, and, after fusing, form the uterus and vagina; while the Wolffian duct gives origin to the vas deferens and ejaculatory duct. When that stage of evolutionary development was reached which demanded a separate excretory organ, the kidney was formed. It arises as a bud from the dorsal side of the Wolffian duct near its termination in the cloaca. This bud pushes upward, gradually elongating the stalk on which it grows. This becomes the ureter. Its course is posterior to the peritoneum, and it does not stop until the upper pole of the kidney has reached the eleventh rib. The lower end of the stalk of the bud, which is the lower end of the ureter, migrates along the Wolffian duct until it leaves it and becomes established in that part of the cloaca from which the bladder is made. Thus, when fully developed, the ureter and kidney are wholly separated from the Wolffian body, although they are derived from it.

All of the structures derived from the Müllerian and Wolffian ducts are activated by the sympathetic system. Gaskell says there is no evidence that the ureter, uterus, and vas deferens have any connection with the pelvic nerve, but Kuntz says they are well supplied with parasympathetics.

The bladder and rectum originally formed a single cavity, but as the excretory function of the urinary apparatus became of greater importance to the animal, these two structures separated and each became a distinct cavity with an external opening of its own. The bladder, rectum, and large intestine correspond to the cloaca in lower life. They are developmentally related and possess similar innervation. In them we have, aside from the usual circular and longitudinal

388

muscles, which are found throughout the gut, a second system of muscles, the sphincters. Their origin is as follows: The cloaca was originally divided into three parts and each of them protected above and below by a circular band of muscle (sphincter). Thus the contents of the small gut would be prevented from entering the cloaca; relaxation of the outer sphincter could permit of the evacuation of urine without feces; or, if both outer and inner rectal sphincters were relaxed, both urine and feces could pass out. It can readily be understood how, when the posterior chamber differentiated into the urinary bladder, it carried with it the outer sphincter musculature which further differentiated into the sphincter of the bladder and the urethral musculature.

The *bladder* and *urethra* then carry with them the same innervation as the systems from which they are embryologically derived. The sphincter, that part of the bladder between the sphincter and the ureteral orifices known as the trigone, and the urethral musculature are activated by the sympathetics and inhibited by the parasympathetics. The body of the bladder is innervated in the same manner as the cloacal walls, activated by the parasympathetics (pelvic nerve) and inhibited by the sympathetics. Thus it is evident that the urogenital structures are more or less complex embryologically and also show this same complexity from the standpoint of innervation.

The foregoing embryologic facts make the relationships of these structures clear. We shall now discuss the innervation of those structures which are derived wholly from the Müllerian and Wolffian ducts, viz:

1. **The Fallopian Tubes, Uterus, Vagina, Vas Deferens, Seminal Vesicles, and Ureter.**—These, except the cervix uteri are activated by the *sympathetics*, the connector fibers arising, according to different observers, from the Xth thoracic to the Vth lumbar (animals). The Xth thoracic to IVth lumbar are the chief sources of supply. *The sympathetics carry the only fibers for most of these structures.* In this way they resemble the dermal musculature. This is to be expected because of the fact that the Müllerian and Wolffian ducts are of epiblastic origin. The uterus, vagina, clitoris, and walls of the urethra, however, are supplied by a few parasympathetic fibers from the sacral nerves.

The separate nerve supply to the cervix which comes from the *sacral nerves*, according to some authors, activates the cervix and

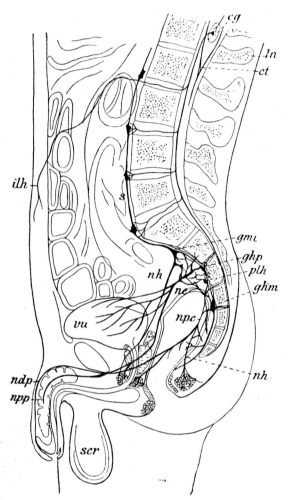

Fig. 76.—Innervation of generative organs (male). *cg*, spinal center for the organs of generation, on level of first lumbar vertebrae; *s*, nervus sympathicus; *ct*, conus terminalis; *ilh*, nervus iliohypogastricus; *gmi*, ganglion mesentericum inferius; *ghp*, ganglion hypogastricus; *plh*, plexus hypogastricus; *ghm*, ganglion hemorrhoidale; *nh*, superior nervus hypogastricus; *ne*, nervus erigens or pelvicus; *npc*, nervus pudendus communis; *nh*, nervus hemorrhoidalis inferior; *ndp*, nervus dorsalis penis; *npp*, nervus peronaei profundus; *vu*, bladder; *scr*, scrotum. (Bechterew.)

produces inhibitory influences on the body of the uterus (Bechterew). Gaskell, however, finds no parasympathetic fibers in the body of the uterus.

The connector neurons which supply these structures pass as medullated fibers through the inferior mesenteric ganglion and end, according to some investigators, in ganglia in the uterovaginal plexus; according to others, in ganglia within the organs, in much the same manner as do the parasympathetics throughout the enteral system.

2. **The Prostate and the Glands of Cowper and Bartholin.**—These are supplied by secretory nerves from the sympathetics. The prostate, however, seems to partake of characteristics of both the Wolffian duct and the cloaca as far as innervation is concerned, as might be inferred from its derivation. The musculature around the prostate is derived from the cloacal structures and innervated by the pelvic nerve. Stimulation of the pelvic nerve probably causes a forcing out of secretion by contracting the musculature, and not by stimulating secreting glands. Stimulation of the hypogastric produces true secretion. Figs. 76 and 77 from Bechterew show the innervation of the organs of generation of the male and female.

3. **The Penis.**—The penis is supplied by *sympathetic* fibers from the hypogastric plexus which go to all the smooth muscles, such as the retractor penis muscle belonging to the dermal system; and by *parasympathetics* from the pelvic nerve (nervus erigens). This nerve was originally named *nervus erigens* from the fact that it was the nerve which is active in producing erection. Later physiologists have given it the name of *pelvic* in order to indicate thereby its greater distribution. When stimulated, this nerve produces a relaxation of the smooth muscle of the corpora cavernosa. At the same time a dilatation of the vessels ensues and they become filled with blood. Simultaneously the muscles, transversus perinei profundus, ischiocavernosus, and bulbocavernosus, contract and increase the hyperemia. This results in an increase in the size of the organ.

4. **The Urinary Bladder.**—The bladder, as previously mentioned, is formed from the cloaca and carries with it both the musculature of the walls of the gut and that of the sphincters. Therefore, the bladder has two distinctly antagonistic systems of innervation.

The *parasympathetics* which supply the bladder run as connector fibers in the pelvic nerve until they reach motor cells which lie on the bladder musculature. They activate the musculature of the bladder walls, except the trigonum; and inhibit the musculature in the trigonum, the sphincter, and urethra. Therefore, stimulation of the pelvic fibers going to the bladder compresses the walls and relaxes the sphincter and thus causes emptying of the viscus.

The *sympathetic* fibers to the bladder antagonize the parasympathetics. When stimulated, they constrict the sphincter and urethral muscle and relax the musculature of the bladder wall, with the excep-

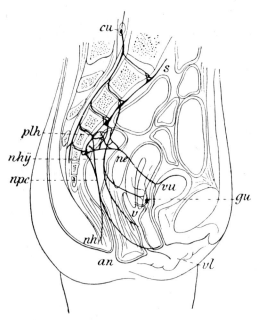

Fig. 77.—Innervation of generative organs (female). Innervation of the uterus and vagina. *cu*, spinal uterus center; *s*, nervus sympathicus and sympathetic ganglia; *plh*, plexus hypogastricus; *nhy*, nervus hypogastricus; *npc*, nervus pudendus communis; *nh*, nervus hemorrhoidalis; *gu*, peripheral ganglion in vaginal wall; *v*, vagina; *vu*, bladder; *vl*, vulva; *an*, anus. (Bechterew.)

tion of the trigonum, which they contract. The trigonum is closely related to the sphincter muscles. The motor cells which give origin to the sympathetic fibers lie in the inferior mesenteric ganglion, and the connector fibers originate in segments between the XIth thoracic and IIIrd lumbar (Riddoch[1]).

5. **Ovary and Testicle.**—The *ovary*, aside from the function of ovulation, produces internal secretions which have a very marked influ-

ence on the individual. It not only influences the growth but exerts an unusual energizing influence throughout life. These internal secretions are at least three in number: one from the interstitial glands, which has to do with growth and metabolism; one from the corpus luteum, which seems to be essential for the retention of the ovum in the uterus; and one from the follicle, described by Allen and Doisy,[2] which seems to control estrus. The ovary is supplied for the most part by sympathetic fibers which arise from the IXth and Xth, or Xth and XIth thoracic segments, pass through the small splanchnic nerves to the aorticorenal ganglion and follow the ovarian artery in the plexus arteriae ovaricae to be distributed to

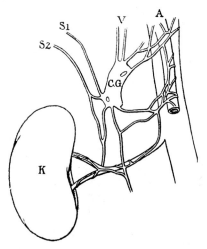

Fig. 78.—Nerve supply of the kidney. (After Renner.) K, kidney; S_1, S_2, major and minor splanchnic nerves; V, vagus; C. G., celiac ganglion; A, aorta.

the ovarian vessels and tissue. These nerves probably produce their effects on the ovary largely through their action on the blood vessels. It is generally assumed that the functions of the ovary are independent of nerve action and dependent on hormones instead. Parasympathetic fibers from the pelvic nerve, according to some authors, enter the ovary but do not effect secretory activity.

The *testes*, aside from the production of spermatozoa, produce an internal secretion which has an influence on metabolism and growth, the lack of which is well illustrated in case of castrated animals and eunuchs.

The testis is supplied by nerves which for the most part course in the blood vessels. They are almost wholly of *sympathetic* origin. They arise from the IXth and Xth, or Xth and XIth thoracic segments, pass through the small splanchnic to the aorticorenal ganglion and spermatic plexus to the testicle.

The *parasympathetics* from the pelvic nerve also enter the gland, but are not activating fibers. According to Kuntz[3] there is much doubt whether secretion on the part of the testis is influenced by nerve stimulation. The internal secretion of the testes is sympathicotropic, according to Wheelon and Shipley.[4]

6. **The Kidney.**—The kidney which arises from a bud from the Wolffian duct, carries an innervation which differs markedly from the other structures which are embryologically related to it. Both sympathetic and parasympathetic nerves go to the kidney, but it is supposed that the control of the blood supply rather than a truly secreting nervous mechanism is the chief factor in altering the secretion of urine.

The *sympathetics* go to the kidney as nonmedullated fibers from the celiac ganglion, which is supplied by connector fibers from the VIth thoracic to the Ist lumbar, chiefly, however, from the Xth, XIth, and XIIth thoracic segments. The sympathetics furnish both vasoconstrictor and vasodilator fibers.

The *parasympathetics* which supply the kidney come from the vagus, but there are no definite data on which to base an opinion that they have a vasodilator effect. They are important, however, in accounting for many of the reflexes which mediate with other parasympathetic fibers when the kidney is inflamed. Fig. 78 from Cushney shows the nerve supply of the kidney.

II. THE UROGENITAL TRACT: CLINICAL CONSIDERATION

1. **Fallopian Tubes, Uterus, Vagina, Vas Deferens, and Seminal Vesicles.**—The reflexes which arise from some of these structures have not been carefully analyzed. If, as seems evident, they are supplied only by sympathetic nerves, one type of reflex—the sympathetic—alone will be found. Clinical observation of the pains and sensations which arise from these structures must of necessity be more or less uncertain.

It has been a common clinical observation that nausea and vomiting and other digestive disturbances, follow inflammation of the uterus and tubes. The vomiting impulse is readily stimulated by inflammation in all structures belonging to the enteral system, yet vomiting is a complex act which is presided over by a definite vomiting center, which is found in the floor of the fourth ventricle, and may be induced by stimuli which reach this center from many sources and from varied causes. Severe pain is at times sufficient to discharge this center, so is a foul odor, a "sickening" sight, and even thoughts of it. Vomiting, like coughing and ejaculation of semen, is a complex act.

MOTOR REFLEX.—The motor reflex from these structures belonging to the genital system is not very pronounced, in spite of the fact that the uterus is one of the very important organs of the body.

SENSORY REFLEX.—The sensory reflex from some of these organs is definite and well recognized, in others it is not as yet well defined. Pain is a common symptom of uterine disease and of considerable importance in tubal disease. As a rule it is not acute.

The location of pain arising in the Fallopian tubes may be felt according to Marcus[5] in the loin, in the iliac fossa, or down the anterior surface of the thigh to the knee, indicating that the nerves of the tubes mediate with neurons arising from the XIth and XIIth dorsal, and Ist, IInd, and IIIrd lumbar segments of the cord.

Uterine pain is found in many women who have, or who have had, uterine disease, particularly those who are below par from both a physical and a nerve standpoint. This pain is usually located in the lumbar region and lower abdomen. Uterine pain, however, may be located anywhere in the areas from the Xth dorsal to the Vth lumbar zones or even in sacral zones. At times there are pains present which seem to be definitely of uterine origin, which are referred to the sacral region, the back of the hip and the thigh. These make it appear as though there is nerve connection with the sacral nerves. However, the impulse responsible for these reflexes might originate in the cervix which is innervated by filaments from the sacral segments (which is most probable) or be transferred in the cord in the same manner as those from the lung to the cervical portion of the cord. The location of uterine, ovarian, and tubal pain is shown in Fig. 79 from Behan.

There are several centers in the central nervous system from which the uterus may be influenced; one of them lies in the lumbar portion of the cord from which the sympathetic connector neurons, which supply the uterus, arise. It is in these areas of the cord that the uterus has its main reflex connection with the spinal nerves, particularly the ischiadicus and cruralis. The uterus is easily stimulated to contraction by ovarian irritation. The impulse which causes this reflex is probably carried to the cord through sensory fibers of the sympathetic connector neurons arising from the IXth, Xth, and XIth thoracic segments, and transferred downward in the cord by associa-

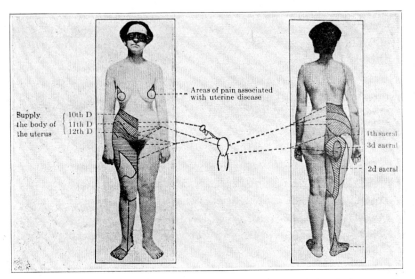

Fig. 79.—Areas of distribution of cord segments involved in uterine, ovarian, and tubal diseases.

The body of the uterus is supplied by the Xth, XIth and XIIth dorsal segments; the cervix by the IIIrd and IVth lumbar and sometimes by the Ist and IInd sacral segments; the ovary by the Xth, and the Fallopian tube by the XIth and XIIth dorsal and the Ist lumbar segments. (Behan.)

tion fibers to the lumbar segments. Some observers state that the uterus receives its sympathetic supply from areas as high in the cord as the Xth thoracic. If so, reflexes from it may course over the same nerves that receive afferent impulses from the ovary.

Stimuli which cause reflex contraction of the uterus may be transmitted from any portion of the spinal cord, according to some writers. Irritation of the mammae and nipples exerts a strong uterine contraction. Stimulation of the central portion of the brachial plexus is also followed by uterine contraction according to Schlesinger.

In the medulla oblongata there is also a center which presides over uterine contraction. It is not impossible that this reflex act, like vomiting, as mentioned above, may be reflexly precipitated through intercalated neurons between the neurons in the lumbar portion of the cord and the center in the medulla.

2. **Prostate.**—The prostate shows viscerosensory reflexes in which, according to Head, the afferent impulses apparently travel central-ward with both sympathetics and parasympathetics; because the pain is expressed in both thoracic and sacral spinal sensory nerves. It would seem that the sympathetic connector fibers going to the prostate should emerge from the upper lumbar segments, but the reflex is shown in the areas of the Xth and XIth thoracic. The parasympa-thetic reflex, through the pelvic nerve, expresses itself in sensory dis-turbances in the Ist, IInd, and IIIrd sacral sensory zones. Pain may be felt in the glans penis; and frequency of urination and discomfort in the rectum may be noted. These reflexes are readily understood because of the connection of the tissues with the pelvic nerve. The areas of pain which are most frequent in prostatic disease are shown in Fig. 80, *A* and *B* and in Fig. 37, page 257.

3. **Penis.**—The penis is more often the subject of reflex sensation than the cause of it. It is closely bound to the urogenital and rectal structures by the filaments of the pelvic nerve, and is the seat of reflex sensory disturbances during inflammations of the kidney, ureter, bladder, and prostate, and at times when the cloacal tissues are involved.

4. **Bladder.**—The bladder having a double innervation of spinal origin, one from the XIth thoracic to IIIrd lumbar segments—sympathetic; and one from the IIIrd and IVth sacral segments—parasympathetic; has two routes (chiefly sympathetic, however) over which afferent sensory impulses may travel to the cord to com-bine with sensory and motor neurons in the production of reflex action.

VISCEROMOTOR REFLEX.—The bladder, when inflamed, at times pro-duces spasm of the lower recti according to Mackenzie. Pain, how-ever, is the chief and most characteristic reflex phenomenon.

VISCEROSENSORY REFLEX.—The pain from diseases of the bladder is reflected through both the sympathetic system (IInd, IIIrd, and IVth lumbar nerves) and the parasympathetic system (IInd, IIIrd, and IVth sacral nerves). The pain from the former is usually found in the areas near the pubis and is not marked, while that from the latter is found in the region of the perineum and penis and is very

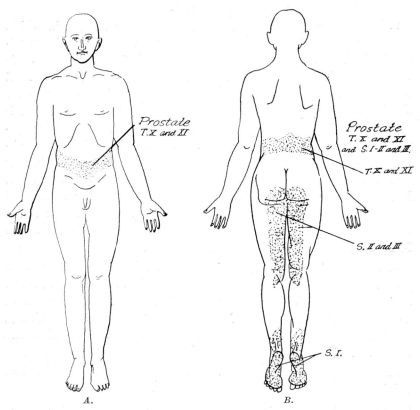

Fig. 80.—A. Anterior view, illustrating area of pain in prostatic disease. The prostate shows both a sympathetic and a parasympathetic reflex. Pain anteriorly is entirely above the pubis and of sympathetic origin.

B. Posterior view, illustrating area of pain in prostatic disease. Pain posteriorly expresses itself not only in the Xth and XIth thoracic segments, but also in the sacral segments of the region of the buttocks and inner surface of the thigh.

important. Fig. 81, A and B shows the common location of reflex pain when the bladder is diseased. Fig. 37, page 257, should also be consulted.

The bladder is influenced reflexly by inflammation in such neighboring structures as the appendix, kidney, Fallopian tubes, uterus, ovary, prostate, and rectum.

5. **The Ovary and Testicle.**—The ovary and the testicle are supplied by sympathetics whose connector neurons arise from the IXth and Xth, or Xth to XIIth thoracic segments of the cord. The fact that their innervation comes from a higher plane in the cord than

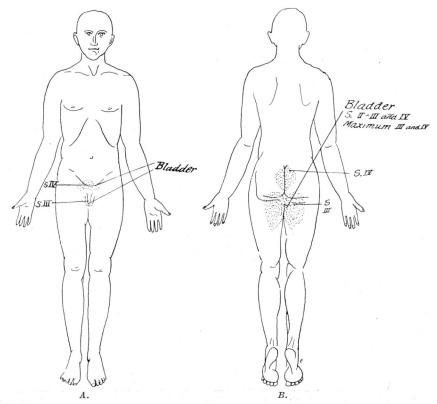

Fig. 81.—*A.* Anterior view, showing the common location of pain when the bladder is inflamed. It will be seen that these are parasympathetic reflexes. While the bladder receives a sympathetic nerve supply from the IInd, IIIrd, and IVth lumbar segments, these rarely give sensory reflexes. The sensory reflex anteriorly is immediately above the pubis and in the region of the scrotum and penis.

B. Posterior view, showing the common location of pain when the bladder is inflamed. The reflex pain from the bladder posteriorly is found in the region of the sacrum and perineum, and the inner surface of the thigh.

that of most of the genital organs is probably significant of the higher position that they occupy in the abdomen in fetal life. The reflexes

from the ovary and testis manifest themselves in the structures above
the pubis, the ovaries higher than the testes.

MOTOR REFLEX.—The visceromotor reflex from the ovary and testis
is of little diagnostic aid. The lowest portion of the abdominal muscles shows rigidity at times when these organs are involved.

SENSORY REFLEX.—The viscerosensory reflexes from the ovary and
testicle are of considerable clinical importance. They produce their

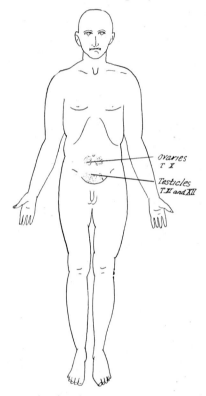

Fig. 82.—Common areas of pain when the testicles or the ovaries are inflamed.
It will be noted that the pain from the ovary is higher than that from the testicle.
Both express themselves near the median line.

pain in the groin in the Xth to XIIth thoracic sensory zones. This
at times seems to radiate down the thigh, and the skin may become
hyperalgesic. Fig. 82 illustrates the common position of pain in diseases of the testicle and ovary.

6. **Kidney and Ureter**.—The kidney and ureter show both visceromotor and viscerosensory reflexes. The kidney receives its sympa-

thetic innervation from the VIth thoracic to Ist lumbar segments. The chief source of nerve supply, however, comes from the lower thoracics, XIth and XIIth and Ist lumbar, and it seems from clinical observation that the visceromotor and viscerosensory reflexes which occur when the renal tissue is involved, are produced by nerves arising from these lower segments.

RENAL VISCEROMOTOR REFLEX.—In 1912,[6] I described a spasm of the lumbar muscles which I noticed when the renal tissue is infiltrated by tuberculosis. This reflex is present in inflammatory conditions of the kidney of nontuberculous as well as those of a tuberculous nature. In order to detect it, the patient should be seated on a stool with the

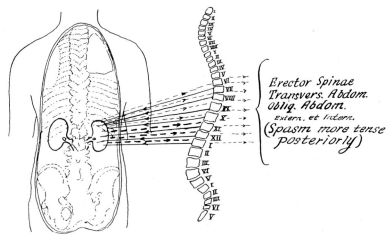

Fig. 83.—Renal visceromotor reflex.
Lines connecting the kidney with the segments of the cord from the VIth thoracic to the Ist lumbar segments, represent sympathetic connector neurons. Solid lines represent the sympathetic nerves supplying the kidney. Broken lines represent afferent fibers of the sympathetic system which carry impulses from the kidney to the cord. Broken lines on the other side of the cord represent corresponding spinal nerves which receive the impulses from the sympathetic afferent system and transmit them to the muscles shown, producing the renal visceromotor reflex.

feet resting on the floor, and the lumbar muscles relaxed as much as possible. Palpation will then reveal the increased tonus in those muscles which show the motor reflex. This increased muscle tonus is of great value in determining the condition of the other kidney before removing one because of tuberculous infection. This reflex is of diagnostic value in all inflammatory processes affecting the kidney. *This is a truly renal reflex and differs from that observed in so-called renal colic, which belongs to the ureter rather than to the kidney.*

As long as the stone remains in the pelvis of the kidney, neither muscle spasm nor pain is prominent; but as soon as the stone is engaged in the ureter, both are present. Fig. 83 shows the muscles which are involved in the renal reflex.

RENAL VISCEROSENSORY REFLEX.—The renal viscerosensory reflex as a rule seems more like an ache than a pain. It often expresses

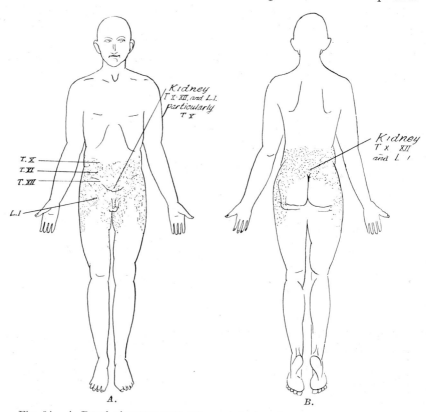

Fig. 84.—*A.* Renal viscerosensory reflex. Anterior view.
It will be noted that the pain from the kidney might be expressed anywhere below the naval and on the inner and external portions of the thigh, including the scrotal area. The severest pain, however, is in the Xth thoracic zone, which lies immediately below the umbilicus.

B. Renal viscerosensory reflex. Posterior view.
Posteriorly, pain may be expressed anywhere over the entire lumbar region and extending down over the external portion of the thighs.

itself in the back alone but may be felt in any sensory zone from the VIth thoracic to the Ist lumbar. It is unlike that of ureteral colic which usually extends from the lumbar region and the iliac fossa over the front of the abdomen and down into the scrotum.   Fig. 84, *A* and *B* shows the common site of pain arising in the kidney.

RENAL VISCEROTROPHIC REFLEX.—The same muscles, skin, and subcutaneous tissue that show the motor and sensory reflexes when the kidney is first inflamed, show degenerative changes when the disease becomes chronic. This degeneration of the lumbar muscles and subcutaneous tissue and skin covering them becomes an important diagnostic sign in tuberculosis or other chronic inflammatory processes involving the renal tissue.

URETERAL VISCEROMOTOR REFLEX.—The abdominal, erector spinae, and cremaster muscles become tense during an attack of *renal colic.*

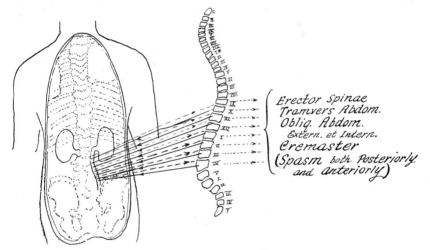

Fig. 85.—Showing the ureteral visceromotor reflex.
The lines connecting the ureter with the segments of the cord from the IXth thoracic to the IVth lumbar represent the sympathetic connectors. Solid lines represent sympathetic nerves which supply the ureter. Broken lines represent afferents of the sympathetic system which carry impulses to the cord. Broken lines on the other side of the cord represent corresponding spinal nerves which receive the impulse from the sympathetic afferent system and transmit them to the muscles shown producing the ureteral visceromotor reflex. The broken lines running from the ureter to the IInd, IIIrd, and IVth lumbar segments are heavier, indicating that these are the principal paths of the impulse.

The fibers arising from the last thoracic and first lumbar spinal nerves are stimulated and cause those portions of the muscles which are supplied by them to contract. The probable explanation of the more extensive and more marked muscle spasm when the ureter, as compared with the renal tissue, is the seat of inflammation, is furnished by the fact that one is a simple inflammation of tissue while the other is an inflammation associated with a tonic spasm and contraction of a muscle belonging to an inflamed hollow organ. The latter condition affords the maximum nerve irritation. Fig. 85 shows the muscles involved in the reflex from the ureter.

URETERAL VISCEROSENSORY REFLEX.—The pain which accompanies *renal colic* is for the most part a ureteral pain. When the stone in

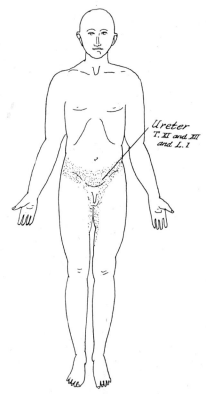

Fig. 86.—Common area of pain in ureteral viscerosensory reflex. This is the common pain of so-called "renal colic." Beginning in the back, it expresses itself for the most part in the groin, running down the inner side of the thigh.

the pelvis of the kidney first engages the ureteral orifice, there is a dull pain in the back which passes out over the iliac fossa toward the front of the abdomen and sometimes down over the anterior aspects of the thigh; in the male it passes down into the testicle as the calculus engages the walls of the ureter. This pain may be slight, or it may be severe. Sometimes the pain is accompanied by a marked hyperalgesia of the skin and muscles in the areas involved. Fig. 86 shows the common areas of pain when the ureter is inflamed as in ureteral, so-called "renal colic."

References

1. Riddoch, George: Conduction of Sensory Impulses From the Bladder by the Inferior Hypogastric and the Central Afferent Connections of These Nerves, Proc. Physiol. Soc., February 12, 1921, Abstracted Physiol. **54:** 134, 1921.
2. Allen, E., and Doisy, E.: An Ovarian Hormone, J. A. M. A. **81:** 819, 1923.
3. Kuntz, Albert: The Autonomic Nervous System, Philadelphia, 1929, Lea and Febiger.
4. Wheelon and Shipley: The Effects of Testicular Transplants Upon Vasomotor Irritability, Am. J. Physiol., 1916, p. 394.
5. Marcus, Maurice: The Radiation of Pain in Lesions of the Fallopian Tube, Brit. M. J. **1:** 185, 1923.
6. Pottenger, F. M.: Muscle Spasm and Degeneration and Light Touch Palpation, St. Louis, 1912, The C. V. Mosby Co., p. 96. Spasm of Lumbar Muscles; a Diagnostic Sign in Inflammation of the Kidney, J. A. M. A. **60:** 980, 1913.

CHAPTER XXXIV

THE SUBDERMAL STRUCTURES

The skin contains structures which are of great importance in the physiologic economy of man, among which are the blood vessels, pilomotor muscles, and sweat glands. Their importance is evident from the fact that these structures are provided with sensory nerves which receive stimuli from all the forces which are found in man's environment, and transfer them to the proper compensating mechanism so that the organism may adjust and maintain its physiologic processes in a state of equilibrium. Furthermore, they have as their special function, the control of body temperature. Between 80 and 85 per cent of the heat of the body is thrown off through the skin, which may be taken to mean that the skin exerts an influence up to this percentage in maintaining body temperature.

I. INNERVATION OF THE SKIN

The structures of the skin, as far as physiologists have been able to determine, possess only sympathetic nerves receiving innervation from the thoracic and upper three lumbar segments.

Since vasomotor, pilomotor, and sweat secretory effects can be produced independently of each other, we assume that there are distinct groups of nerves presiding over each of these functions. Both activating and inhibiting effects are produced by nerves belonging to the sympathetics.

Afferent Components of Skin Reflexes.—These afferent impulses, which originate in the skin, course centralward and pass through the posterior root ganglion and mediate in the central nervous system with sympathetic neurons to produce vasoconstrictor, pilomotor, or sweat secretory effects. They are also responsible for many visceral reflexes.

Efferent Components of Skin Reflexes.—The efferent components are of two kinds: activating and inhibiting. They both arise from the same centers, but the vasoconstrictors, pilomotor, and sweat activators pass peripheralward with the motor spinal nerves, while vasodilators, pilomotor and sweat inhibitors course peripheralward with

406

the sensory spinal nerves. There are also certain cranial and sacral fibers which belong to the parasympathetics which produce regional vasodilator effects, notably the chorda tympani and the nervus erigens.

II. THE SKIN: CLINICAL CONSIDERATION

Body Temperature.—The skin organs are influenced in the maintenance of normal temperature by reflex stimulation. Heat relaxes the dermal structures and dilates the vessels; cold contracts both muscles and vessels. Heat regulating impulses also affect the sweat glands, bringing them into play when they are necessary to the maintenance of the temperature within normal limits. The centers in the cord and brain are influenced by reflex effects, the temperature and quality of the blood, and by psychic stimuli.

Skin Reflexes.—One of the interesting phenomena associated with the skin is its color reaction to stimulation. This is sometimes limited in extent, being due to reflexes mediated in the cord. At other times it is more widely spread, under which circumstances higher centers and the emotions come into evidence.

Skin reflexes affecting large areas may at times be noted in wide vasomotor and pilomotor effects in distant parts, as may be noted in the application of cold to the feet and hands, or following a hot foot bath. The vasomotor effects, goose flesh and outbreak of sweat following fright, are well known, so is the blush following emotional stimuli due to timidity and shame. Sometimes widespread vasomotor and pilomotor effects follow tactile stimuli of mild degree. I have often noted, during examination, a flushing and outbreak of sweat over the shoulders and upper portion of the chest follow coughing when the effort was repeated several times in succession.

Dermographism.—One of the very interesting phenomena connected with the innervation of the skin is dermographism. It will be noticed that there is a wide variation in the skin reactions of different individuals, a fact which must always be taken into consideration in studying these interesting phenomena. Since the skin reactions are so closely associated with the state of the blood vessels, the various color reactions following stroking have come to be taken as a measure of the relative tonus of the sympathetic activators and inhibitors, as described in Chapter VI. Among the many interesting studies of this subject I would particularly call attention to those of Ebbecke,[1, 2] Müller,[3] and Lewis.[4]

The White Line.—If a blunt point is drawn lightly over the warm skin, a white line (The White Line of Sergent) follows, which remains for an instant. This is due to the pressure of the instrument on the vessels, causing a temporary emptying. As soon as the pressure is released, however, the vessels again begin to fill. After the lapse of a few seconds another wider white line appears, soon reaching its maximum. The cause of the white line is undoubtedly a contraction of the minute skin vessels which remains after the irritation ceases, thus resisting refilling.

The Red Line.—The red line on the skin is caused by fairly heavy stroking. It results from a greater force than that which produces the white line. It appears in a few seconds after the stimulus is applied, and remains for a variable length of time. I have seen it remain for many minutes. It is caused by a dilatation of the minute skin vessels, arterioles, capillaries, and venules.

While both the white and red lines seem to represent local effects, we must not forget that mild stimuli may be picked up by the extremely sensitive nerves of the skin and carried centralward to produce reflex effects. Any stroke, on the other hand, might set free histamine-like substances which cause vascular dilatation.

Spreading Flush.—When the stroking of the skin is unusually strong, or when it is repeated several times, a blush extends several centimeters to the side of the path of stimulation. The color is much brighter than that of the red line. This originates in the arterioles and is dependent upon the cutaneous nerves for its existence.

Wheal.—If the irritation is still greater, then local edema in the form of a wheal or urticarial patch takes place. This seems to have as its cause the same dilatation of arterioles that causes the flush produced by the nerve reflex, and, added to this, an increased permeability of the vessel walls, permitting exudation to take place.

Cause of Various Reactions of Skin to Injury.—It will be seen that the minute vessels, including the arterioles, are involved in these reactions. In some the vascular nerves are evident in the production of reflex effects. But, according to Lewis, there is still a chemical factor found in all, a histamine-like substance which results from the injury of the tissues produced by the application of the stimulus. Urticaria and the effects produced by the application of heat and cold, ultraviolet light, x-ray, and various irritants are all brought within the same causative influence according to the work of Lewis and his coworkers.

Cutaneous Anaphylactic Phenomena.—The urticaria which follows food poisoning, serum reaction, and local irritation in the group of individuals who are susceptible to such stimuli, can all be accounted for as a local release of some histamine-like substance which produces local vessel dilatation and increased vascular permeability. The wheal occurs at the point where the reaction between the antigen and antibody takes place.

III. THE PILOMOTOR MUSCLES

As the cutaneous sensory branches of the spinal nerves follow out the segmentation of the body in their distribution, so do the sympathetic fibers to the pilomotor muscles. The segmental distribution is not followed, however, by the connector neurons going to the lateral ganglia, for they send off collateral branches to ganglia other than the one corresponding to the segment of the cord from which they rise. A stimulation of the motor cells in a given ganglion of the gangliated cord will stimulate only the pilomotor muscles in the segment supplied by the sensory nerves arising from the corresponding spinal segment; but a stimulus applied to the connector fiber before it reaches the lateral ganglion, may through its collateral fibers stimulate several lateral ganglia and cause an erection of hairs in several spinal segments.

It is to Langley that we owe much of our knowledge of the sympathetic system. Table IX worked out by him and quoted by Gaskell[5] shows the extent to which each connector fiber from the IVth thoracic to the IIIrd lumbar through its collateral branches and lateral ganglia, influences sensory body segments through spinal sensory nerves. It will be noted that each spinal nerve is associated with several sympathetic ganglia and each sympathetic ganglion sends, through its gray rami, fibers to its corresponding spinal nerve. Therefore stimulation of the connector fibers from one spinal segment often causes pilomotor action in several segments.

Not only do the pilomotor muscles of animals which have hair belong to this system, but also the entire subdermal smooth musculature—that which moves the skin causing goose flesh when contracted, the smooth subdermal musculature around the anus and vagina, and the retractor penis muscle.

TABLE IX

CONNECTION OF THE SPINAL NERVES OF THE CAT FROM THE FOURTH THORACIC TO THE THIRD LUMBAR WITH THOSE LATERAL GANGLIA OF THE SYMPATHETIC INCLUDED BETWEEN THE GANGLION STELLATUM AND THE COCCYGEAL GANGLIA

SPINAL NERVE			SYMPATHETIC GANGLIA
	IV	g. st.	
	V	"	
	VI	"	
	VII	"	4 5 6 7 8 9 Thoracic
Thoracic	VIII	"	4 5 6 7 8 9 10
	IX	"	4 5 6 7 8 9 10 11
	X		- - - - 8 9 10 11 12 13
	XI		- - - - - - - - — 12 13 1 2 3 Lumbar
	XII		- - - - - - - — — 13 1 2 3 4 5 6 7
	XIII		- - - - - - - — — — 1 2 3 4 5 6 7 1 Sacral
	I		- - - - - - - — — — - 2 3 4 5 6 7 1 2
Lumbar	II		- - - - - - - — — — - - 3 4 5 6 7 1 2 3
	III		- - - - - - - — — — - - - 4 5 6 7 1 2 3 coc.

IV. THE SWEAT GLANDS

The innervation of the sweat glands is puzzling to both physiologists and clinicians. Langley has shown definitely that secretion of sweat is produced by stimulation of the sympathetics. Gaskell[6] says, in speaking of the nerves of the sweat glands, that it has been conclusively shown, "(1) that these nerves belong to the sympathetic system, and (2) that their connector fibers are in anterior roots."

The sweat glands are supplied with smooth muscle which when stimulated causes an expression of sweat, and Gaskell says that the action of this smooth muscle must be considered in the process of sweating.

Pharmacologically, the secretion of sweat does not take place following the injection of adrenalin. In this it differs from all other supposedly sympathetic actions. It is stopped by atropine which inhibits vagus secretory activity, and is induced by pilocarpine which is distinctly vagotropic in action. In spite of this, Luciani[7] says: "But the experimental data adduced are ambiguous and do not prove the existence of a double order of nerves for the regulation of cutaneous secretion." This may now be explained by the theory that sweating is caused by the cholinergic rather than adrenergic neurons of the sympathetics.

Clinically, we find sweating in toxic states, usually after the temperature has reached its maximum and is receding. It does not accompany the early vasoconstriction or the pilomotor stimulation which precedes chill and is present in the early stage of temperature rise. When vasodilatation is occurring, and heat is rapidly dissipating, sweating which accompanies such toxic states as those found in tuberculosis and malaria, ensues.

Sweating often accompanies severe fright, but is not prone to occur in moderate degrees of fright. It comes in those conditions which we designate as neurasthenic or psychasthenic, whenever the nervous and psychic equilibrium is disturbed. It is frequent in conditions of general weakness, as during convalescence from disease. Vagotonics are prone to it. In this group the sweating of the hands and feet is often very annoying. This is probably an expression of unstable equilibrium, rather than an indication that the parasympathetic nerves have an influence in the causation of sweating.

We also see it in severe pain, which acts strongly on the sympathetics. Rapid peristalsis is accompanied at times by marked sweating. This could be through sympathetic connection with the spinal sensory nerves in the cord. Sweating, such as occurs in cases of asphyxia and in death agony, is due, most likely, to stimulation of nerve centers rather than peripheral irritation, according to Luciani.

References

1. Ebbecke, U.: Capillarerweiterung, Urticaria, und Shock, Klin. Wchnschr. 2: 1725, 1923.
2. Ebbecke, U.: Ueber Gwebsreizung und Gefässreaktion, Arch. f. d. ges. Physiol. 199: 197, 1923.
3. Müller, L. R.: Studien über den Dermographismus und dessen diagnostiche Bedeutung, Deutsche Ztschr. f. Nervenh. 47: 413, 1913.
4. Lewis, Thomas: The Blood Vessels of the Human Skin and Their Responses, London, 1927, Shaw and Sons, Ltd.
5. Gaskell: The Involuntary Nervous System, London, 1916, Longmans, Green & Co., p. 38.
6. Gaskell: Loc. cit., p. 37.
7. Luciani: Human Physiology, London, 1913, Macmillan Co., Vol. II, p. 497.

CHAPTER XXXV

ENDOCRINE GLANDS

The present monograph is not intended to treat of the specific problems of endocrinology, but is chiefly concerned with the subject of its relationship to the vegetative nervous system.

Visceral Neurology and Endocrinology Inseparable.—Studies of visceral neurology and endocrinology are inseparable, as must be apparent from the fact that the vegetative nervous system and the endocrine glands furnish the two regulating and correlating mechanisms which affect vegetative functions throughout the body. This is still further evident from the developmental relationship that exists between these two systems. The endocrine system, furnishing the normal chemical control, is older; in fact, in lower life, it is the only control of activity found in smooth musculature and secreting glands aside from the normal rhythmic action which is inherent in every cell. As the organism became more complex, however, a more rapid response in the correlation of vegetative activities became necessary and so the vegetative nervous system was evolved. So the endocrine and vegetative nervous systems became supplementary to each other.

Any disturbance in balance on the part of the vegetative nerves causes a disturbed equilibrium in the endocrine system, and vice versa. This must be so because both systems exert their effects upon cells, and cells have only two phases—activity and rest. Equilibrium in vegetative structures, however, depends upon the colloidal complex of the cell and its content in ions. Nerve impulses and hormones produce different effects according as the chemical and physical conditions of the cell differ. A patient with hyperirritability of the sympathetic system will show reflexes when the neurons of this system are acted upon by sympathicotropic stimuli which would not cause action in a normal person. The same is true with the parasympathetic system.

Uncompensated overaction on the part of such sympathicotropic glands as the adrenals, thyroid, and parathyroid must heighten sympathetic effects, while uncompensated overaction on the part of such parasympathetic glands as the pancreas, and the secretin-producing glands increases certain parasympathetic effects.

In the near future many of the clinical problems which, at present, are beyond solution, will be simplified by a better understanding of the normal and pathologic physiology of the vegetative nerves, the endocrine glands, and the electrolytic balance of the tissues.

Certain endocrine glands stimulate the sympathetics, others the parasympathetics. Still others seem to produce, now one effect, now another. Certain glands, on the other hand, are stimulated to action by the sympathetics and others by the parasympathetics.

Innervation of Endocrine Glands.—Unfortunately our knowledge of the innervation of the endocrine glands is incomplete. We know that the thyroid, adrenals, pancreas, pituitary, and the glands of the intestinal mucous membrane have activating neurons. The secretion of the testicle and ovary, on the other hand, do not seem to be under direct nerve control. Nevertheless vegetative innervation is indicated by reflexes in other tissues, as discussed in Chapter XXXIII, which are caused by stimuli arising in them.

We know that hormones exert an influence upon fecundation, the maturation of the embryo, and sexual development; that they are determining factors in the somatic and psychic spheres. They influence growth and metabolic activity, exert a control over the electrolytes and pH of the tissues, and provide a chemical regulating and correlating mechanism for the body (Pottenger[1]). The temperature, water, fat, sugar, calcium, potassium, sodium, and cholesterol balances are all under the influence of one or more of these glands.

Since nerve action in vegetative structures is either that of activation or inhibition, whether manifested in secretory, motor, or sensory phenomena, we must assume that the secretions of endocrine glands produce action which is identical with or similar to nerve stimulation. Therefore, we are probably warranted in assuming that in any given structure on which it acts the secretion of an endocrine gland acts with and reinforces effects which are characteristic of action in one or the other division of the vegetative nervous system and produces effects on smooth muscle and glandular structure similar to that produced by nerve stimulation.

While the secretion of the thyroid gland seems at times to show a preference for stimulating the parasympathetics, for most of its action it may be classed among the sympathicotropic group of glands. It stimulates the adrenals which produce the sympathicotropic adrenalin.

Interrelation of Various Glands.—Knowledge of the interrelation between the various glands is very important to clinical medicine. The key gland seems to be the pituitary, which, aside from numerous general effects, produces a substance which stimulates growth; others are gonadotropic, thyrotropic, and adrenotropic. It seems also to have special relation to the parathyroid. It shows its influence upon sugar metabolism by the fact that when it is removed before the pancreas, the animal fails to develop diabetes. It influences fat metabolism and water balance. The reaction of each gland is complex and the interrelation of the many glands is more complex.

The interrelation of these glands is shown by the fact that many of them influence the same body function. It would seem that Nature never leaves an important function to depend on a single mechanism.

Gonadotropic effects are produced by the pituitary, adrenals, and thyroid. Blood sugar is influenced by adrenals, pituitary, thyroid, and pancreas. Growth is stimulated by the thyroid, pituitary, gonads, and adrenals. Energy is stimulated by the adrenals, thyroid, gonads, and pituitary. Calcium is influenced by the thyroid, parathyroid, pituitary, adrenals, and gonads. Metabolism and blood pressure are influenced by all of the glands.

It is the multiplicity of control that makes for the safety of the organism, and also adds to the difficulties of unraveling the story of endocrinology.

The difficulty in securing active principles for therapeutic use has interfered much with the development of clinical knowledge. Doses that are being used are often far too small to produce results.

THE THYROID

The thyroid gland is supplied by both sympathetics and parasympathetics.

Sympathetics.—The sympathetic supply of the thyroid comes from the three cervical ganglia, the connector fibers arising in the upper thoracic segments of the cord. The sympathetic fibers not only supply the blood vessels but also go to the secreting cells which they activate. Stimulation of the sympathetics causes an increased secretion on the part of the glandular structures of the thyroid. This has been proved by Cannon and Cattell.[2]

Parasympathetics.—The parasympathetic nerves arise from the superior and inferior laryngeals and a branch from the main vagus nerve. Stimulation of the vagus fails to produce secretion. We are justified in considering the possibility of their opposing the action of the sympathetics because the glandular portion of the thyroid arises from the hypoblast of the pharyngeal structures in which such antagonistic nerve action is evident; yet, Cannon failed in "obtaining any evidence of any influence of vagus impulse on the thyroid gland," and further states that the interpretation of ten experiments "proves that the vagus has been neither an excitor nor an inhibitor of thyroid activity."

The internal secretion of the thyroid may be stimulated by the thyrotropic hormone from the anterior pituitary, by the adrenals, and by the sympathetic nerves.

The effect of the sympathetics is seen in the increased activity which follows toxic and emotional states. It would seem that the relation with the anterior pituitary is especially close, and reciprocal.

The chief function of the thyroid is to increase oxidative processes. This is shown in its stimulation of growth and metabolic processes generally.

Between hyperthyroidism, as indicated by a high metabolic rate, and the hypothyroidism of myxedema and cretinism there are many pathologic states of great importance to the organism. The influence upon bone development, sexual phenomena, blood sugar, blood pressure, water balance, hemopoiesis, on the heart, liver, and sympathico-adrenal mechanism makes the thyroid an organ of great importance to man. This is further emphasized by its influence on man's psychic state.

No recognized reflex symptoms arise from the thyroid gland, but Wilson has observed pathologic changes in the muscles of the shoulder girdle. Pathologic change also occurs in the cervical sympathetic ganglia when the patient suffers from toxic goiter. This has been described by Wilson[3] and by Wilson and Durante.[4]

The thyroid gland is of special interest to students of endocrinology because we are familiar in clinical experience with many conditions which represent both a hypoactivity and hyperactivity of the gland.

The gland is one of an important group whose function we are gradually understanding better. Each endocrine gland produces some substance or substances which influence other glands and other structures which are not in direct connection with it.

Plummer believed that the chief action of thyroxin is that of a catalytic agent which controls cellular energy output. The theory, which is generally held, that the secretion of the thyroid is wholly dependent upon iodine for its action, is no longer believed. Iodine is not essential to the action of thyroxin but is essential to its most efficient action. According to Plummer's views the varied effects upon the nervous system noted in hyperthyroid states are accompanying manifestations, and do not represent the primary effect of the thyroid substance upon the tissues.

Aub[5] and his coworkers have recently shown that when the thyroid is very active, it mobilizes the calcium in the bones and, further, that in hypothyroid states calcium is stored in the bones. It exerts a control over the bony development of the child. Its relationship to calcium indicates its sympathicotropic effects.

THE ADRENALS

Sympathetics.—The adrenals consist of two portions: the cortex and the medulla. In some of the lower forms of life these portions are two distinct organs. In man, however, they are combined in one. The cortical substance is formed from the Wolffian duct, while the medulla is derived from the phaeochromoblasts, one of the two groups of embryonic cells into which the primary sympathetic cells which migrate from the central nervous system become differentiated. Therefore, the medullary portion is derived from the nervous system and must be looked upon as being a tissue very closely related to the motor cells of the sympathetic ganglia. In fact, cells of the medulla are connected directly with the cord by medullated connector fibers, which pass from the Vth to the IXth thoracic segments of the cord through the lateral and the semilunar ganglia without meeting their sympathetic motor cells until the chromaffin cells of the medulla are attained. In this the cells of the medulla have the same function as motor cells in sympathetic ganglia. This direct innervation of the chromaffin cells in the adrenal medulla, without the intervention of a sympathetic ganglion, is shown schematically in Fig. 87.

Stimulation of the *splanchnics* activates the chromaffin cells of the adrenal gland and causes them to secrete adrenalin, a product which enters the blood stream and acts peripherally (either on the ganglion cells or at the myoneural junction) on all structures supplied by the sympathetic nerves, except the sweat glands. It produces and prolongs the same action as results from sympathetic stimulation. Adrenalin also stimulates the thyroid gland to secretory activity.

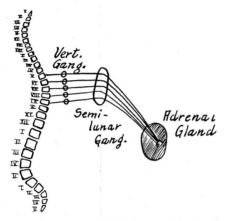

Fig. 87.—Showing the direct sympathetic innervation of chromaffin cells of the medulla of the adrenal body.

The connector neurons pass through the vertebral ganglia and the semilunar ganglion, and do not meet their motor cells until they reach the medulla of the adrenal body itself.

Parasympathetics.—Parasympathetic fibers from the vagus also supply the adrenals, but have no part in the production of adrenalin.

Adrenalin.—The action of adrenalin is fairly well known. As stated elsewhere, with the exception of failing to produce sweating, adrenalin produces the same effects as stimulation of the sympathetic nervous system.

Whether or not adrenalin influences body cells under normal conditions of physiologic balance is doubted by some authorities. The adrenalin-producing cells probably exert much the same influence upon the physiologic economy during normal life as the cells of sympathetic ganglia to which they are embryonically related. This has been pointed out by Swale Vincent, Hoskins, and Stewart; but when conditions arise which stimulate the splanchnics, the chromaffin cells and the medulla of the adrenals partake of the stimulation and produce adrenalin. This being thrown into the blood stream, circulates and acts upon sympathetically innervated structures and exerts the same influence as though the sympathetic nerves were centrally stimulated. Adrenalin is not normally in control of blood pressure as has been generally believed, but in times of stress produces a varying influence according to the degree of stimulation.

Adrenalin does not act with equal force upon blood vessels in all structures. Its action also differs according to the dosage. Small doses cause vasoconstriction in the vessels of the skin, mucous membranes, and abdominal organs, and drive the blood into the vessels supplying the skeletal muscles which are dilated. Larger amounts dilate the splanchnic vessels, as is shown in the quotation from Hartman, page 363.

Adrenalin and thyroxin are reciprocal substances, as shown by Hoskins. One gland cannot be activated without the other, for their secretions are reciprocally stimulating. Likewise, adrenalin and the internal secretions of the pancreas, and thyroid secretion and the internal secretion of the pancreas exert a reciprocally antagonistic action.

Cortical Substances.—Effects caused by the secretion of the cortical portion are more numerous and more complicated than those from the medullary portion. The secretion from the cortical portion of the adrenal has many functions. It furnishes one of the energizing substances in the body. It exerts an influence on growth, metabolism, sexual development, increases energy, protects against infections, and acts synergistically with adrenalin in relieving anaphylactic and allergic phenomena. When deficient, the body chlorides, sodium, and glucose decrease and the pH of the blood becomes less. The potassium, nonprotein nitrogen, and cholesterol increase.

The idea has been expressed that the primary function of the cortex is to regulate the volume of circulating blood, and that when the adrenals are removed the patient quickly develops a condition of dehydration.

When after adrenalectomy the animal begins to lose sodium and with this, chlorides and bicarbonate, the normal amount of water is not held in the tissues, and the animal goes into a state of shock. This condition may be partially relieved by the administration of salt and wholly by supplying the cortical hormone.

Retention of potassium in excessive amounts in the blood occurs, and with its close relationship to parasympathetic stimulation we would expect Addison's disease to show parasympathetic effects. This it does in its reduction of blood pressure, and in its gastrointestinal manifestations.

PITUITARY

It is generally stated that no definite relationship between pituitary secretion and nerve stimulation has been shown, yet Ranson[6] has shown that the sympathetics send antidiuretic nerves to the posterior lobe.

The situation at least seems different from what is found in the adrenals and thyroid where the activity of the gland is stimulated by the sympathetics, and the glands in turn secrete substances which increase the susceptibility of tissues to sympathetic action.

There seems to be scarcely an effect in body function, produced by any other endocrine organ that is not influenced directly or indirectly by the pituitary. Body growth; development, somatic and psychic; sexual development and maturity; sugar, water, pH, fat, and protein metabolism are all influenced either through this gland or through its stimulation of the particular mechanisms which control these processes. It also produces thyrotropic, adrenotropic, gonadotropic, and parathyrotropic substances. While many have made important contributions to the study of the pituitary, Evans, Smith, Collip, Riddle, Houssay and their coworkers have been especially active in developing our knowledge of this gland.

THE PANCREAS

The pancreas is innervated by both the sympathetic and parasympathetic systems, as discussed in Chapter XXI.

Both internal and external secretory activity are influenced by nerves. Stimulation of the vagus of the parasympathetic system causes secretion of insulin. The effects of the sympathetics on insulin have not been determined.

It is an interesting fact that the secretion of insulin is favored by parasympathetic stimulation and that insulin also produces parasympathetic effects.

Experimental diabetes may be produced by removal of the pancreas. If, however, the pituitary is first removed, diabetes does not occur. Houssay[7] has shown that if the pituitary is removed in a pancreatectomized dog, glycosuria, hyperglycemia, and acidosis are considerably relieved.

Collip[8] discusses these experiments which have proved the existence of a diabetogenic principle in the pituitary in a recent review of the subject.

THYMUS

The thymus is richly supplied with both sympathetic and parasympathetic nerves. There has been a difference of opinion among observers as to whether or not the thymus can be considered as a gland of internal secretion, but recent experiments seem to give an affirmative answer to the question.

Rowntree, Clark and Hanson[9] have shown an increasing precocity in growth and development of successive generations of animals, physically, sexually, and psychically, when treated by thymus preparations.

The sudden deaths caused by so-called persistent thymus continues to be somewhat of a riddle.

The thymus seems to oppose the thyroid in certain activities.

TESTES

The innervation of the testes has been discussed in a preceding chapter.

Testicular hormones when administered to normal individuals stimulate metabolism and growth, have an energizing effect, influence the sexual power to a certain degree, and in the immature stimulate secondary sex characteristics.

The testes are stimulated by secretions from many endocrine glands, particularly the pituitary, thyroid, adrenal, and thymus.

OVARY

Nerves which activate the internal secretory portion of the ovary have not been definitely proved.

The internal secretion of the ovary seems to be largely controlled by the pituitary. It is influenced in different ways by the gonadotropic substances from the hypophysis, pregnancy urine, and the placenta.

Collip[10] sums up the effect of various stimulating substances upon the ovary as follows:

"It seems necessary at the present time to postulate two hypophyseal gonadotropic hormones, one follicle stimulating and one that luteinizes the theca and the mature granulosa while it has no effect on the immature granulosa cells. The so-called prolan A of menopausal urine appears to consist chiefly of the former, or at least to resemble it closely, whereas the placental hormone of pregnancy urine ("prolan A" plus "prolan B" of Zondek's original terminology) is more comparable, in its biologic relations, to the luteinizing fraction."

References

1. Pottenger, F. M.: Neural and Endocrine Factors in Bodily Defense, President's Address, Association for the Study of Internal Secretions, Kansas City, Missouri, May 11, 1936; Endocrinology 21: 449, 1937.
2. Cannon and Cattell: The Secretory Activity of the Thyroid Gland, Am. J. Physiol. 41: 58, 1916.
3. Wilson: Pathologic Changes in the Sympathetic System in Goiter, Am. J. M. Sc. 152: 799, 1916.
4. Wilson and Durante: Changes in the Superior Cervical Sympathetic Ganglia Removed for the Relief of Exopthalmos, J. Med. Research 34: No. 3, 1916 (New Series 29: No. 3).
5. Aub, Joseph C.: The Relation of the Internal Secretions to Calcium Metabolism, Particularly the Thyroid and Parathyroid. Read before the meeting of the Association for the Study of Internal Secretions, Minneapolis, Minn., June 12, 1928.
6. Ranson, S. Walter: Some Functions of the Hypothalamus, The Harvey Lectures, 1936-7, p. 92.
7. Houssay, B. A., and Biasotti, A.: Hypophysis, Carbohydrate Metabolism and Diabetes, Endocrinology 15: 511, 1931.
8. Collip, J. B.: Diabetogenic, Thyrotropic, Adrenotropic and Parathyrotropic Factors in the Pituitary, 1936, Glandular Physiology and Therapy, A. M. A., p. 85.
9. Rowntree, L. G., Clark, J. H., and Hanson, A. M.: The Biological Effects of Thymus Extract (Hanson), J. A. M. A. 103: 1425, 1934.
10. Collip, J. B.: Loc. cit. p. 79.

Those who are particularly interested in endocrinology will find the developments in this important field of medicine recorded year by year in *Endocrinology,* the bulletin of the Association for the Study of Internal Secretions. Recently the American Medical Association published a group of authoritative articles in the *Journal of the American Medical Association.* These have been reprinted in book form under the title *Glandular Physiology and Therapy.*

AUTHORS INDEX

A

ABDERHALDEN, EMIL, 119
ADSON, A. W., 367
ALLEN, E., 393
ALVAREZ, W. C., 255, 266
ANDERSON, J. J., 98, 200, 256
ANDRUS, E. C., 119
ARQUIN, SERGIUS, 132
AUB, JOSEPH C., 416
AUER, J., 119

B

BACQ, Z. M., 45
BAILEY, F. R., 36, 102
BAINBRIDGE, F. A., 279
BANTING, F. G., 285
BARD, PHILIP, 75
BAYLISS, W. M., 28, 36, 39, 113, 114, 119, 287, 362, 366
BECHTEREW, W. V., 36, 99, 256, 345
BEHAN, RICHARD J., 395
BERG, B. N., 90, 119
BERNARD, CLAUDE, 22, 27, 98
BERRY, E. L., 363
BEST, C. H., 285
BICKEL, A., 243
BIEDL, A., 36, 108
BISHOP, G. H., 175, 357, 361
BRADFORD, J. R., 360
BRODIE, T. G., 344
BROWN, GEORGE E., 367
BROWN, LANGDON W., 217
BROWN, P. K., 349
BRÜCKE, ERNST, 89
BURDENKO, NIKOLAI N., 368
BURNS, DAVID, 28, 113, 114, 119, 121, 138
BURRIDGE, W., 119

C

CAJAL, RAMON Y., 100
CALLENDER, C. L., 367
CANNON, W. B., 36, 45, 76, 88, 100, 135, 217, 276, 279, 363, 415
CARLSON, A. J., 127, 194, 237, 241, 243, 253, 259, 279
CARRION, H., 36
CARTER, E. P., 119
CATTELL, McK., 415

C (continued)

CHILD, CHARLES M., 37
CLARK, A. J., 119, 134
CLARK, J. H., 420
COFFEY, W. B., 348
COLLIP, J. B., 420
CRILE, G. W., 200, 217
CROSBY, ELIZABETH C., 74
CUSHING, HARVEY, 78

D

DALE, H. H., 45, 355, 379
DALY, I. DE B., 119, 134
DASTRE, A., 329
DAVIS, L., 175
DE BOER, 201
DEJERINE, J., 214
DOISY, E., 393
DUKE, W. W., 45, 116, 119
DURANTE, L., 415
DUSSER DE BARENNE, J. G., 201

E

EBBECKE, U., 366, 408
EDINGER, LUDWIG, 210
ELLIOTT, T. R., 45, 103
ENGELBACH, WM., 122
ENGELMANN, J., 114
EPPINGER, H., 36, 50, 106, 121, 295
EVANS, HERBERT M., 419

F

FALTA, WILHELM, 36
FONTAINE, RENÉ, 349
FRIEDLANDER, A., 260
FROEHLICH, A., 108

G

GASKELL, W. H., 36, 48, 56, 82, 84, 85, 86, 93, 97, 99, 102, 114, 119, 207, 228, 233, 241, 256, 258, 345, 360, 388, 409, 410
GAUCKLER, 214
GLEY, E., 36
GUILLAUME, A. G., 36
GUNN, JAMES A., 114
GUNNING, R. E. L., 363

SUBJECT INDEX

A

Abdominal organs reflect in diaphragm, 288
  viscera, ganglia supplying vasomotors to, 360
Accessorius, pulmonary reflexes through, 330
Acetylcholine, acts chiefly on parasympathetics, 46, 104
  may cause sympathetic effects, 104
  produces vasodilator effects, 104
  test for parasympathicotonia, 111
Acid-base balance affects symptoms, 138
  equilibrium, effect of toxins on, 144
Activation in vegetative structures, 88
Activity, protoplasmic, control of, 36
Adequate stimulus, 57
  lowered in chronic disease, 188
  necessary to cause reflex, 162, 164
Adrenal cortex, action of, 418
  medulla, connector neurons of, 103
    formation of, 102
    related to sympathetic nerves, 102, 417
    test for sympathicotonia, 109
Adrenalin, 40, 102
  action of, compared with ergotoxine, 105
  in vascular control, 356, 363
  and sympathetic stimulation, 45
  causes same effect as sympathetic stimulation, 103, 417, 418
  does not cause sweating, 410
  emergency action of, 356
  in hyperexia, 365
Adrenals, internal secretion of, 417-419
  parasympathetics of, 417
  sympathetics of, 415, 416
Adrenergic transmission of nerve impulse, 46
Afferent fibers of sympathetic system, 191
  neurons, 94
    basis of the reflex, 166
    of all tissues, somatic, 55, 173
    paths from skin, 406
Allergic inflammation, 171
Anaphylactic phenomena, cutaneous, 409
Anaphylaxis, a parasympathetic hyperirritability, 123, 223

Anaphylaxis—Cont'd
  favorably influenced by adrenalin, calcium, and atropine, 124
  syndrome of, 223
  vegetatively considered, 123
Anger, action of, on intestinal tract, 277
Angina, surgical treatment of, 348, 349
Antagonism of calcium and potassium, 89, 90, 113
  of calcium and sodium, 120
  of H and OH ions, 89, 90, 113
  of sympathetics and parasympathetics, 241
    shown pharmacologically, 108
Antidromic impulse, 362
  causes herpes zoster, 362
  trophic changes, 362
Antigen-tissue reaction, symptoms due to, 135
Aorta, innervation of, 352
  parasympathetics of, 352
  segmental relation of, to skin, 155
  spread of pain from, 353
  sympathetics of, 352
  vagus fibers to, regulate blood pressure, 353
Aortic pain, location of, 352, 353
Appendicitis, motor reflex in, 260
  pain in, 261, 262
Argyll Robertson's pupil, 383
Arterial tone, 362
Arteries, contractility an important function of, 354, 355
  innervation of, 67, 74, 352, 354, 356, 360, 361
  sensibility of, 177
  structure and function of, 354
Asphyxia, sympathetics combat, 223
Asthma, a parasympathetic syndrome, 124, 125
  hypermotility in, 251
  reflex, from nasal chambers, 375
    from other viscera, 332
  treatment of, by adrenalin, atropine, calcium, increasing acidity of tissues, and sympathetic stimulation, 124, 125
Atrophy of facial muscles in pulmonary tuberculosis, 330

426

Metabolism and endocrines, 30
and vegetative nervous system, 30
regulators of, 28
Metabolites, acid, cause vasodilation, 361
Meteorologic factors, man's response to, 44
Mucous colitis, vegetatively considered, 126
Müller, muscle of, nerve supply of, 380
Muscarin, 107
Muscles, broad, do not contract as whole, 197
reflexes in, 198, 199
endodermal, nerve supply of, 48, 229
involved in pleural motor reflex, 337
pulmonary visceromotor reflex, 309-311
only mildly sensitive, 176
pilomotor, sympathetics supply, 48, 409
segmentation of, 149
slightly sensitive, 176
striated, effect of sympathetics on, 201, 202
subdermal, innervation of, 48, 228, 406, 407, 409
urogenitodermal, sympathetics supply, 48, 388
Musculature, vasodermal, innervation of, 228
Myogenic theory of muscle activity, 112, 114

N

Narcotics, action of, on cell, 112
Nasal chambers, bradycardia caused by irritation of, 375
mucous membrane, innervation of, 373
Nausea, reflex, 252, 253
Neck, vasomotors of, 357
Nerve action, influenced by ionic content of cell, 112
by physical state of cell, 112
control, of body activity, 29, 39, 40
nature of, 40, 41
impulse, adrenergic, 45, 46
chemical transmission of, 45, 46
cholinergic, 45, 46
response, vegetative and voluntary compared, 83
trigeminus, relation of, to parasympathetic reflexes, 207
Nerves, afferent, all belong to somatic system, 36, 194

Nerves—Cont'd
cranial, vegetative, 71
effect of toxins on, 142, 143
inhibitory action of, 41
motor, action of, 37
of capillaries, 355
part of, in body control, 116
in cellular activity, 115
sacral, vegetative, 71
segmentation of, 145
sensory, belong to somatic system, 36
spinal, of diaphragm, 289
relation of, to vertebrae, 145-147
splanchnic, 255, 256, 360
sympathetic, distribution of, 191
sympathetics and parasympathetics antagonize each other, 224
vasodilator, 361
vasomotor, 354, 356
vegetative, cause of disequilibrium in, 121
depend on ionic content of cell, 118
form connecting path from skin to viscera, 195, 196
motor only, 36
sensory, and pain, 36
structures supplied by, 228
voluntary, 37
Nervous system, adjustment to environment made through, 80
and electrolytes act reciprocally, 90, 91
development of, 42
divisions of, 36
effect of toxins on, 142, 143
parasympathetic, 50, 159
origin of, 47
relationship of vegetative to central, 82
significance of, 42
sympathetic, 50, 158
distribution of, 84
origin of, 47
vegetative, 157
a correlating mechanism, 81
anatomy of, 61
and metabolism, 30
divisions of, 49
embryological considerations of, 53
general considerations of, 36
origin of, 47
physiology of, 80
protective features of, 80, 81
significance of, 46